# TEST BANK

## to accompany

# COLLEGE PHYSICS

# TEST BANK

## to accompany

Paul A. Tipler
# COLLEGE PHYSICS

**Charles E. Robertson**
Bellevue Community College

**J. P. Svenne**
University of Manitoba

WORTH PUBLISHERS, INC.

**Test Bank**
to accompany
COLLEGE PHYSICS  by Paul A. Tipler
By Charles E. Robertson and J. P. Svenne

Printed in the United States of America
ISBN: 0-87901-271-4
First Printing, March 1988

**Worth Publishers, Inc.**
33 Irving Place
New York, New York 10003

# Preface

This Test Bank has been developed for use with **College Physics** by Paul Tipler. The test questions emphasize the same topics as the textbook, and they use the same symbols and notation.

Each Test Bank chapter consists of conceptual, numerical, and factual questions. Many of the conceptual questions require proportional reasoning skills or the ability to analyze graphs. The numerical questions test students' problem-solving skills. Occasionally it was difficult to distinguish conceptual and numerical questions: Those questions involving proportional reasoning that can be carried out without paper and pencil are designated conceptual; those requiring paper and pencil or a calculator are designated numerical.

In addition to being categorized by type, the questions are identified by the corresponding textbook headings, enabling you to scan questions quickly and select the appropriate balance of questions from the topics you wish to cover.

The incorrect choices accompanying the correct answer to each question often reflect common student misconceptions. By looking at a student's incorrect responses you may be able to gain insight into the mistaken understanding or reasoning that was the source of the student's error. (Answers to numerical questions are given to two significant figures except where the question merits a more exact calculation.)

Most of the questions in this Test Bank have been student tested at the authors' respective institutions. However, time did not permit us to test all of the questions; in these cases, the questions were read and worked by at least one other physics instructor. Inevitably some questions will not be as clear to the user of this Test Bank as they were to the authors. If you have any corrections, questions, or suggestions please contact Worth Publishers, Inc. or Charles E. Robertson, Bellevue Community College, 3000 Landerholm Circle S. E., Bellevue, WA 98007. (BITNET address: CER@UWPHAST)

We would like to thank the many people who helped us complete this project. David VanHarlingen (Raritan Valley Community College) contributed some of the conceptual questions. Arthur West (Bellevue Community College) edited questions and checked their answers. A special thanks goes to John Stewart (Bellevue Community College) who supplied many questions, checked for correct answers, and helped with the editing. Without their help, this job could not have been done.

April 1988                                               Charles E. Robertson

                                                         Juris P. Svenne

# Contents

CHAPTER 1     **Introduction**

**0101    1-1   Units,   Factual,   c**

Which of the following is a fundamental unit of the SI system of units?

a.   kilometre
b.   joule
c.   kilogram
d.   gram
e.   newton

**0102    1-1   Units,   Factual,   c**

The prefix *giga* means

a.   $10^3$
b.   $10^6$
c.   $10^9$
d.   $10^{12}$
e.   $10^{15}$

**0103    1-1   Units,   Factual,   c**

Which of the following is NOT one of the fundamental physical quantities in the SI system?

a.   mass
b.   length
c.   force
d.   time
e.   All of the above are fundamental physical quantities.

**0104    1-1   Units,   Factual,   d**

The prefix *mega* means

a.   $10^{-9}$
b.   $10^{-6}$
c.   $10^{-3}$
d.   $10^6$
e.   $10^9$

**0105   1-1   Units,   Factual,   a**

The prefix *pico* means

   a.  $10^{-12}$
   b.  $10^{-6}$
   c.  $10^{-3}$
   d.  $10^{6}$
   e.  $10^{9}$

**0106   1-1   Units,   Factual,   c**

Which of the following prefixes does NOT represent a fractional part of a whole unit?

   a.  nano
   b.  micro
   c.  kilo
   d.  milli
   e.  deci

**0107   1-1   Units,   Factual,   e**

Which of the following prefixes does NOT represent a quantity larger than a single unit?

   a.  kilo
   b.  mega
   c.  giga
   d.  tera
   e.  femto

**0108   1-1   Units,   Factual,   a**

Which of the following is NOT one of the fundamental units in the SI system?

   a.  newton
   b.  metre
   c.  kilogram
   d.  second
   e.  All of the above are fundamental units.

**0109   1-1   Units,   Factual,   e**

The standard for the metre was originally the distance between two scratches on a platinum-iridium bar kept in France.  This is no longer the case because

   a.  the bar was stolen.
   b.  the bar was damaged in a fire.
   c.  the scratches were found to have been incorrectly marked.
   d.  its length was too easily affected by temperature changes.
   e.  the standard is now defined in terms of the speed of light.

**0110    1-1   Units,   Factual,   c**

Someone you don't know too well who has heard you speak tells your friend that you are "centimental."  You should

a.   be pleased at the acknowledgement of your higher than average intelligence.
b.   be slightly annoyed at the suggestion your intelligence is only about average.
c.   be upset at the suggestion your mental powers are tiny.
d.   correct the person's spelling.
e.   find a new friend.


**0111    1-1   Units,   Factual,   b**

Millicent Fenwick is a former member of Congress from New Jersey.  What fraction of a dollar is a millicent?

a.   $10^{-6}$
b.   $10^{-5}$
c.   $10^{-3}$
d.   $10^{-1}$
e.   $10^{+1}$


**0112    1-2   Conversion of Units,   Numerical,   e**

The density of sea water was measured to be 1.07 $g/cm^3$.  This density in SI units is

a.   $1.07 \times 10^{-3} kg/m^3$
b.   $(1/1.07) \times 10^3 kg/m^3$
c.   $1.07 \times 10^3 kg$
d.   $1.07 \times 10^{-3} kg$
e.   $1.07 \times 10^3 kg/m^3$


**0113    1-2   Conversion of Units,   Numerical,   b**

To convert a quantity from km/h to m/s, you must

a.   multiply by 1000 and divide by 60.
b.   multiply by 1000 and divide by 3600.
c.   multiply by 60 and divide by 1000.
d.   multiply by 3600 and divide by 1000.
e.   None of the above is correct.


**0114    1-2   Conversion of Units,   Numerical,   d**

To convert a quantity from  m/s to km/h, you must

a.   multiply by 1000 and divide by 60.
b.   multiply by 1000 and divide by 3600.
c.   multiply by 60 and divide by 1000.
d.   multiply by 3600 and divide by 1000.
e.   None of the above is correct.

**0115    1-2    Conversion of Units,    Numerical,    b**

To convert a quantity from km/hr/s to m/s$^2$, you must

a.   multiply by 1000 and divide by 60.
b.   multiply by 1000 and divide by 3600.
c.   multiply by 60 and divide by 1000.
d.   multiply by 3600 and divide by 1000.
e.   None of the above is correct.


**0116    1-2    Conversion of Units,    Numerical,    c**

To convert from g/cm$^3$ to kg/m$^3$, you must

a.   multiply by 0.01.
b.   multiply by 100.
c.   multiply by 1000.
d.   multiply by 0.001.
e.   multiply by 1,000,000.


**0117    1-2    Conversion of Units,    Numerical,    d**

In doing a calculation, you arrive at a situation where the numerator is in kilometres and the denominator is in m/s.  When the calculation is completed, your resulting units will be

a.   metres, if you divide by 1000.
b.   metres, if you multiply by 1000.
c.   seconds, if you divide by 1000.
d.   seconds, if you multiply by 1000.
e.   metres squared per second, if you multiply by 1000.


**0118    1-2    Conversion of Units,    Conceptual,    d**

In doing a calculation, you end up with m/s in the numerator and m/s$^2$ in the denominator. The resulting units will be

a.   m$^2$/s$^3$
b.   1/s
c.   s$^3$/m$^2$
d.   s
e.   m/s


**0119    1-3    Dimensions of Physical Quantities,    Conceptual,    d**

The dimensions of density are

a.   $MLT^{-1}$
b.   $ML^3$
c.   $ML^2$
d.   $ML^{-3}$
e.   None of the above is correct.

**0120    1-3    Dimensions of Physical Quantities,    Conceptual,    d**

The dimensions of two quantities MUST be identical if you are either _____ or _____ the quantities.

a.  adding; multiplying
b.  subtracting; dividing
c.  multiplying; dividing
d.  adding; subtracting
e.  All of the above are correct.


**0121    1-4    Scientific Notation,    Numerical,    d**

Compute $\dfrac{(3 \times 10^8)(8 \times 10^4)}{(6 \times 10^5)}$

a.  $144 \times 10^{17}$
b.  $6 \times 10^7$
c.  $8 \times 10^{17}$
d.  $4 \times 10^7$
e.  None of these is correct.


**0122    1-4    Scientific Notation,    Numerical,    d**

Compute $\dfrac{(6.2 \times 10^{-4}) + (4.0 \times 10^{-5})}{(2 \times 10^{-3})}$

a.  $3.3 \times 10^{-6}$
b.  $5.1 \times 10^6$
c.  $5.1 \times 10^{-12}$
d.  $3.3 \times 10^{-1}$
e.  None of these is correct.


**0123    1-5    Significant Figures,    Conceptual,    c**

The number 0.0005130 has ____ significant figures.

a.  one
b.  three
c.  four
d.  seven
e.  eight


**0124    1-5    Significant Figures,    Conceptual,    e**

The number 23.0040 has ____ significant figures.

a.  two
b.  three
c.  four
d.  five
e.  six

**0125    1-5   Significant Figures,   Numerical,   d**

The number of seconds in a month has an order of magnitude of

a.   $10^1$
b.   $10^3$
c.   $10^5$
d.   $10^6$
e.   $10^7$

**0126    1-5   Significant Figures,   Factual,   c**

The number of people living in the United States has an order of magnitude of

a.   $10^6$
b.   $10^7$
c.   $10^8$
d.   $10^9$
e.   $10^{10}$

**0127    1-5   Significant Figures,   Numerical,   c**

The chemical agent dioxin can be toxic or hazardous to humans in concentrations as small as one part per billion.  If I am testing a soil sample that has a mass of 1.0 kg, how much dioxin would have to be present for me to label it toxic or hazardous?

a.   a picogram
b.   a nanogram
c.   a microgram
d.   a milligram
e.   a kilogram

**0128    1-5   Significant Figures,   Numerical,   b**

An impurity in a manufacturing process will cause a batch to be rejected if the impurity exceeds one part per million.  What is the maximum amount of impurity that could be present if the batch contains 100 kg of the product?

a. 100 micrograms
b. 100 milligrams
c. 100 grams
d. 100 megagrams
e. 100 nanograms

**0129    1-5   Significant Figures,   Factual,   b**

The tallest mountains on earth are how many orders of magnitude high?

a.   $10^3$ m
b.   $10^4$ m
c.   $10^5$ m
d.   $10^6$ m
e.   $10^8$ m

**0130**   **1-5   Significant Figures,   Numerical,   e**

Light travels at $3 \times 10^8$ m/s and it takes about eight minutes for light from the sun to arrive at the earth.  Based on this, the order of magnitude of the distance from the sun to the earth is

a.   $10^6$ m
b.   $10^8$ m
c.   $10^9$ m
d.   $10^{10}$ m
e.   $10^{11}$ m

CHAPTER 2     Motion in One Dimension

0201    **2-1   Speed, Displacement, and Velocity,   Numerical,   d**

A particle moves from $x_0 = 30$ cm to $x = -40$ cm in 5 s.  The average velocity of the particle over the time interval is

a.   2 cm/s
b.   -2 cm/s
c.   14 cm/s
d.   -14 cm/s
e.   -140 cm/s

0202    **2-1   Speed, Displacement, and Velocity, Numerical, a**

You drive for 30 minutes at 100 km/h and then stop for 15 minutes.  You then drive for 45 minutes at 80 km/h.  Your average speed for the entire trip is

a.   73 km/h
b.   83 km/h
c.   88 km/h
d.   90 km/h
e.   97 km/h

0203    **2-1   Speed, Displacement, and Velocity,   Conceptual,   c**

The displacement of an object for a round trip between two locations

a.   is always greater than zero.
b.   is always less than zero.
c.   is zero.
d.   may be greater than or less than but not equal to zero.
e.   may have any value.

**0204   2-1   Speed, Displacement, and Velocity,   Conceptual,   b**

The displacement of an object over any time interval is always _____ the distance it travels over that same time interval.

a.   greater than or equal to
b.   less than or equal to
c.   equal to
d.   greater than
e.   less than

**0205   2-1   Speed, Displacement, and Velocity,   Conceptual,   b**

An object moves along the $x$ axis as shown in the diagram.  At which point is the object farthest from its starting point?

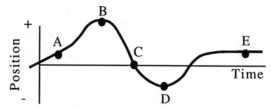

a.   A
b.   B
c.   C
d.   D
e.   E

**0206   2-1   Speed, Displacement, and Velocity,   Conceptual,   b**

The graph shows how the position of a particle depends on time.  Which choice is closest to the average speed of the particle in the time interval between 0 and 6 seconds?

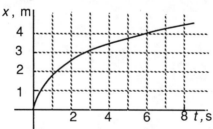

a.   0.40  m/s
b.   0.67  m/s
c.   0.75  m/s
d.   1.50  m/s
e.   2.22  m/s

**0207    2-1   Speed, Displacement, and Velocity,   Conceptual,  b**

Which graph of $v$ versus $t$ best describes the motion of a particle whose velocity is constant and negative.

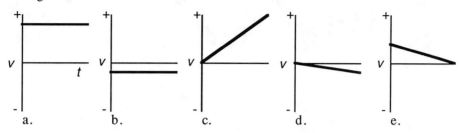

   a.             b.            c.            d.           e.

**0208    2-1   Speed, Displacement, and Velocity,   Conceptual,  d**

In which graph of $v$ versus $t$ does the particle end up the closest to its starting point?

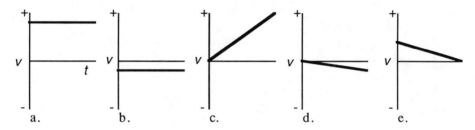

   a.             b.            c.            d.           e.

**0209    2-1   Speed, Displacement, and Velocity,   Conceptual,  a**

In which graph of $v$ versus $t$ does the particle end up the farthest from its starting point?

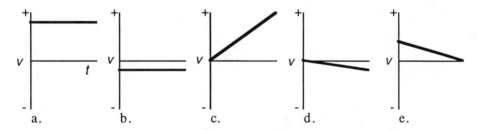

   a.              b.            c.            d.           e.

**0210    2-1   Speed, Displacement, and Velocity,   Conceptual,  b**

If the speed of particle A is twice that of particle B, the distance particle B travels in a given interval of time as compared to particle A is

a.   twice as far.
b.   half as far.
c.   the same.
d.   four times as far.
e.   one-fourth as far.

0211    2-1   Speed, Displacement, and Velocity,  Numerical,  d

Assume that the Dechutes River has straight and parallel banks and that the current is 0.75 m/s.  A student drifting down the river falls out of his raft and grabs a piling of the Warm Springs bridge.  The student holds on and is stationary for 40 s.  He then swims after the boat with a speed relative to the water of 0.95 m/s.  The distance of the boat downstream from the bridge when the student catches it is

a.  67 m
b.  90 m
c.  78 m
d.  54 m
e.  120 m

0212    2-1   Speed, Displacement, and Velocity,  Numerical,  b

You are traveling in your car at 82 km/h (23 m/s) when an emergency arises.  If your car is 4 m long, how many car lengths do you travel during the 0.7 s of reaction time (i.e., the time interval between when you see the emergency and when your foot hits the brake pedal)?

a.  2
b.  4
c.  6
d.  8
e.  10

0213    2-2   Instantaneous Velocity,  Conceptual,  c

On a graph on which the position of an object is plotted vertically and the time is plotted horizontally, the instantaneous velocity at a particular time is

a.  the height of the curve at that time.
b.  the total length of the curve.
c.  the slope of the tangent to the curve at that time.
d.  the area under the curve up to that time from zero.
e.  impossible to determine from this type of plot.

0214    2-2   Instantaneous Velocity,  Conceptual,  c

If an object is moving at uniform speed in a straight line, its instantaneous velocity halfway through any time interval is

a.  greater than its average velocity.
b.  less than its average velocity.
c.  the same as its average velocity.
d.  half of its average velocity.
e.  twice its average velocity.

**0215    2-2   Instantaneous  Velocity,   Conceptual,   a**

The graph shows how the position of a particle depends on time.  Which choice is closest to the instantaneous speed of the particle at time equals 3 s?

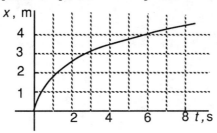

a.   0.40 m/s
b.   0.67 m/s
c.   0.75 m/s
d.   1.50 m/s
e.   2.22 m/s

**0216    2-2   Instantaneous  Velocity,   Conceptual,   d**

On a graph of position on the vertical axis and time on the horizontal axis, a straight line with a positive slope represents

a.   a constant positive acceleration.
b.   a constant negative acceleration.
c.   zero velocity.
d.   a constant positive velocity.
e.   a constant negative velocity.

**0217    2-2   Instantaneous  Velocity,   Conceptual,   e**

On a graph of position on the vertical axis and time on the horizontal axis, a straight line with a negative slope represents

a.   a constant positive acceleration.
b.   a constant negative acceleration.
c.   zero velocity.
d.   a constant positive velocity.
e.   a constant negative velocity.

**0218   2-2   Instantaneous Velocity,   Conceptual,   e**

In which graph is the particle the furthest from the origin at $t = 5$ s?

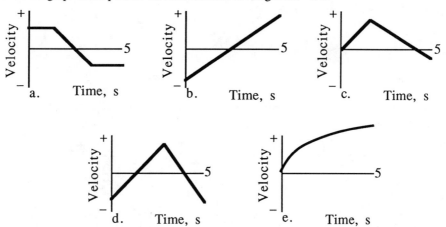

**0219   2-2   Instantaneous Velocity,   Conceptual,   b**

An object moves along the $x$ axis as shown in the diagram.  At which point or points is the magnitude of its velocity a minimum?

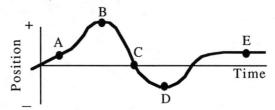

a.   A and E
b.   B, D, and E
c.   C only
d.   E only
e.   None of these is correct.

**0220   2-2   Instantaneous Velocity,   Conceptual,   b**

An object moves along the $x$ axis as shown in the diagram.  At which point or points is the object not moving?

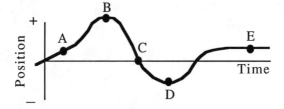

a.   A and E
b.   B, D, and E
c.   C only
d.   E only
e.   None of these is correct.

0221    2-3   Acceleration,   Numerical,   d

A car starts from rest and accelerates uniformly to a speed of 20 m/s at the end of one minute; it then accelerates uniformly to a speed of 40 m/s at the end of the next minute.  The average speed of the car is

a.   7.5 m/s
b.   13 m/s
c.   15 m/s
d.   40  m/s
e.   57 m/s


0222    2-3   Acceleration,   Numerical,   c

An object is moving in a straight line.  At $t = 0$ its speed is 5.0 m/s.  From $t = 0$ to $t = 4.0$ s, its acceleration is 2.5 m/s$^2$.  From $t = 4.0$ s to $t = 11.0$ s, its speed is constant. The average speed over the entire time interval is

a.   9.5 m/s
b.   15 m/s
c.   13 m/s
d.   21 m/s
e.   8.2 m/s


0223    2-3   Acceleration,   Numerical,   d

A particle that is moving along a straight line decelerates uniformly from 40 cm/s  to 20 cm/s in 5.0 s and then has a constant acceleration of 20 cm/s$^2$ during the next 4.0 s.  The average speed over the whole time interval is

a.   57 cm/s
b.   140 cm/s
c.   86 cm/s
d.   43 cm/s
e.   97 cm/s


0224    2-3   Acceleration,   Numerical,   d

A particle accelerates from a speed of 30 cm/s to 40 cm/s in 5 s and thereafter moves at a constant speed of 40 cm/s for an additional 3 s.  The average speed over this total time interval is

a.   35 cm/s
b.   27 cm/s
c.   0.45  cm/s
d.   37 cm/s
e.   73 cm/s


0225    2-3   Acceleration,   Conceptual,   c

For uniformly accelerated motion, which of the following quantities must be zero?

a.   the initial velocity
b.   the initial displacement
c.   the rate of change of the acceleration
d.   the rate of change of the velocity
e.   the rate of change of the displacement

**0226    2-3   Acceleration,   Numerical,   a**

A particle decelerates from a speed of 30 cm/s to rest in a time interval of 5.0 s. It then has a uniform acceleration of 10 cm/s$^2$ for another 5.0 s. The particle moves in the same direction along a straight line. The average speed over the whole time interval is

a.   20 cm/s
b.   35 cm/s
c.   38 cm/s
d.   100 cm/s
e.   12 cm/s

**0227    2-3   Acceleration,   Numerical,   a**

A Triumph sports car starts at rest and accelerates to a speed of 27.0 m/s in 11.8 s. Calculate the distance the car traveled during the acceleration.

a.   160 m
b.   320 m
c.   1900  m
d.   640 m
e.   350 m

**0228    2-3   Acceleration,   Conceptual,   a**

On a graph with position on the vertical axis and time on the horizontal axis, a parabola that opens upward represents

a.   a positive acceleration.
b.   a negative acceleration.
c.   no acceleration.
d.   a positive followed by a negative acceleration.
e.   a negative followed by a positive acceleration.

**0229    2-3   Acceleration,   Conceptual,   b**

On a graph with position on the vertical axis and time on the horizontal axis, a parabola that opens downward represents

a.   a positive acceleration.
b.   a negative acceleration.
c.   no acceleration.
d.   a positive followed by a negative acceleration.
e.   a negative followed by a positive acceleration.

**0230    2-3   Acceleration,   Conceptual,   c**

On a graph with velocity on the vertical axis and time on the horizontal axis, zero acceleration is represented by

a.   a straight line with a positive slope.
b.   a straight line with a negative slope.
c.   a straight line with zero slope.
d.   either a, b, or c.
e.   None of the above is correct.

0231    2-3   **Acceleration,   Conceptual,   d**

On a graph with velocity on the vertical axis and time on the horizontal axis, constant acceleration is represented by

a.   a straight line with a positive slope.
b.   a straight line with a negative slope.
c.   a straight line with zero slope.
d.   either a, b, or c.
e.   None of the above is correct.


0232    2-3   **Acceleration,   Conceptual,   c**

On a graph with velocity on the vertical axis and time on the horizontal axis, the area under the curve represents

a.   average acceleration.
b.   average velocity.
c.   displacement.
d.   average speed.
e.   nothing special.


0233    2-3   **Acceleration,   Conceptual,   e**

On a graph with position on the vertical axis and time on the horizontal axis, the area under the curve represents

a.   average acceleration.
b.   average velocity.
c.   displacement.
d.   average speed.
e.   nothing special.


0234    2-3   **Acceleration,   Conceptual,   e**

Which graph of $v$ versus $t$ best describes the motion of a particle with positive velocity and negative acceleration?

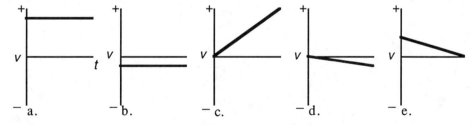

**0235   2-3   Acceleration,   Conceptual,   d**

Which graph of *v* versus *t* best describes the motion of a particle with negative velocity and negative acceleration?

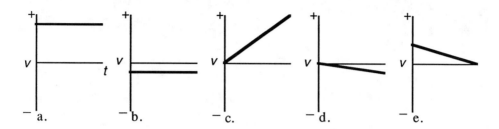

**0236   2-3   Acceleration,   Conceptual,   c**

In which graph of *v* versus *t* is the magnitude of the particle's acceleration the greatest?

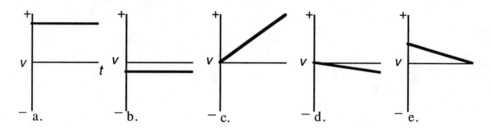

**0237   2-3   Acceleration,   Conceptual,   c**

A car and a truck, starting from rest, have the same acceleration but the truck accelerates for twice the length of time.  Compared to the car, the truck will travel

a.   twice as far.
b.   three times as far.
c.   1.4 times as far.
d.   four times as far.
e.   one-half as far.

**0238   2-3   Acceleration,   Conceptual,   a**

An object moves along the *x* axis as shown on the diagram.  At which point or points is its acceleration zero?

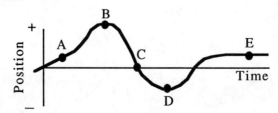

a.   A and E
b.   B, D, and E
c.   C only
d.   E only
e.   B and D

**0239   2-4   Motion with Constant Acceleration,   Conceptual,   d**

An object is dropped from rest.  If the time interval during which it falls is cut in half, the distance it falls will

a.   double.
b.   decrease by one-half.
c.   increase by a factor of four.
d.   decrease by a factor of four.
e.   not change.

**0240   2-4   Motion with Constant Acceleration,   Conceptual,   c**

An object is dropped from rest.  If the time interval during which it falls is doubled, the distance it falls will

a.   double.
b.   decrease by one-half.
c.   increase by a factor of four.
d.   decrease by a factor of four.
e.   not change.

**0241   2-4   Motion with Constant Acceleration,   Conceptual,   c**

A car accelerates uniformly from a speed of 10 km/h to 30 km/h in one minute.  Which graph best describes the motion of the car?

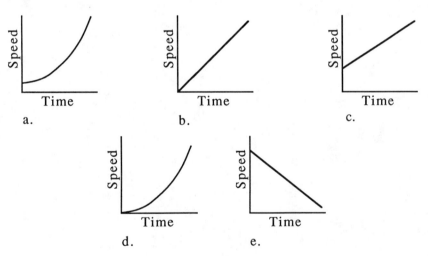

**0242   2-4   Motion with Constant Acceleration,   Numerical,   c**

A projectile with a mass of 130 kg is fired vertically upward with a speed of 62 m/s.  The maximum height the projectile attains is

a.   $2.5 \times 10^4$ m
b.   98 m
c.   200 m
d.   $1.9 \times 10^4$ m
e.   3 m

**0243    2-4  Motion with Constant Acceleration,  Numerical,  d**

A ball with a mass of 30 grams is dropped from the top of a building.  The ball hits the ground with a speed of 49 m/s.  The height of the building is

a.   25 m
b.   5 m
c.   240 m
d.   120 m
e.   10 m

**0244    2-4  Motion with Constant Acceleration,  Conceptual,  a**

In which graph does the particle have no acceleration at $t = 5$ s?

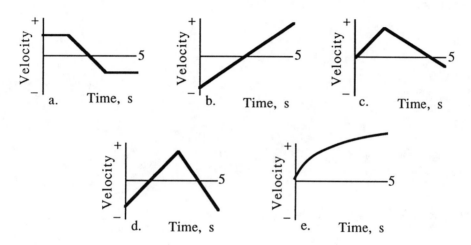

**0245    2-4  Motion with Constant Acceleration,  Conceptual,  b**

In which graph does the particle have a constant acceleration for the entire 5 seconds?

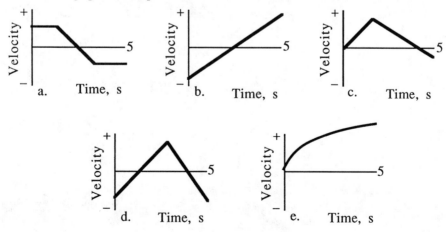

**0246   2-4   Motion with Constant Acceleration,   Conceptual,   e**

In which graph does the particle never have a constant acceleration?

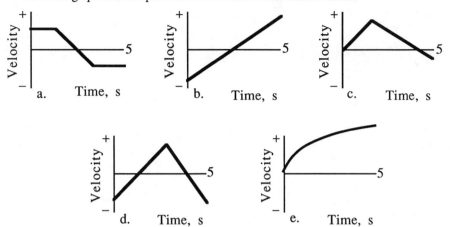

**0247   2-4   Motion with Constant Acceleration,   Conceptual,   b**

An object is at $x = -3$ m and has a velocity of 4 m/s.  It is observed to be slowing down.  Its acceleration is

a.   positive.
b.   negative.
c.   zero.
d.   impossible to determine based on the information provided.

**0248   2-4   Motion with Constant Acceleration,   Conceptual,   e**

A graph of the motion of an object is plotted with the velocity on the vertical axis and the time along the horizontal axis.  The graph is a straight line.  Which of these quantities CANNOT be determined from this graph?

a.   the displacement from time $t = 0$
b.   the initial velocity at $t = 0$
c.   the acceleration of the object
d.   the average velocity of the object
e.   All four of the quantities can be determined from the graph.

CHAPTER 3   # Motion in Two and Three Dimensions

0301    **3-1  The Displacement Vector,  Conceptual,  e**

The displacement of a particle is _____ the distance the object has traveled.

a.  larger than
b.  smaller than
c.  may be either larger or smaller than
d.  the same as
e.  smaller than or equal to


0302    **3-1  The Displacement Vector,  Conceptual,  b**

Which of the following quantities are vectors:  (a) the wind velocity,  (b) the population of Winnipeg,  (c) the tension in a chain pulling a disabled car,  (d) the weight of your physics book, (e) the total amount of blood pumped by your heart per hour.

a.  (a) and (c)
b.  (a), (c), and (d)
c.  (a), (c), (d), and (e)
d.  All of them are vector quantities.
e.  None of them are vector quantities.


0303    **3-1  The Displacement Vector,  Numerical,  c**

A vector has an $x$ component of -5.51 units and a $y$ component of +9.52 units.  The angle between the positive direction of the vector and the positive direction of the $x$ axis is

a.  125°
b.  60°
c.  120°
d.  150°
e.  -60°


0304    **3-2  Addition of Vectors by Components,  Conceptual,  c**

The components of a vector are $A_x = -10$ units and $A_y = 6$ units.  What angle does this vector make with the positive $x$ axis?

a.  31°
b.  -31°
c.  180° - 31°
d.  180° + 31°
e.  90° - 31°

**0305**   **3-2   Addition of Vectors by Components,   Conceptual,   a**

What is the least number of vectors that can be added to give a resultant equal to zero?

a.   2
b.   3
c.   4
d.   An infinite number can be added to give a resultant equal to zero.
e.   It cannot be done.

**0306**   **3-2   Addition of Vectors by Components,   Numerical,   d**

Three vectors **A**, **B**, and **C** have the following $x$ and $y$ components:

|              | A   | B   | C   |
|--------------|-----|-----|-----|
| $x$ component | +6  | -3  | +2  |
| $y$ component | -3  | +4  | +5  |

The magnitude of the resultant sum of **A**, **B**, and **C** is

a.   3.3
b.   5.0
c.   11
d.   7.8
e.   14

**0307**   **3-2   Addition of Vectors by Components,   Numerical,   c**

Three vectors **A**, **B**, and **C** have the following $x$ and $y$ components:

|              | A   | B   | C   |
|--------------|-----|-----|-----|
| $x$ component | +6  | -3  | +2  |
| $y$ component | -3  | +4  | +5  |

The angle which the resultant sum makes with the positive direction of the $x$ axis is

a.   $1.2°$
b.   $36°$
c.   $50°$
d.   $40°$
e.   $70°$

**0308**   **3-2   Addition of Vectors by Components,   Numerical,   a**

A car proceeding due south at 60 km/h (**V₁**) takes 10 seconds to make a right turn, after which it is traveling due west at 80 km/h (**V₂**).  What is its change in velocity (**V₂ − V₁**)?

a.   100 km/h 37° north of west
b.   100 km/h 37° south of west
c.   20 km/h west
d.   20 km/h 37° north of west
e.   20 km/h 37° south of west

**0309    3-2   Addition of Vectors by Components,   Numerical,   b**

Two vectors **A** and **B** are added together to give a resultant **R**.  The components of **A** are $A_x$ = -8.0 units and $A_y$ = 6.0 units while the components of **R** are $R_x$ = -7.0 units and $R_y$ = 5.0 units.  The magnitude of vector **R** is

a.  -1.0 units.
b.  +8.6 units.
c.  +19 units.
d.  +2.0 units.
e.  -3.2 units.


**0310    3-2   Addition of Vectors by Components,   Numerical,   c**

The vector **A** has components $A_x$ = +4.0 units and $A_y$ = +3.2 units, whereas the vector **B** has components $B_x$ = +2.5 units and $B_y$ = +5.5 units.  The angle <u>between</u> the two vectors is

a.  24°
b.  65°
c.  27°
d.  39°
e.  14°


**0311    3-2   Addition of Vectors by Components,   Numerical,   b**

The vectors **A**, **B**, and **C** have the following components expressed in arbitrary units:

|              | **A**  | **B**  | **C**  |
|--------------|--------|--------|--------|
| $x$ component | +4.60  | -3.10  | +5.30  |
| $y$ component | -3.10  | +2.30  | -2.50  |

A vector **D** is defined so that
$$\mathbf{A} + \mathbf{B} + \mathbf{C} + \mathbf{D} = 0$$

The magnitude and direction of **D** relative to the positive $x$ axis are

a.  7.6 units at -26°
b.  7.6 units at 150°
c.  14 units at 26°
d.  3.5 units at 29°
e.  10 units at 29°

0312   **3-2   Addition of Vectors by Components,   Numerical,   a**

Vectors **A** and **B** have the following components:

$$A_x = 5 \text{ units} \qquad A_y = 2 \text{ units}$$
$$B_x = 3 \text{ units} \qquad B_y = 4 \text{ units}$$

The angle between the positive $x$ axis and the vector **A** - **B** is

a.   14°
b.   194°
c.   37°
d.   54°
e.   86°


0313   **3-2   Addition of Vectors by Components,   Numerical,   d**

Vectors **A** and **B** have the following components:

|               | **A**       | **B**       |
|---------------|-------------|-------------|
| $x$ component | +5 units    | -3 units    |
| $y$ component | -2 units    | -4 units    |

The magnitude of the vector **A** - **B** is

a.   6.3 units.
b.   10.0 units.
c.   2.8 units.
d.   8.2 units.
e.   16 units


0314   **3-2   Addition of Vectors by Components,   Numerical,   d**

The components of four vectors are as follows:

|               | **A**       | **B**       | **C**       | **D**       |
|---------------|-------------|-------------|-------------|-------------|
| $x$ component | +2.5 units  | +6.1 units  | -3.6 units  | -1.5 units  |
| $y$ component | +4.3 units  | -2.1 units  | +1.0 units  | -7.3 units  |

The angle which the resultant vector makes with the positive $x$ axis is

a.   40°
b.   59°
c.   50°
d.   37°
e.   23°

**0315    3-2   Addition of Vectors by Components,   Numerical,   b**

Vectors **A, B, C,** and **D** have the following components:

|  | **A** | **B** | **C** | **D** |
|---|---|---|---|---|
| $x$ component | +2.5 units | +6.1 units | -3.6 units | -1.5 units |
| $y$ component | +4.3 units | -2.1 units | +1.0 units | -7.3 units |

The magnitude of the resultant sum is

a.  -4.6 units.
b.  5.4 units.
c.  29 units.
d.  3.5 units.
e.  7.3 units.

**0316    3-2   Addition of Vectors by Components,   Conceptual,   b**

A velocity vector has an $x$ component of +5.5 m/s and $y$ component of -3.5 m/s. The diagram that gives the direction of the vector is

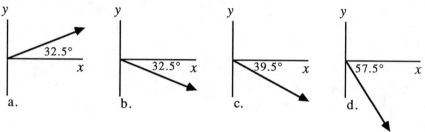

e.  None of these is correct.

**0317    3-2   Addition of Vectors by Components,   Numerical,   a**

The initial path of a rocket is 30° above the horizontal and the horizontal component of the rocket's speed is 326 m/s. The initial <u>vertical</u> component of the rocket's speed is

a.  190 m/s
b.  330 m/s
c.  380 m/s
d.  280 m/s
e.  250 m/s

**0318    3-2   Addition of Vectors by Components,   Numerical,   c**

A particle has an initial velocity of 4.8 m/s toward the south and a final velocity of 7.1 m/s toward the east. The particle is accelerated for 0.25 s. The magnitude and the direction of the acceleration is

a.  8.6 m/s$^2$ at 34.1° north of east.
b.  260 m/s$^2$ at 34.1° south of east.
c.  34 m/s$^2$ at 34.1° north of east.
d.  34 m/s$^2$ at 34.1° south of east.
e.  8.6 m/s$^2$ at 34.1° south of east.

0319   **3-3   Velocity and Acceleration Vectors,   Conceptual,   e**

If an object is moving toward the west, its acceleration

a.   is north.
b.   is east.
c.   is west.
d.   is south.
e.   may be any direction.

0320   **3-3   Velocity and Acceleration Vectors,   Conceptual,   d**

A river is 0.76 km wide.  The banks are straight and parallel.  The current is 5.0 km/h and is parallel to the banks.  A boat has a maximum speed of 3 km/h in still water..  The pilot of the boat wishes to go on a straight line from A to B, where AB is perpendicular to the banks.  The pilot should

a.   head directly across the river.
b.   head 68° upstream from the line AB.
c.   head 22° upstream from the line AB.
d.   give up.  The trip from A to B is not possible with this boat.
e.   None of these is correct.

0321   **3-4   Projectile Motion,   Conceptual,   d**

A stone with a mass $m$ is dropped from an airplane with a horizontal velocity $v$ at a height $h$ above a lake.  The horizontal distance $R$ from the point on the lake directly below the point of release to the point where the stone strikes the water is given by the formula

a.   $R = v(2h/g)^2$
b.   $R = (1/2)gt^2$
c.   $R = 2mv\sqrt{2h/g}$
d.   $R = v\sqrt{2h/g}$
e.   None of these is correct.

0322   **3-4   Projectile Motion,   Numerical,   a**

A plane is flying horizontally at a height of 0.5 km and a constant speed of 429 km/h when an object is projected vertically downward at an initial speed of 35 m/s.  Assume no air resistance.  The average speed of the object in the vertical direction between its release and its striking the ground is

a.   70 m/s
b.   $5.5 \times 10^3$ m/s
c.   140 m/s
d.   105 m/s
e.   35 m/s

**0323    3-4   Projectile Motion,   Conceptual,   b**

A projectile is shot at an angle of 45° to the horizontal.  When it reaches the highest point of its trajectory, its speed is 150 m/s.  In a second trial with the same projectile, the initial speed is the same but the angle is now 37° with the horizontal.  At its highest point in this trajectory, the speed of the projectile would be

a.  $\dfrac{\sin 45°}{\sin 37°}$ x  150 m/s

b.  $\dfrac{\cos 37°}{\cos 45°}$ x  150 m/s

c.  $\dfrac{\sin 37°}{\sin 45°}$ x  150 m/s

d.  $\dfrac{37}{45}$ x  150 m/s

e.   None of these is correct.


**0324    3-4   Projectile Motion,   Numerical,   b**

An airplane is diving toward its target at an angle of 37° below the horizontal with a speed of 250 m/s.  It releases a survival package when it is at an altitude of 600 m, and the package hits the intended target.  The horizontal distance of the target from the plane at the moment of the package's release is

a.   $2.8 \times 10^3$ m
b.   720 m
c.   $6.8 \times 10^3$ m
d.   420 m
e.   $5.5 \times 10^3$ m


**0325    3-4   Projectile Motion,   Conceptual,   d**

A golfer drives her ball from the tee a distance of 240 yards down the fairway in a high arcing shot.  When the ball is at the highest point of its flight,

a.   its velocity and acceleration are both zero.
b.   its velocity is zero but its acceleration is nonzero.
c.   its velocity is nonzero but its acceleration is zero.
d.   its velocity and acceleration are both nonzero.
e.   Insufficient information is given to answer correctly.


**0326    3-4   Projectile Motion,   Numerical,   b**

A particle has a speed of 4.0 m/s along the $x$ axis when it is accelerated at 3.0 m/s$^2$ along the $y$ axis for 2.0 s.  The final speed of the particle is

a.   -2.0 m/s
b.   7.2 m/s
c.   6.0 m/s
d.   10 m/s
e.   None of these is correct.

**0327**   **3-4   Projectile Motion,   Conceptual,   e**

A projectile was fired at 35° above the horizontal.  At the highest  point in its trajectory its speed was 200 m/s.  The initial velocity had a horizontal component of

a.  zero
b.  200 cos(35°) m/s
c.  200 sin(35°) m/s
d.  200/cos(35°) m/s
e.  200 m/s

**0328**   **3-4   Projectile Motion,   Conceptual,   a**

A student shoots an archery arrow in a high arc toward a target located some distance away. At the highest point in its flight, the arrow's

a.  velocity and acceleration are both nonzero.
b.  velocity is zero but its acceleration is nonzero.
c.  velocity is nonzero but its acceleration is zero.
d.  velocity and acceleration are both zero.
e.  Insufficient information is given to answer correctly.

**0329**   **3-4   Projectile Motion,   Conceptual,   b**

In projectile motion, the _____ of the projectile remains constant.

a.  velocity vector
b.  $x$-component of the velocity vector
c.  $y$-component of the velocity vector
d.  speed
e.  range

**0330**   **3-4   Projectile Motion,   Conceptual,   d**

The figure represents the parabolic trajectory of a ball going from A to E.  What is the direction of the acceleration at point B?

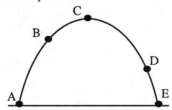

a.  It is up and to the right.
b.  It is down and to the left.
c.  It is straight up.
d.  It is straight down.
e.  The acceleration of the ball is zero.

**0331    3-4    Projectile Motion,    Conceptual,    d**

The figure represents the parabolic trajectory of a ball going from A to E. What is the direction of the acceleration at point C?

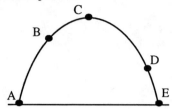

a.  It is to the right.
b.  It is to the left.
c.  It is straight up.
d.  It is straight down.
e.  The acceleration of the ball is zero.

**0332    3-4    Projectile Motion,    Conceptual,    d**

The figure represents the parabolic trajectory of a ball going from A to E. At point C the velocity of the ball is

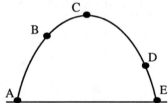

a.  directed to the right.
b.  directed to the left.
c.  a maximum.
d.  a minimum.
e.  zero.

**0333    3-4   Projectile Motion,  Conceptual,  a**

A projectile is fired horizontally with an initial speed $v_O$. Which of the following graphs is representative of the projectile's motion?

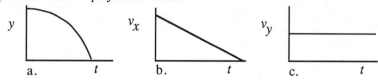

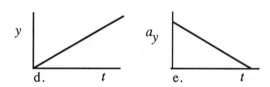

**0334    3-4   Projectile Motion,  Conceptual,  b**

The figure represents the parabolic trajectory of a ball going from A to E.  What is the speed at point C compared to that at point A?

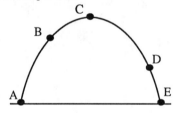

a.   It is greater at C than at A.
b.   It is less at C than at A.
c.   The speeds are identical.

**0335    3-4   Projectile Motion,  Conceptual,  c**

If the initial speed of a projectile is doubled, its range will

a.   double.
b.   decrease by one-half.
c.   increase by a factor of four.
d.   decrease by a factor of four.
e.   not change.

**0336     3-5   Circular Motion,   Conceptual,   b**

A car going around a curve of radius $R$ at a speed $V$ experiences a centripetal acceleration $A_C$. What is its acceleration if it goes around a curve of radius $3R$ at a speed of $2V$?

a.   $(2/3)A_C$
b.   $(4/3)A_C$
c.   $(2/9)A_C$
d.   $(9/2)A_C$
e.   $(3/2)A_C$

**0337     3-5   Circular Motion,   Numerical,   a**

A particle moving with uniform circular motion has a period of 0.24 s and a speed of 420 cm/s. The radius of the path of the particle is

a.   16 cm
b.   2.6 cm
c.   100 cm
d.   0.062 cm
e.   1.4 cm

**0338     3-5   Circular Motion,   Numerical,   d**

A particle is moving uniformly in a circle with radius 50 cm. The linear speed of the particle is 60 cm/s. The acceleration of the particle has a magnitude of

a.   zero
b.   $3600 \text{ cm/s}^2$
c.   $1.8 \times 10^5 \text{ cm/s}^2$
d.   $72 \text{ cm/s}^2$
e.   $360 \text{ cm/s}^2$

**0339     3-5   Circular Motion,   Conceptual,   d**

A car going around a curve of radius $R$ at a speed $V$ experiences a centripetal acceleration $A_C$. What is its acceleration if it goes around a curve of radius $2R$ at a speed of $3V$?

a.   $(2/3)A_C$
b.   $(4/3)A_C$
c.   $(2/9)A_C$
d.   $(9/2)A_C$
e.   $(3/2)A_C$

**0340     3-5   Circular Motion,   Conceptual,   b**

A car experiences both a centripetal and a tangential acceleration. For which of the following would this be true?

a.   It is going around a curve at a constant speed.
b.   It is going around a curve and slowing down.
c.   It is going down a straight road at a constant speed.
d.   It is going down a straight road and increasing its speed.
e.   It is going down a straight road and decreasing its speed.

CHAPTER 4   Newton's Laws

**0401   4-1  Force and Mass,   Conceptual,   d**

A body moves with constant speed in a straight line.  Which of the following statements must be true?

a.   No force acts on the body.
b.   A single constant force acts on the body in the direction of motion.
c.   A single constant force acts on the body in the direction opposite to the motion.
d.   A net force of zero acts on the body.
e.   A constant net force acts on the body in the direction of motion.

**0402   4-1  Force and Mass,   Conceptual,   c**

A body of mass $M$ accelerates under the action of a force.  The same force applied to a second body produces three times the acceleration.  What is the mass of the second object?

a.   $M$
b.   $3M$
c.   $M/3$
d.   $9M$
e.   $M/9$

**0403   4-1  Force and Mass,   Conceptual,   b**

A body of mass $M$ accelerates under the action of a force.  A second body requires twice as much force to produce the same acceleration as the first.  What is the mass of the second body?

a.   $M$
b.   $2M$
c.   $M/2$
d.   $4M$
e.   $M/4$

**0404   4-1  Force and Mass,   Numerical,   e**

A net force of 64 N acts on a mass of 16 kg.  The resulting acceleration is

a.   $16 \text{ m/s}^2$
b.   $510 \text{ m/s}^2$
c.   $64 \text{ m/s}^2$
d.   $9.0 \text{ m/s}^2$
e.   $4.0 \text{ m/s}^2$

0405   **4-1   Force and Mass,   Numerical,   d**

A particle that has a mass of 200 g is acted on by a force of 4.5 N.  The acceleration of the particle is

a.   $0.90 \text{ m/s}^2$
b.   $0.022 \text{ m/s}^2$
c.   $900 \text{ m/s}^2$
d.   $22 \text{ m/s}^2$
e.   $9 \text{ m/s}^2$


0406   **4-1   Force and Mass,   Numerical,   c**

A mass of 25.0 kg is acted upon by two forces:  $F_1$ is 15.0 N due east and $F_2$ is 10.0 N and due north.  The acceleration of the mass is

a.   $0.72 \text{ m/s}^2$,  56.3° north of east.
b.   $0.20 \text{ m/s}^2$,  due east.
c.   $0.72 \text{ m/s}^2$,  33.7° north of east.
d.   $1.0 \text{ m/s}^2$,  33.7° north of east.
e.   $0.20 \text{ m/s}^2$,  56.3° north of east.


0407   **4-1   Force and Mass,   Numerical,   b**

A mass $m$ is traveling at an initial speed $v_0 = 25.0$ m/s.  It is brought to rest in a distance of 62.5 m when a force of 15.0 N acts on it.  The mass $m$ is

a.   37.5 kg
b.   3.00 kg
c.   1.50 kg
d.   6.00 kg
e.   3.75 kg


0408   **4-1   Force and Mass,   Conceptual,   b**

If one applies the same force to objects with masses $M$ and $4M$, the acceleration of the mass $M$ will be

a.   the same as for the mass $4M$.
b.   four times the acceleration of the mass $4M$.
c.   one-fourth the acceleration of the mass $4M$.
d.   twice the acceleration of the mass $4M$.
e.   one-half the acceleration of the mass $4M$.


0409   **4-1   Force and Mass,   Conceptual,   d**

An object is moving to the right with a constant speed.  Which of the following statements must be incorrect?

a.   There are no forces acting on the object.
b.   There is a larger number of forces acting on the object to the right than to the left.
c.   There may be many forces acting on the object to the right.
d.   There is no net force acting on the object.
e.   There is just one force acting on the object and it is to the right.

**0410   4-1   Force and Mass,   Conceptual,   d**

A force $F$ produces an acceleration $a$ on an object of mass $m$. A force of $3F$ is exerted on a second object and an acceleration $8a$ results. What is the mass of the second object?

a. $3m$
b. $9m$
c. $24m$
d. $(3/8)m$
e. $(8/3)m$

**0411   4-1   Force and Mass,   Conceptual,   a**

The law of inertia is Newton's _____ law.

a. first
b. second
c. third
d. None of these is correct.

**0412   4-1   Force and Mass,   Conceptual,   a**

A 10-N force is applied to mass $M$. The same force is applied to mass $4M$. The ratio of the acceleration of the smaller mass to the acceleration of the larger mass is

a. 4 to 1.
b. 20 to 1.
c. 1 to 1.
d. 1 to 2.
e. 1 to 4.

**0413   4-1,   Force and Mass   Conceptual,   c**

Snoopy the dog (of mass $m$) walks into an elevator and steps on a scale. The elevator begins to accelerate toward the basement. While the elevator is accelerating, the scale reads

a. more than the value $mg$.
b. the same as the value $mg$.
c. less than the value $mg$.
d. Insufficient information is given to answer correctly.

**0414   4-2   The Force Due to Gravity: Weight,   Factual,   d**

The weight of a body is

a. the mass of the body.
b. the quantity of matter in the body.
c. the mass of the body times 9.81.
d. the gravitational force acting on the body.
e. the reading on a spring scale attached to the body.

**0415   4-2   The Force Due to Gravity: Weight,  Conceptual,  b**

A body is sent out in space.  As it moves away from the earth, which of the following
statements is true?

a.   The body's mass and weight remain constant.
b.   The body's mass remains constant, and its weight decreases.
c.   The body's mass decreases, and its weight remains constant.
d.   The body's mass and weight decrease.
e.   The body's mass decreases, and its weight increases.


**0416   4-2   The Force Due to Gravity: Weight,  Conceptual,  e**

A person of weight $w$ is in an upward moving elevator when the cable suddenly brakes.
What is the person's apparent weight immediately after the elevator starts to fall?

a.   $w$
b.   Greater than $w$
c.   Less than $w$
d.   $9.8w$
e.   Zero


**0417   4-2   The Force Due to Gravity: Weight,  Factual,  a**

The SI unit of weight is the

a.   newton.
b.   gram.
c.   pound.
d.   kilogram.
e.   None of these is correct.


**0418   4-2   The Force Due to Gravity: Weight,  Factual,  c**

In the cgs system, the units of force are

a.   $g \cdot cm$
b.   $g \cdot cm^2/s^2$
c.   $g \cdot cm/s^2$
d.   $g \cdot s/cm$
e.   $cm\ s^2$


**0419   4-2   The Force Due to Gravity: Weight,  Numerical,  b**

An astronaut lands on an earth-like planet and drops a small lead ball with a mass of 76.5 g
from the top of her spaceship.  The point of release is 18 m above the surface of the planet
and the ball takes 2.5 s to reach the ground.  The astronaut's mass on earth is 68.5 kg.  Her
<u>weight</u> on the planet is

a.   69 N
b.   390 N
c.   670 N
d.   990 N
e.   1020 N

0420   **4-2   The Force Due to Gravity:   Weight,   Conceptual,   b**

A shopper steps on an escalator moving downward at a constant speed toward the bargain basement in a large department store.  On her way down, the normal force exerted on her by the step of the escalator is

a.   greater than her weight when off of the escalator.
b.   equal to her weight when off of the escalator.
c.   less than her weight when off of the escalator.
d.   Insufficient information is given to answer correctly.


0421   **4-2   The Force Due to Gravity:   Weight,   Conceptual,   c**

On the moon, the acceleration due to gravity is only about 1/6 of that on earth.  An astronaut whose weight on earth is 600 N travels to the lunar surface.  His mass as measured on the moon will be

a.   600 kg
b.   100 kg
c.   60 kg
d.   10 kg
e.   360 kg


0422   **4-2   The Force Due to Gravity:   Weight,   Conceptual,   a**

A bathroom scale reads

a.   apparent weight.
b.   mass.
c.   its mass times the acceleration due to gravity.
d.   the gravitational force on it.
e.   the gravitational field.


0423   **4-3   Units of Force and Mass,   Factual,   c**

Which of the following is NOT a unit of force?

a.   Newton
b.   Pound
c.   Slug
d.   Dyne
e.   kg·m/s$^2$


0424   **4-3   Units of Force and Mass,   Factual,   a**

Which of the following is NOT a unit of mass?

a.   Pound
b.   Kilogram
c.   Gram
d.   Slug
e.   Milligram

0425    4-3  **Units of Force and Mass,  Numerical,  a**

What is the weight of a 50-kg girl on the moon, where the acceleration due to gravity is 1.6 $m/s^2$?

a.  80 N
b.  110 lb
c.  490 N
d.  50 N
e.  80 lb


0426    4-3  **Units of Force and Mass,  Conceptual,  c**

The units of force are

a.  $m^2/s^2$
b.  $kg/m/s^2$
c.  $kg \cdot m/s^2$
d.  $N \cdot s$
e.  $N/kg$


0427    4-4  **Newton's Third Law,  Conceptual,  b**

An 80-kg man on ice skates pushes a 40-kg boy also on skates with a force of 100 N.  The force exerted by the boy on the man is

a.  200 N
b.  100 N
c.  50 N
d.  40 N
e.  zero, unless the boy pushes back.


0428    4-4  **Newton's Third Law,  Conceptual,  d**

A boy holds a bird in his hand.  The reaction force to the normal force exerted on the bird by the boy's hand is

a.  the force of the earth on the bird.
b.  the force of the bird on the earth.
c.  the force of the hand on the bird.
d.  the force of the bird on the hand.
e.  the force of the earth on the hand.


0429    4-4  **Newton's Third Law,  Conceptual,  b**

A boy holds a bird in his hand.  The reaction force to the weight of the bird is

a.  the force of the earth on the bird.
b.  the force of the bird on the earth.
c.  the force of the hand on the bird.
d.  the force of the bird on the hand.
e.  the force of the earth on the hand.

**0430   4-4   Newton's Third Law,   Conceptual,   a**

A body of weight $w$ is in free-fall near the surface of the earth.  What force does the body exert on the earth?

a.   $w$
b.   Greater than $w$
c.   Less than $w$
d.   9.8$w$
e.   Zero

**0431   4-4   Newton's Third Law,   Conceptual,   a**

A body of weight $w$ rests on the surface of the earth.  What force does the body exert on the earth? (Ignore the earth's rotation.)

a.   $w$
b.   Greater than $w$
c.   Less than $w$
d.   9.8$w$
e.   Zero

**0432   4-4   Newton's Third Law,   Conceptual,   b**

A horse exerts a force $F$ on a cart, causing the cart to move with increasing speed.  What force does the cart exert on the horse?

a.   Zero
b.   $F$
c.   Greater than $F$
d.   Less than $F$
e.   The force cannot be determined unless the acceleration is given.

**0433   4-4   Newton's Third Law,   Conceptual,   c**

A baseball player hits a ball with a bat.  If the force with which the bat hits the ball is considered the action force, what is the reaction force?

a.   The force the bat exerts on the batter's hands.
b.   The force on the ball exerted by the glove of the person who catches it .
c.   The force the ball exerts on the bat.
d.   The force the pitcher exerts on the ball while throwing it.
e.   Friction, as the ball rolls to a stop.

**0434   4-5   Springs, Strings, and Support Forces,   Conceptual,   c**

If a force $F$ is required to extend a spring by 20 cm, what force is required to extend it by 30 cm?

a.   $F$
b.   (20/30)$F$
c.   (30/20)$F$
d.   600$F$
e.   (30/50)$F$

0435   **4-5   Springs, Strings, and Support Forces,   Conceptual,   d**

If a force $F$ is required to extend a spring a distance $5y$, how far will it be extended by a force $3F$ ?

  a.   $5y$
  b.   $(3/5)y$
  c.   $(5/3)y$
  d.   $15y$
  e.   $(3/8)y$

0436   **4-6   Applications to Problem Solving: Constant Forces,   Numerical,   b**

A horse-drawn coach is decelerating at 3.0 m/s$^2$ while moving in a straight line.  A mass $m$ = 350 g is hanging on a string 1.6 m long from the ceiling of the coach.  The angle that the string makes with the vertical is

  a.   9.3° toward the front of the coach.
  b.   17° toward the front of the coach.
  c.   9.3° toward the back of the coach.
  d.   2.5° toward the front of the coach.
  e.   0° or straight down.

0437   **4-6   Applications to Problem Solving: Constant Forces,   Conceptual,   d**

Two masses $m_1$ and $m_2$ connected together by a massless string are accelerated uniformly on a frictionless surface as shown.  The ratio of the tensions $T_1/T_2$ is given by

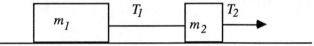

  a.   $m_1/m_2$
  b.   $m_2/m_1$
  c.   $(m_1 + m_2)/m_2$
  d.   $m_1/(m_1 + m_2)$
  e.   $m_2/(m_1 + m_2)$

0438   **4-6   Applications to Problem Solving: Constant Forces,   Numerical,   a**

A car is accelerating at a rate of 2.5 m/s$^2$.  A mass of 250 g is hanging from the ceiling on a string 1.2 m long.  The angle that the string makes with the vertical is

  a.   14° toward the back of the car.
  b.   76° toward the back of the car.
  c.   7° toward the front of the car.
  d.   14° toward the front of the car.
  e.   0° or straight down.

**0439    4-6   Applications to Problem Solving: Constant Forces,   Numerical,   b**

A lamp with a mass $m = 42.6$ kg is hanging from wires as shown.  The tension $T_1$ in the vertical wire is

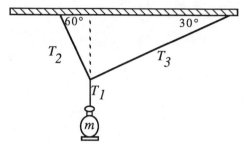

a.  210 N
b.  420 N
c.  570 N
d.  360 N
e.  730 N

**0440    4-6   Applications to Problem Solving: Constant Forces,   Numerical,   e**

A lamp with a mass $m$  is suspended from the ceiling by two cords as shown below.  The ratio of the magnitude of the vertical component of the tension in $T_2$  to that in $T_3$  is

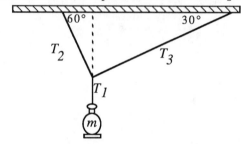

a.  1:1
b.  1:2
c.  $\sqrt{3}:3$
d.  3:2
e.  3:1

**0441    4-6   Applications to Problem Solving: Constant Forces,   Conceptual,   a**

A boy sits in a tire attached to a rope that passes over a pulley fastened to the ceiling and then back down to the boy.  The weight of the boy is $W$.  The force with which the boy must pull down on the free end of the rope in order to support his weight while sitting in the tire is

a.  $(1/2)W$
b.  $W$
c.  $2W$
d.  $(2/3)W$
e.  $(3/2)W$

**0442    4-6    Applications to Problem Solving: Constant Forces,   Numerical,   a**

A vertical rope is attached to an object that has a mass of 40.0 kg and is at rest.  The tension in the rope needed to give the object an upward speed of 3.50 m/s in 0.700 s is

a.  590 N
b.  390 N
c.  200 N
d.  980 N
e.  720 N


**0443    4-6    Applications to Problem Solving: Constant Forces,   Conceptual,   a**

A mass 2*m* is attached by a string to another mass *m*, as illustrated.  A force of *N* newtons acts on mass *m* to accelerate the system.  The force *F* in the string, which acts on mass 2*m*, is

a.  2*N*/3 newtons.
b.  *N* newtons.
c.  2*N* newtons.
d.  3*N* newtons.
e.  3*N*/2 newtons.


**0444    4-6    Applications to Problem Solving: Constant Forces,   Numerical,   e**

A particle of mass 1.3 kg is sliding down a frictionless slope inclined at 30° to the horizontal.  The acceleration of the particle down the slope is

a.  1.3 m/s$^2$
b.  9.8 m/s$^2$
c.  0.5 m/s$^2$
d.  8.5 m/s$^2$
e.  4.9 m/s$^2$


**0445    4-6    Applications to Problem Solving: Constant Forces,   Numerical,   b**

A student wishes to elope by sliding down a nylon rope made by tying stockings together.  The rope will withstand a maximum tension of 300 N without breaking.  The student's mass is 61.2 kg.  The magnitude of the smallest acceleration *a* with which the student can slide down the rope is

a.  9.8 m/s$^2$
b.  4.9 m/s$^2$
c.  zero
d.  2.4 m/s$^2$
e.  19.6 m/s$^2$

**0446    4-6   Applications to Problem Solving: Constant Forces,   Numerical,   a**

A student is riding an elevator that is accelerating upward at 2.20 m/s$^2$.  He has a spring balance accurately calibrated in newtons.  When he hangs a mass of 10.0 kg on the balance, the reading of the balance is

 a.   120 N
 b.   98 N
 c.   76 N
 d.   10 N
 e.   9.8 N

**0447    4-6   Applications to Problem Solving: Constant Forces,   Numerical,   a**

An object with a mass $M$ = 250 g is on a plane inclined at 30° above the horizontal and is attached by a string to a mass $m$ = 150 g.  There is no friction and mass $m$ hangs freely. When mass $m$ has dropped a distance $h$ = 10 cm, its speed is

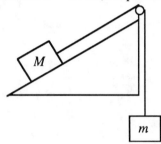

 a.   35 cm/s
 b.   7 cm/s
 c.   140 cm/s
 d.   110 cm/s
 e.   70 cm/s

**0448    4-6   Applications to Problem Solving: Constant Forces,   Numerical,   b**

A mass $m$ is hanging on a string that passes over a pulley and is attached to another mass $3m$ that is resting on a horizontal table.  Neglect friction.  Mass $m$ is held motionless and is then released.  When it has fallen a distance $h$, it has a speed $v$ that can be calculated from the formula

 a.   $v = \sqrt{gh/4}$
 b.   $v = \sqrt{gh/2}$
 c.   $v = \sqrt{gh}$
 d.   $v = \sqrt{2gh}$
 e.   None of these is correct.

**0449    4-6   Applications to Problem Solving: Constant Forces,   Numerical,   c**

A mass of 4.2 kg has three forces, **X**, **Y**, and **Z**, acting on it.  The forces are:

> **X** = 2.0 N acting to the east
> **Y** = 5.0 N acting 45° to the north of east
> **Z** = 4.0 N acting 30° to the north of west

The magnitude of the net acceleration of the mass is

a.  2.9 m/s$^2$
b.  5.3 m/s$^2$
c.  1.4 m/s$^2$
d.  0.0 m/s$^2$
e.  18 m/s$^2$

**0450    4-6   Applications to Problem Solving: Constant Forces,   Numerical,   c**

A mass of 4.2 kg has three forces, **X**, **Y**, and **Z** acting on it.  The forces are:

> **X** = 2.0 N acting to the east
> **Y** = 5.0 N acting 45° to the north of east
> **Z** = 4.0 N acting 30° to the north of west

The direction of the net acceleration

a.  cannot be determined since the acceleration is zero.
b.  is 61° north of east.
c.  is 70° north of east.
d.  is 51° north of east.
e.  is 44° north of east.

**0451    4-6   Applications to Problem Solving: Constant Forces,   Numerical,   d**

Eighty grams of blood is pumped from the heart with each heartbeat.  The blood starts from rest and reaches a speed of 0.60 m/s in the aorta.  If the pumping takes 0.16 s, the average force on the blood is

a.  3.0 x10$^2$ N
b.  0.22 N
c.  0.16 N
d.  0.30 N
e.  0.98 N

**0452    4-6   Applications to Problem Solving: Constant Forces,   Conceptual,   a**

If two blocks of metal of different masses slide freely down the same frictionless incline, which one of the following will be true?

a.  They will have equal accelerations.
b.  They will have unequal accelerations, but the forces acting on them will be equal.
c.  The more massive one will reach the bottom first.
d.  The less massive one will reach the bottom first.
e.  None of these is correct.

**0453   4-6   Applications to Problem Solving: Constant Forces,   Conceptual,   d**

A 15-kg block sitting on a smooth table is connected to a 5-kg mass by a stretchless, massless cord that hangs over a small frictionless pully.  The acceleration of the two-block system is

a.   equal to $g$.
b.   half of $g$.
c.   one-third of $g$.
d.   one-quarter of $g$.
e.   zero.


**0454   4-6   Application to Problem Solving: Constant Forces,   Conceptual,   d**

A 6-kg block sitting on a smooth table is connected to a 2-kg mass by a stretchless, massless cord that hangs over a small frictionless pulley.  The acceleration of the two-block system is

a.   equal to $g$.
b.   half of g.
c.   one-third of $g$.
d.   one-quarter of $g$.
e.   two-thirds of $g$.


**0455   4-6   Applications to Problem Solving: Constant Forces,   Conceptual,   d**

A man riding in an elevator has an apparent weight greater than his actual weight.  Which of the following statements could be true?

a.   The elevator moves upward with constant speed.
b.   The elevator moves downward with constant speed.
c.   The elevator moves upward with decreasing speed.
d.   The elevator moves downward with decreasing speed.
e.   The elevator moves downward with increasing speed.


**0456   4-6   Applications to Problem Solving: Constant Forces,   Conceptual,   c**

A body hangs from a blue rope.  A red rope attached to the side of the body is pulled in the horizontal direction.  This causes the blue rope to make an angle with the vertical.  Which of the following statements is true?

a.   The red rope is under greater tension than the blue rope.
b.   The red rope is under the same tension as the blue rope.
c.   The blue rope is under greater tension than the red rope.
d.   The tensions cannot be compared unless the mass of the body is given.
e.   The tensions cannot be compared unless the angle that the blue rope makes with the vertical is given.


**0457   4-6   Applications to Problem Solving: Constant Forces,   Conceptual,   e**

A net force is exerted on an object toward the north.  The object

a.   is moving toward the north.
b.   is moving toward the east.
c.   is moving toward the west.
d.   is moving toward the south.
e.   may be moving in any direction.

0458   **4-6   Applications to Problem Solving: Constant Forces,   Conceptual,   b**

A box sets on an inclined plane without sliding.  As the angle of inclination increases, the normal force

a.   increases.
b.   decreases.
c.   does not change.
d.   is directed upward.
e.   is directed in the direction of the gravitational force.

0459   **4-6   Applications to Problem Solving: Constant Forces,   Conceptual,   d**

In the diagram, what happens to the tension $T_1$ as the mass $m$ is moved to the left and the angle Ø increases?

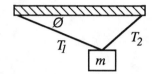

a.   It will not change.
b.   It approaches zero.
c.   It approaches $m$.
d.   It increases.
e.   It decreases.

0460   **4-6   Applications to Problem Solving: Constant Forces,   Factual,   d**

As it applies to forces, the word *normal* means

a.   usual.
b.   mean.
c.   average.
d.   perpendicular.
e.   straight up, in the direction opposite to the force of gravity.

0461   **4-6   Applications to Problem Solving: Constant Forces,   Conceptual,   c**

A lamp of mass $m$ hangs from a spring scale that is attached to the ceiling of an elevator. When the elevator is stopped at the fortieth floor, the scale reads $mg$.  What does it read when the elevator descends toward the ground floor at a constant speed?

a.   more than $mg$
b.   less than $mg$
c.   $mg$
d.   This cannot be answered without knowing how fast the elevator is descending.

0462   **4-6   Applications to Problem Solving: Constant Forces,   Numerical,   d**

A particle has a mass of $6.0 \times 10^{-6}$ kg and a velocity of 800 m/s along the $x$ axis when a force of $14.4 \times 10^{-5}$ N along the $y$ axis acts on the particle at right angles to the velocity. The acceleration of the particle is

a.   24 m/s$^2$ along the $x$ axis.
b.   zero.
c.   impossible to determine; forces never act at right angles to velocities.
d.   24 m/s$^2$ along the $y$ axis.
e.   tangential.

**0463   4-6   Applications to Problem Solving: Constant Forces,   Numerical,   d**

A force of 3 N acts on a body along a direction 30° above the horizontal.  In addition there a gravitational force of 4 N downward.  The resultant force has magnitude of

a.  7.0 N
b.  6.8 N
c.  6.1 N
d.  3.6 N
e.  5.0 N

**0464   4-6   Applications to Problem Solving: Constant Forces,   Numerical,   b**

For this problem, assume there is no friction.  A mass $m_2$ = 3.5 kg rests on a horizontal table and is attached by strings to masses $m_1$ = 1.5 kg and $m_3$ = 2.5 kg as shown.  The masses $m_1$ and $m_3$ hang freely.  The system is initially held at rest.  After it is released, the acceleration of mass $m_2$ is

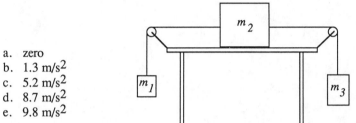

a.   zero
b.   1.3 m/s$^2$
c.   5.2 m/s$^2$
d.   8.7 m/s$^2$
e.   9.8 m/s$^2$

**0465   4-6   Applications to Problem Solving: Constant Forces,   Conceptual,   a**

A lamp of mass $m$ hangs from a spring scale that is attached to the ceiling of an elevator.  When the elevator is stopped at the fortieth floor, the scale reads $mg$.  What does it read while the elevator slows down to stop at the ground floor?

a.  More than $mg$
b.  Less than $mg$
c.  $mg$
d.  One cannot tell without knowing how fast the elevator is stopping.

**0466   4-6   Applications to Problem Solving: Constant Forces,   Conceptual,   b**

A lamp of mass $m$ hangs from a spring scale which is attached to the ceiling of an elevator.  When the elevator is stopped at the fortieth floor, the scale reads $mg$.  What does it read while the elevator slows down to stop at the forty-fifth floor?

a.  More than $mg$
b.  Less than $mg$
c.  $mg$
d.  One cannot tell without knowing how fast the elevator is stopping.

**0467   4-6   Applications to Problem Solving: Constant Forces,   Conceptual,   c**

Three boxes are connected by stretchless strings and are pulled by a force $F$ as shown in the figure.  Which string has to be the strongest so as not to break?

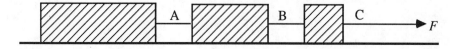

a.  A
b.  B
c.  C
d.  They all have to be equally strong.

**0468   4-6   Applications to Problem Solving: Constant Forces,   Conceptual,   d**

Three boxes are connected by stretchless strings and are pulled by a force $F$ as shown in the figure. Which box has the greatest acceleration?

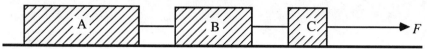

a.   A
b.   B
c.   C
d.   They all have the same acceleration.

**0469   4-6   Applications to Problem Solving: Constant Forces,   Conceptual,   e**

Which of the following free-body diagrams represents a block sliding down a frictionless inclined surface?

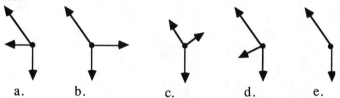

**0470   4-6   Applications to Problem Solving: Constant Forces,   Conceptual,   c**

Which of the following free-body diagrams represents a car going uphill at a constant speed?

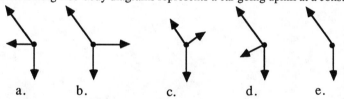

**0471   4-6   Applications to Problem Solving: Constant Forces,   Conceptual,   c**

Which of the following free-body diagrams represents a car going downhill without acceleration?

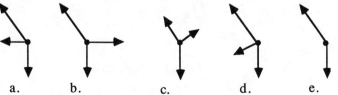

**0472   4-6   Applications to Problem Solving: Constant Forces,   Conceptual,   b**

A net force is exerted toward the east on an object that is initially at rest. Which direction will the object start to move?

a.   North
b.   East
c.   West
d.   South
e.   It may start to move in any of these directions.

CHAPTER 5     Applications of Newton's Laws

**0501     5-1   Friction,   Conceptual,   c**

A tired worker pushes on a heavy (100-kg) crate resting on a thick pile carpet. The coefficients of static and kinetic friction are 0.6 and 0.4, respectively. The worker pushes with a force of 500 N. The frictional force exerted by the surface is

a.  1000 N
b.  600 N
c.  500 N
d.  400 N
e.  100 N

**0502     5-1   Friction,   Conceptual,   d**

A block of mass $m$ is at rest on an inclined plane that makes an angle of 30° with the horizontal, as shown in the figure. Which of the following statements about the force of static friction is true?

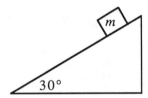

a.  $f_s > mg$
b.  $f_s > mg \cos 30°$
c.  $f_s = mg \cos 30°$
d.  $f_s = mg \sin 30°$
e.  None of these statements is true.

**0503     5-1   Friction,   Conceptual,   b**

Two objects are initially sliding at the same speed across a wooden surface. The coefficient of kinetic friction between the first object and the surface is twice that between the second object and the surface. The distance traveled before stopping by the first object is $S$. The distance traveled by the second object is

a.  impossible to determine without knowing the masses involved.
b.  2$S$
c.  $S/2$
d.  $S$
e.  4$S$

**0504   5-1   Friction,   Conceptual,   b**

A 10-kg block is initially at rest on a level surface, where the coefficient of static friction is 0.6 and that for kinetic friction is 0.4, when a 50-N horizontal force is applied. The frictional force on the block is

a.   60 N
b.   50 N
c.   40 N
d.   20 N
e.   10 N

**0505   5-1   Friction,   Conceptual,   c**

A worker pulls horizontally on a rope that is attached to a 10-kg crate resting on a rough floor. The coefficients of static and kinetic friction are 0.5 and 0.3, respectively. The worker pulls with a force of 40 N. The frictional force exerted by the surface is

a.   100 N
b.   50 N
c.   40 N
d.   30 N
e.   10 N

**0506   5-1   Friction,   Conceptual,   c**

A heavy truck and a light car are both traveling at the same speed on the same roadway. If the coefficients of static friction between their tires and the road are the same, which vehicle will be able to stop in the shortest distance?

a.   The car
b.   The truck
c.   Both will be able to stop in the same distance.
d.   Cannot tell without knowing their coefficients of kinetic friction.
e.   Cannot tell without knowing their individual masses.

**0507   5-1   Friction,   Factual,   e**

Which of the following statements is NOT true about friction?

a.   $\mu_k$ is less than $\mu_s$.
b.   $\mu_k$ is independent of the relative speed of the surfaces in the range of about 1 cm/s to several metres per second.
c.   $\mu_k$ depends on the relative speed of the surfaces at speeds over several metres per second.
d.   The coefficients of friction depend on the nature of the surfaces.
e.   The force of static friction depends on the area of contact between the two surfaces.

**0508   5-1   Friction,   Numerical,   d**

An object with a mass of 5.5 kg is allowed to slide from rest down an inclined plane. The plane makes an angle of 30° with the horizontal and is 72 m long. The coefficient of friction between the plane and the object is 0.35. The speed of the object at the bottom of the plane is

a.   5.3 m/s
b.   15 m/s
c.   24 m/s
d.   17 m/s
e.   11 m/s

**0509   5-1   Friction,   Conceptual,   e**

A block of wood is pulled by a horizontal string across a rough surface at a constant velocity with a force of 20 N.  The coefficient of kinetic friction between the surfaces is 0.3.  The force of friction is

a.   impossible to determine without knowing the mass of the block.
b.   impossible to determine without knowing the speed of the block.
c.   0.3 N
d.   6 N
e.   20 N

**0510   5-1   Friction,   Conceptual,   e**

A block of mass $m$ is pulled across a rough surface at a constant velocity by a string in the direction shown in the figure.  The magnitude of the frictional force is

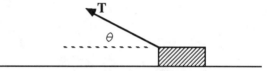

a.   $\mu_k mg$
b.   $\mu_k T \cos \theta$
c.   $\mu_k (T - mg)$
d.   $\mu_k T \sin \theta$
e.   $\mu_k (mg - T \sin \theta)$

**0511   5-1   Friction,   Numerical,   b**

An object is accelerating down a plane that is inclined at an angle of 27.5° above the horizontal.  The acceleration is 3.65 m/s².  The coefficient of friction $\mu_k$  between the plane and the object is

a.   $\mu_k = 0.52$
b.   $\mu_k = 0.10$
c.   $\mu_k = 0.20$
d.   $\mu_k = 0.30$
e.   $\mu_k = 0.40$

**0512   5-1   Friction,   Numerical,   b**

A mass $M = 5.6$  kg is on a horizontal table and is pulled by a horizontal string that passes over a frictionless pulley to another mass $m = 3.4$ kg hanging on the end of the string.  The coefficient of friction between $M$ and the table is 0.28.  The acceleration of $M$ is

a.   3.7 m/s²
b.   2.0 m/s²
c.   2.2 m/s²
d.   0.20 m/s²
e.   0.49 m/s²

**0513**   **5-1   Friction,   Numerical,   a**

An object with a mass $M = 250$ g is at rest
on a plane that makes an angle $\theta = 30°$
above the horizontal. The coefficient of
kinetic friction between $M$ and the plane is
$\mu_k = 0.100$. Mass $M$ is attached by a string
to another mass $m = 200$ g, which hangs
freely. When mass $m$ has fallen 30.0 cm,
its speed is

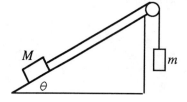

a.   83 cm/s
b.   48 cm/s
c.   160 cm/s
d.   59 cm/s
e.   72 cm/s


**0514**   **5-1   Friction,   Numerical,   b**

A mass $M = 4.0$ kg is on a horizontal table and is pulled by a horizontal string that passes
over a pulley to a mass $m = 1.9$ kg, which hangs at the end of the string. The coefficient of
kinetic friction between $M$ and the table is $\mu_k = 0.25$. The acceleration of $M$ is

a.   5.2 m/s$^2$
b.   1.5 m/s$^2$
c.   3.2 m/s$^2$
d.   4.8 m/s$^2$
e.   6.4 m/s$^2$


**0515**   **5-1   Friction,   Factual,   e**

The SI units for the coefficient of friction are

a.   newtons per metre.
b.   metres.
c.   newtons.
d.   newtons times metres.
e.   The coefficient of friction has no units.


**0516**   **5-1   Friction,   Numerical,   b**

A horizontal force $F$ acts on a mass $m$, that lies on a horizontal surface. The acceleration of
$m$ is $a$. The coefficient of kinetic friction $\mu_k$ between mass $m$ and the surface can be
calculated from

a.   $\mu_k = a/g$
b.   $\mu_k = (F/mg) - (a/g)$
c.   $\mu_k = (F/mg) + (a/g)$
d.   $\mu_k = 0$
e.   None of these is correct.

**0517   5-1   Friction,   Numerical,   a**

A mass $m_2 = 1.5$ kg rests on a horizontal table.  The coefficient of friction between $m_2$ and the table is $\mu_s = 0.3$ and $\mu_k = 0.25$.  The mass $m_2$ is attached by a string to masses $m_1 = 2.5$ kg and $m_3 = 4.5$ kg.  Masses $m_1$ and $m_3$ hang freely.  The system is initially held at rest.  After it is released, the acceleration of $m_2$ is

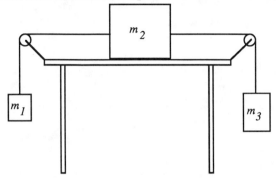

a.   11 m/s$^2$.
b.   2.4 m/s$^2$.
c.   3.0 m/s$^2$.
d.   zero.
e.   13 m/s$^2$.

**0518   5-1   Friction,   Numerical,   c**

A horizontal force $F$ is being used to push an object of mass $m$ up an inclined plane.  The angle between the plane and the horizontal is $\phi$.  The normal reaction force of the plane acting on the mass $m$ is

a.   $mg \cos \phi + F \cos \phi$
b.   $mg \cos \phi$
c.   $mg \cos \phi + F \sin \phi$
d.   $mg \cos \phi - F \cos \phi$
e.   impossible to determine because the coefficient of friction is not given.

**0519   5-1   Friction,   Numerical,   b**

A block with a mass of 10 kg is at rest on a horizontal surface.  The coefficient of static friction between the block and the surface is 0.30 and the coefficient of kinetic friction is 0.25.  A force of 20 N acts on the block toward the left.  The magnitude of the frictional force on the block is

a.   10 N
b.   20 N
c.   100 N
d.   30 N
e.   3 N

**0520    5-1  Friction,   Conceptual,   b**

A block of mass $m$ is pulled by a string in the direction shown in the figure across a rough surface with a constant acceleration $a$ .  The magnitude of the frictional force is

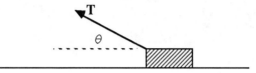

a.  $\mu_k mg$
b.  $T \cos\theta - ma$
c.  $\mu_k(T - mg)$
d.  $\mu_k T \sin\theta$
e.  $\mu_k(mg + \sin\theta)$

**0521    5-2  Static Equilibrium of an Extended Body,   Conceptual,   c**

The horizontal bar in the diagram will remain horizontal if

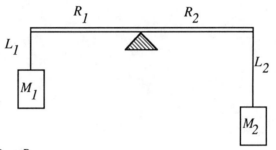

a.  $L_1 = L_2$ and $R_1 = R_2$
b.  $L_1 = L_2$ and $M_1 = M_2$
c.  $R_1 = R_2$ and $M_1 = M_2$
d.  $L_1 M_1 = L_2 M_2$
e.  $R_1 L_1 = R_2 L_2$

**0522    5-2  Static Equilibrium of an Extended Body,   Numerical,   d**

If the force $F$ shown in the diagram is 840 N and the bottom right edge of the box is slightly off the ground, what is the weight of the box?    [HINT: With the right edge slightly off the ground, the forces applied by the floor and the ridge must be at the bottom left corner of the box.]

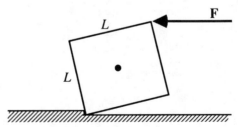

a.   420 N
b.   590 N
c.   840 N
d.   $1.7 \times 10^3$ N
e.   $2.4 \times 10^3$ N

0523   **5-2  Static Equilibrium of an Extended Body,  Conceptual,  d**

A 10-m long plank (of negligible mass) is supported at each end by vertical cables. A person of unknown weight sits on the plank between the cables. The tension in the left cable is 300 N, and in the right cable it is 200 N. The person's weight is

a.   100 N
b.   300 N
c.   400 N
d.   500 N
e.   700 N

0524   **5-2  Static Equilibrium of an Extended Body,  Conceptual,  c**

A 10-m long plank (of negligible mass) is supported at each end by vertical cables. A person of unknown weight sits on the plank between the cables. The tension in the left cable is 300 N, and in the right cable it is 200 N. How far is the person sitting from the left cable?

a.   2.0 m
b.   3.0 m
c.   4.0 m
d.   6.0 m
e.   7.0 m

0525   **5-2  Static Equilibrium of an Extended Body,  Conceptual,  c**

Under which of the following conditions can a ladder standing on a frictionless horizontal floor and leaning against a rough vertical wall be in equilibrium?

a.   The normal force exerted by the floor on the ladder equals the normal force the wall exerts on the ladder.
b.   The weight of the ladder is equal in magnitude to the frictional force the wall exerts on the ladder.
c.   A ladder in this situation cannot be in equilibrium.
d.   The normal force exerted by the floor on the ladder equals the weight of the ladder.
e.   The normal force exerted by the floor on the ladder equals the frictional force the wall exerts on the ladder.

0526   **5-3  Stability of Equilibrium and Balance,  Conceptual,  c**

Which of the following objects is nearest to being in unstable equilibrium?

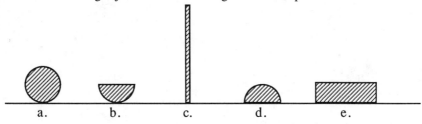

a.            b.            c.            d.            e.

0527   **5-3   Stability of Equilibrium and Balance,   Conceptual,   e**

An upright refrigerator will tip over if

a.   its height is greater than its width.
b.   its center of mass is below the middle of the refrigerator.
c.   its center of mass is above the middle of the refrigerator.
d.   its center of mass is at the middle of the refrigerator.
e.   its center of mass is not over the bottom of the refrigerator.


0528   **5-4   Circular Motion,   Conceptual,   b**

On an icy winter day, the coefficient of friction between the tires of a car and a roadway might be reduced to one-half of its value on a dry day.  As a result, the maximum speed at which a curve of radius $R$ can be safely negotiated is

a.   the same as on a dry day.
b.   reduced to 70% of its value on a dry day.
c.   reduced to 50% of its value on a dry day.
d.   reduced to 25% of its value on a dry day.
e.   reduced by an unknown amount depending on the car's mass.


0529   **5-4   Circular Motion,   Conceptual,   d**

Our moon's mass is about 1% that of the earth.  Relative to the gravitational force that the earth exerts on our moon, the centripetal force that keeps our moon in its orbit around the earth

a.   is much smaller.
b.   depends on the phase of the moon.
c.   is much greater.
d.   is the same.
e.   I cannot answer; we haven't studied Newton's law of gravity yet


0530   **5-4   Circular Motion,   Conceptual,   b**

A car is traveling around a curve at a uniform speed.  Which of the following statements is true?

a.   The net force on it is zero.
b.   The net force on it is toward the center of the curve.
c.   The net force on it is away from the center of the curve.
d.   The net force on it is tangent to the curve.
e.   None of these is correct.

**0531    5-4  Circular Motion,  Conceptual,  c**

A block slides on a frictionless surface along a loop-the-loop shown in the figure.  Which free-body diagram is correct for the block when it is located at point A?

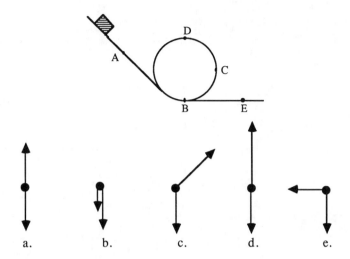

a.          b.          c.          d.          e.

**0532    5-4  Circular Motion,  Conceptual,  d**

A block slides on a frictionless surface along a loop-the-loop shown in the figure.  Which free-body diagram is correct for the block when it is located at point B?

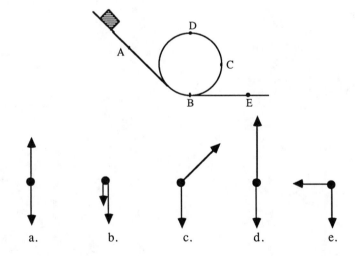

a.          b.          c.          d.          e.

**0533   5-4   Circular Motion,   Conceptual,   e**

A block slides on a frictionless surface along a loop-the-loop shown in the figure.  Which free-body diagram is correct for the block when it is located at point C?

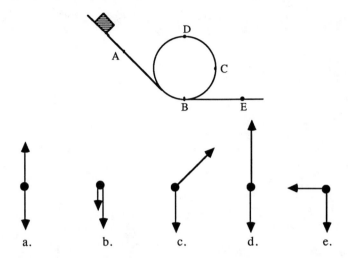

a.            b.            c.            d.            e.

**0534   5-4   Circular Motion,   Conceptual,   b**

A block slides on a frictionless surface along a loop-the-loop shown in the figure.  Which free-body diagram is correct for the block when it is located at point D?

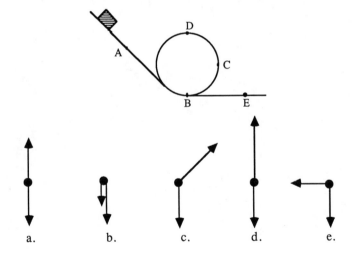

a.            b.            c.            d.            e.

**0535    5-4  Circular Motion,  Conceptual,  a**

A block slides on a frictionless surface along a loop-the-loop shown in the figure. Which free-body diagram is correct for the block when it is located at point E?

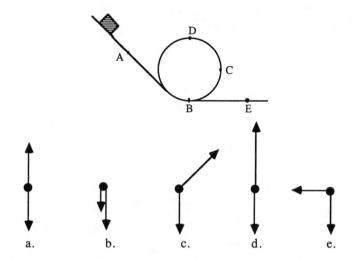

a.                  b.                  c.                  d.                  e.

**0536    5-4  Circular Motion,  Conceptual,  d**

A person rides a loop-the-loop at an amusement park. The cart circles the track at a constant speed. At the top of the loop, the normal force exerted by the seat is equivalent to the force of gravity (one "gee"). At the bottom of the loop, the rider will experience

a.  no force from the seat (weightlessness).
b.  a normal force equivalent to ordinary gravity (one "gee").
c.  a normal force equivalent to two "gee's."
d.  a normal force equivalent to three "gee's."
e.  a normal force greater than one "gee," but it cannot be calculated from the information given.

**0537    5-4  Circular Motion,  Numerical,  b**

An engineer who did poorly in college physics has designed a racetrack that is banked the wrong way, that is, away from the center. The angle of outward banking is $\phi = 9.0°$. The coefficient of friction between the tires and the road is $\mu_s = 0.45$. The radius of curvature of the track is $R = 50.0$ m. The largest speed at which the race car can negotiate the track without skidding is

a.  13.8 m/s
b.  11.5 m/s
c.  10.1 m/s
d.  8.8 m/s
e.  6.1 m/s

**0538   5-4   Circular Motion,   Numerical,   a**

A car speeds around the curved exit ramp of a freeway.  The radius of the curve is 80 m.  A 70-kg passenger holds the arm rest of the car door with a 220 N force in order to keep from sliding across the front seat of the car.  (Assume the exit ramp is not banked and ignore friction with the car seat.)  What is the car's speed?

   a.  16 m/s
   b.  57 m/s
   c.  18 m/s
   d.  50 m/s
   e.  28 m/s

**0539   5-4   Circular Motion,   Conceptual,   c**

A body moves with constant speed in a circle.  Which of the following statements is true?

   a.  No force acts on the body.
   b.  A single constant force acts in the direction of motion.
   c.  A net force acts toward the center of the circle.
   d.  A net force of zero acts on the body.
   e.  A net force acts away from the center of the circle.

**0540   5-4   Circular Motion,   Numerical,   b**

A car is moving around an <u>unbanked</u> horizontal curve of a radius 300 m.  The static-friction force of the road on the tires of the car provides the centripetal force that enables the car to make the curve.  If the coefficient of static friction is $\mu_s = 0.477$, the maximum speed at which the car can make it around the curve is

   a.  The answer cannot be found since the mass of the car is not given.
   b.  37 m/s
   c.  68 m/s
   d.  14 m/s
   e.  200 m/s

**0541   5-4   Circular Motion,   Numerical,   c**

A stone with a mass $m = 95$ g is being whirled in a horizontal circle on the end of a string that is 85 cm long.  The length of time required for the stone to make one complete revolution is 1.22 s.  The angle which the string makes with the horizontal is

   a.  52°
   b.  46°
   c.  26°
   d.  23°
   e.  3°

**0542   5-4   Circular Motion,   Numerical,   d**

A race-car driver wishes to go around a banked, icy curve ($\mu_s = 0$) without skidding.  The curve is banked at 24° above the horizontal, and the radius of curvature is 65 m.  The speed of the car should be

   a.  28 m/s
   b.  15 m/s
   c.  13 m/s
   d.  17 m/s
   e.  8.7 m/s

**0543    5-4   Circular Motion,   Numerical,   b**

A stone of mass $m$ is attached to a light string that is 80 cm long.  The string makes an angle of 25° with the horizontal while the stone moves in a horizontal circle.  How much time is required for the stone to make one complete revolution?

a.  The problem cannot be solved because the mass of the stone is not given.
b.  1.2 s
c.  3.9 s
d.  5.4 s
e.  15 s

**0544    5-4   Circular Motion,   Conceptual,   c**

If a particle that is moving with uniform circular motion has a constant speed,

a.  the force on the particle is zero.
b.  the acceleration of the particle is zero.
c.  the acceleration, which is constant in magnitude, is at right angles to the direction of the velocity.
d.  the tangential acceleration equals the centripetal acceleration.
e.  None of these is correct.

**0545    5-4   Circular Motion,   Numerical,   b**

A road that is banked at an angle of 24° above the horizontal has a radius of curvature of 65 m.  A driver wishes to negotiate the curve at 29.5 m/s.  The minimum coefficient of friction between the tires and the road must be

a.    0.46
b.    0.57
c.    0.40
d.    0.70
e.    1.0

**0546    5-4   Circular Motion,   Numerical,   a**

A centrifuge is rotating 60,000 revolutions per minute.  The force required to keep a particle of mass $6.2 \times 10^{-6}$ kg at distance of 5.0 cm from the axis of rotation is

a.  12 N
b.  $1.9 \times 10^{-3}$ N
c.  0.31 N
d.  $4.4 \times 10^{4}$ N
e.  $8.1 \times 10^{2}$ N

0547   **5-4   Circular Motion,   Conceptual,   e**

A particle is traveling in a vertical circle at constant speed.  One can conclude that the
_____ is constant.

a.   velocity
b.   acceleration
c.   net force
d.   apparent weight
e.   None of these are constant.

0548   **5-4   Circular Motion,   Conceptual,   c**

A frictional force $f$ provides the centripetal force as a car goes around a curve of radius $r$ at a
speed $v$.  If the speed of the car is tripled to $3v$, the frictional force must be

a.   $3f$
b.   $(1/3)f$
c.   $9f$
d.   $(1/9)f$
e.   It cannot be determined without knowing the coefficient of static friction.

0549   **5-4   Circular Motion,   Conceptual,   c**

Which of the following free-body diagrams is correct for a car going around a banked
curve?

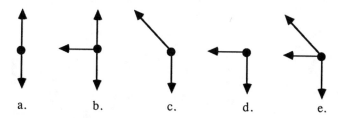

a.              b.              c.              d.              e.

0550   **5-4   Circular Motion,   Conceptual,   e**

Which of the following free-body diagrams could represent a car going around a curve
without friction?

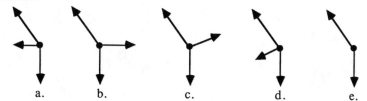

a.              b.              c.              d.              e.

0551   **5-5   Drag Forces,   Conceptual,   e**

The net force acting on an object is zero.  One can therefore definitely conclude that

a.   the object is at rest.
b.   the object is moving in a straight line at constant speed.
c.   the object is moving in a circle at constant speed.
d.   the object is undergoing an acceleration.
e.   the object is either at rest or moving in a straight line at constant speed.

**0552    5-5   Drag Forces,   Numerical,   b**

An object with a mass of $m = 12.0$ g is falling through a resistive fluid, where $g$ is constant. The retarding frictional force due to the fluid is $F = bv$, where $F$ is the force in newtons, $b$ is a constant, and $v$ is the speed in metres per second.  If $F = 3.2 \times 10^{-2}$ N when $v = 16.0$ m/s, the terminal speed of the object falling through the fluid is

a.   0.12 m/s
b.   59 m/s
c.   190 m/s
d.   16.0 m/s

**0553    5-5   Drag Forces,   Factual,   c**

In the equation $F = bv$, $F$ is the force on an object that is moving in a viscous medium, $b$ is a constant, and $v$ is the speed of the falling object.  The SI units of the constant $b$ are

a.   m/s
b.   kg·s
c.   kg/s
d.   kg·m
e.   m/s$^2$

**0554    5-5   Drag Forces,   Conceptual,   e**

As a skydiver falls through the air, her terminal speed

a.   depends on her mass.
b.   depends on the position in which she is falling.
c.   equals her weight.
d.   depends on the density of the air.
e.   All of the above are correct.

CHAPTER 6   **Work and Energy**

**0601    6-1  Work  and  Kinetic  Energy,   Conceptual,   b**

A body of mass $M$ slides a distance $d$ along a horizontal surface.  What work is done by gravity?

a.  $Mgd$
b.  Zero
c.  $-Mgd$
d.  Positive
e.  Negative

**0602    6-1  Work  and  Kinetic  Energy,   Conceptual,   e**

A body moves with decreasing speed.  Which of the following statements is true?

a.  The net work done on the body is positive, and the kinetic energy is increasing.
b.  The net work done on the body is positive, and the kinetic energy is decreasing.
c.  The net work done on the body is zero, and the kinetic energy is decreasing.
d.  The net work done on the body is negative, and the kinetic energy is increasing.
e.  The net work done on the body is negative, and the kinetic energy is decreasing.

**0603    6-1  Work  and  Kinetic  Energy,   Conceptual,   c**

A block slides a certain distance down an incline.  The work done by gravity is $W$.  What is the work done by gravity if this block slides the same distance up the incline?

a.  $W$
b.  Zero
c.  $-W$
d.  Gravity can't do work; some other force does work.
e.  Cannot be determined unless given the distance traveled.

**0604    6-1  Work  and  Kinetic  Energy,   Conceptual,   d**

A body initially has kinetic energy $E$ .  The body then moves in the opposite direction with three times its initial speed.  What is the kinetic energy now?

a.  $E$
b.  $3E$
c.  $-3E$
d.  $9E$
e.  $-9E$

0605   **6-1   Work  and  Kinetic  Energy,   Factual,  e**

The SI unit of energy can be expressed as

  a.  kg·m/s
  b.  kg·m/s$^2$
  c.  m/(kg·s)
  d.  kg·m·s$^2$
  e.  None of these is correct.


0606   **6-1   Work  and  Kinetic  Energy,   Numerical,   e**

The average marathon runner can complete the 42.2 km distance of the marathon in 3 hours and 30 minutes.  If the runner's mass is 75 kg, what is the runner's average kinetic energy during the run?

  a.  842 J
  b.  5.45 x 10$^3$ J
  c.  251 J
  d.  126 J
  e.  421 J


0607   **6-1   Work  and  Kinetic  Energy,   Numerical,  b**

A 6.0-kg block slides from position A down a frictionless curve to position B (see figure). After B, a friction force opposes the motion of the block so that it comes to a stop 2.5 m from B.  Calculate the coefficient of kinetic friction between the block and the surface after position B.

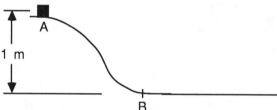

  a.  2.5
  b.  0.40
  c.  > 0.40
  d.  0.40 N
  e.  2.5 N


0608   **6-1   Work  and  Kinteic  Energy,   Numerical,   c**

The work expended to accelerate a car from 0 to 30 m/s

  a.  is more than that required to accelerate it from 30 m/s to 60 m/s.
  b.  is equal to that required to accelerate it from 30 m/s to 60 m/s.
  c.  is less than that required to accelerate it from 30 m/s to 60 m/s.
  d.  may be any of the above, depending on the time taken.
  e.  depends on the mass of the car.

**0609    6-1  Work and Kinetic Energy,   Numerical,   c**

The kinetic energy of a car is $1.00 \times 10^5$ J.  If the car's speed is increased by 20%, the kinetic energy of the car becomes

a.   $4.00 \times 10^3$ J
b.   $1.20 \times 10^5$ J
c.   $1.44 \times 10^5$ J
d.   $1.04 \times 10^5$ J
e.   The answer depends on the mass of the car, which is not given.

**0610    6-1  Work and Kinetic Energy,   Numerical,   a**

A bullet with a mass of 12 g moving horizontally strikes a fixed block of wood and penetrates a distance of 5.2 cm.  The speed of the bullet just before the collision is 640 m/s. The average force that the wood exerted on the bullet was

a.   $4.7 \times 10^4$ N
b.   74 N
c.   $4.7 \times 10^6$ N
d.   The mass of the wood is required.
e.   None of these is correct.

**0611    6-1  Work and Kinetic Energy,   Numerical,   d**

A bullet with a mass of 10.0 g and an initial speed of 800 m/s is stopped in a fixed block of wood and penetrates a distance of 5.00 cm into the block.  The average force exerted by the block on the bullet was

a.   160 N
b.   $1.3 \times 10^5$ N
c.   $1.3 \times 10^3$ N
d.   $6.4 \times 10^4$ N
e.   $6.4 \times 10^5$ N

**0612    6-1  Work and Kinetic Energy,   Conceptual,   a**

A 5-kg object slides down a frictionless surface inclined at an angle of 30° from the horizontal.  The total distance moved by the object along the plane is 10 metres.  The work done on the object by the normal force of the surface is

a.   zero
b.   500 J
c.   433 J
d.   577 J
e.   250 J

**0613    6-1  Work and Kinetic Energy,   Conceptual,   d**

The speed of an object is doubled.  Its kinetic energy is therefore

a.   the same.
b.   doubled.
c.   tripled.
d.   quadrupled.
e.   halved.

**0614**   **6-1  Work and Kinetic Energy,   Conceptual,   d**

Negative work means

a.  the kinetic energy of the object increases.
b.  the applied force is variable.
c.  the applied force is perpendicular to the displacement.
d.  the applied force is opposite to the displacement.
e.  nothing; there is no such thing as negative work.

**0615**   **6-1  Work and Kinetic Energy,   Conceptual,   a**

A particle moves halfway around a circle of radius $R$.  It is acted on by a radial force of magnitude $F$.  The work done by the radial force is

a.  zero
b.  $FR$
c.  $F\pi R$
d.  $2FR$
e.  $2\pi R$

**0616**   **6-2  Work Done by a Variable Force,   Conceptual,   b**

A variable force is represented on an $F$-versus-$x$ graph.  Which of the following is the work done by this force?

a.   The slope of the curve
b.   The area bounded by the curve and the $x$ axis
c.   The area bounded by the curve and the $F$ axis
d.   The $F$ value multiplied by the $x$ value
e.   The $F$ value divided by the $x$ value

**0617**   **6-2  Work Done by a Variable Force,   Conceptual,   a**

Two skiers start at the same place and finish at the same place.  Skier A takes a straight, smooth route to the finish, whereas Skier B takes a curvy, bumpy route to the finish.  Assuming friction is negligible, which of the following statements is true?

a.  Skier A has the same speed as skier B at the finish.
b.  Skier B has the greater speed at the finish.
c.  Skier A has the greater speed at the finish because his route is straight.
d.  Skier A has the greater speed at the finish because his route is smooth.
e.  Skier A has the greater speed at the finish because his route is both straight and smooth.

**0618  6-2  Work Done by a Variable Force,  Numerical,  d**

A particle subject to a variable force travels a total distance of 20 m in a straight line in the same direction as the force.  The force varies as follows:

First 5.0 m, $F = 0$
Next 5.0 m, $F = 3.0$ N
Next 5.0 m, $F = 6.0$ N
Last 5.0 m, $F$ decreases uniformly from 6.0 N to zero.

What was the total work done by this force during the full 20-m trip?

a.  15 J
b.  30 J
c.  45 J
d.  60 J
e.  75 J

**0619  6-2  Work Done by a Variable Force,  Numerical,  a**

A mass $m = 2.5$ kg is sliding along a frictionless table with initial speed $v$ as shown in the figure.  It strikes a coiled spring, with a force constant $k = 500$ N/m, and compresses it a distance $x_2 - x_1 = -5.0$ cm.  The initial speed $v$ of the block was:

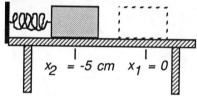

a.  0.71 m/s
b.  1.0 m/s
c.  1.4 m/s
d.  0.50 m/s
e.  1.7 m/s

**0620  6-2  Work Done by a Variable Force,  Numerical,  b**

A 6.0-kg block slides from rest at position A down a frictionless incline to position B.  The speed of the block at B is

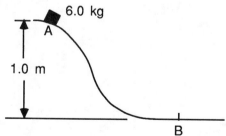

a.  3.1 m/s
b.  4.4 m/s
c.  11 m/s
d.  1.8 m/s
e.  20 m/s

0621    6-3   **Potential Energy,   Conceptual,   a**

A woman runs up a flight of stairs.  The gain in her gravitational potential energy is $U$.  If she runs up the same stairs with twice the speed, what will be her gain in potential energy?

a.   $U$
b.   $2U$
c.   $U/2$
d.   $4U$
e.   $U/4$


0622    6-3   **Potential Energy,   Conceptual,   c**

Person A ascends a mountain via a short, steep trail.  Person B ascends the same mountain via a long, gentle trail.  Which of the following statements is true?

a.   Person A gains more gravitational potential energy than Person B.
b.   Person A gains less gravitational potential energy than Person A.
c.   Person A gains the same gravitational potential energy as Person B.
d.   To compare energies, we must know the height of the mountain.
e.   To compare energies, we must know the lengths of the two trails.

0623    6-3   **Potential Energy,   Conceptual,   e**

The reference point for gravitational potential energy

a.   must be at the initial position of the object.
b.   must be at the final position of the object.
c.   must be at ground level.
d.   must be at the lowest position ever reached by the object.
e.   can be chosen arbitrarily.


0624    6-3   **Potential Energy,   Conceptual,   d**

Which of the following statements is true?

a.   The kinetic and potential energies of an object must always be positive quantities.
b.   The kinetic and potential energies of an object must always be negative quantities.
c.   Kinetic energy can be negative, but potential energy cannot.
d.   Potential energy can be negative, but kinetic energy cannot.
e.   None of the preceding statements is true.


0625    6-3   **Potential Energy,   Numerical,   a**

A 75-kg man climbs the stairs to the fifth floor of a building, a total height of 16 m.  His potential energy has increased by

a.   $1.2 \times 10^4$ J
b.   $5.9 \times 10^4$ J
c.   $4.7 \times 10^4$ J
d.   $3.8 \times 10^4$ J
e.   $5.9 \times 10^3$ J

**0626   6-3   Potential Energy,   Numerical,   c**

A 5200-kg cable car in San Francisco is pulled a distance of 360 m up a hill inclined at 12° from the horizontal.  The change in the potential energy of the car is

a.   $1.8 \times 10^7$ J
b.   $1.2 \times 10^7$ J
c.   $3.8 \times 10^6$ J
d.   $6.0 \times 10^7$ J
e.   $1.8 \times 10^6$ J

**0627   6-3   Potential Energy,   Numerical,   a**

A block with a mass $M = 4.85$ kg is resting on a slide that has a curved surface.  There is no friction.  The speed of the block after it has slid along the slide sufficiently far for its vertical drop to be 19.6 m is

a.   19.6 m/s
b.   384 m/s
c.   73 m/s
d.   43.2 m/s
e.   The problem cannot be solved because the shape of the curved slide is not given.

**0628   6-3   Potential Energy,   Numerical,   e**

A spring with force constant $k = 300$ N/m is compressed 9.0 cm. What is the potential energy in the spring?

a.   $1.2 \times 10^4$ J
b.   2.4 J
c.   $2.7 \times 10^4$ J
d.   27 J
e.   1.2 J

**0629   6-4   Conservative Forces and the Conservation of Energy,   Conceptual,   b**

A body falls through the atmosphere (air resistance is present), gaining 20 J of kinetic energy.  How much gravitational potential energy did it lose?

a.   20 J
b.   More than 20 J
c.   Less than 20 J
d.   It is impossible to tell without knowing the mass of the body.
e.   It is impossible to tell without knowing how far the body falls.

**0630   6-4   Conservative Forces and the Conservation of Energy,   Conceptual,   d**

A projectile of mass $m$ is propelled from ground level with kinetic energy of 450 J.  At the exact top of its trajectory, its kinetic energy is 250 J.  To what height above the starting point does the projectile rise?

a.   $450/(mg)$ m
b.   $250/(mg)$ m
c.   $700/(mg)$ m
d.   $200/(mg)$ m
e.   $350/(mg)$ m

**0631   6-4   Conservative Forces and the Conservation of Energy, Conceptual, e**

A block of mass $m$ is pushed up against a spring, compressing it a distance $X$, and is then released. The spring projects the block along a frictionless horizontal surface, giving the block a speed $V$. The same spring projects a second block of mass $4m$, giving it a speed $3V$. What distance was the spring compressed in the second case?

a.   $X$
b.   $2X$
c.   $3X$
d.   $4X$
e.   $6X$

**0632   6-4   Conservative Forces and the Conservation of Energy, Numerical, c**

A roller coaster car of mass 1500 kg starts a distance $H = 23$ m above the bottom of a loop. If the loop is 15 m in diameter, the downward force of the rails on the car when it is upside down at the top of the loop is

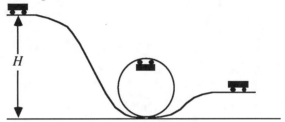

a.   4.6 x 10$^4$ N
b.   3.1 x 10$^4$ N
c.   1.7 x 10$^4$ N
d.   980 N
e.   1.6 x 10$^3$ N

**0633   6-4   Conservative Forces and the Conservation of Energy, Numerical, c**

A mass $m$ on a string is released from rest at point A. As it passes the lowest point B, the tension in the string is

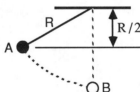

a.   impossible to determine; the answer depends on the length of the string.
b.   $mg$
c.   $2\,mg$
d.   $3\,mg$
e.   None of these is correct.

0634    6-4   Conservative Forces and the Conservation of Energy,   Numerical,   c

A person on a bicycle traveling at 10 m/s on a horizontal road stops pedaling as she starts up a hill inclined at 3.0° to the horizontal.  Ignoring friction forces, how far up the hill will she travel before stopping?

a.   5.1 m
b.   30 m
c.   97 m
d.   10.2 m
e.   The answer depends on the mass of the person.


0635    6-4   Conservative Forces and the Conservation of Energy,   Conceptual,   a

Two unequal masses are connected by a massless cord passing over a frictionless pulley. The following is true about the gravitational potential energy ($U$) and the kinetic energy of the system ($E_k$) after the masses are released from rest:

a.   $\Delta U < 0$ and  $\Delta E_k > 0$
b.   $\Delta U = 0$ and  $\Delta E_k > 0$
c.   $\Delta U < 0$ and  $\Delta E_k = 0$
d.   $\Delta U = 0$ and  $\Delta E_k = 0$
e.   $\Delta U > 0$ and  $\Delta E_k < 0$


0636    6-4   Conservative Forces and the Conservation of Energy,   Numerical,   d

A child is sitting on the seat of a swing with ropes 10.0 m long.  Her mother pulls the swing back till the ropes make a 37° angle with the vertical and then releases the swing.  Neglecting air resistance, what is the speed of the child at the bottom of the arc of the swing when the ropes are vertical?

a.   11 m/s
b.   8.8 m/s
c.   14 m/s
d.   6.3 m/s
e.   12 m/s


0637    6-4   Conservative Forces and the Conservation of Energy,   Numerical,   b

A simple pendulum has a bob of mass $M$.  The bob is on a light string of length $l$ .  The string is fixed at C.  At position A, the string is horizontal and the bob is at rest.  The bob is released from A and swings to B, where the string is vertical.  The tension in the string when the bob first reaches B is

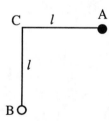

a.   $\frac{M}{2\pi}\sqrt{l/g}$
b.   $3Mg$
c.   $Mg$
d.   $Mgl$
e.   None of these is correct.

**0638**   **6-5   Simple Machines,   Conceptual,   a**

Which of the following is true of simple machines?

a.   Energy in equals energy out, and force in is less than force out.
b.   Energy in is less than energy out, and force in is less than force out.
c.   Energy in is less than energy out, and force in equals force out.
d.   Energy in is greater than energy out, and force in equals force out.
e.   Energy in equals energy out, and force in equals force out.

**0639**   **6-5   Simple Machines,   Numerical,   d**

What is the mechanical advantage of the system of pulleys shown in the figure?

a.   1
b.   2
c.   3
d.   4
e.   5

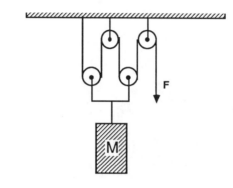

**0640**   **6-5   Simple Machines,   Numerical,   a**

A farmer wishes to move a boulder weighing 3800 N.  She has a 3-m pole that she will use as a lever, and she is able to exert a 670 N force on the lever.  How far from the end of the pole under the boulder must she put another rock to serve as a pivot in order to lift the boulder?

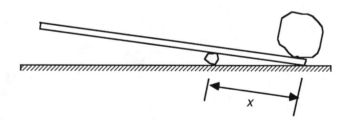

a.   0.45 m
b.   0.53 m
c.   1.0 m
d.   2.55 m
e.   0.05 m

**0641**   **6-6   Power,   Factual,   b**

The SI unit of power is named for

a.   James Watt, the former Secretary of the Interior of the United States.
b.   James Watt, the Scottish inventor.
c.   Key-Lo Watt, a Chinese advisor to Genghis Khan.
d.   James P. Joule, who studied the relation of heat to work.
e.   None of the above are correct.

0642   **6-6   Power,   Conceptual,   c**

Consider two engines.  The larger is rated at 2 hp; the smaller is rated at 1 hp.  The smaller one can do a certain quantity of work in two hours.  The larger one can do twice as much work in a time of

   a.   30 minutes.
   b.   1 hour.
   c.   2 hours.
   d.   4 hours.
   e.   1.4 hours.

0643   **6-6   Power,   Numerical,   c**

A motor is lifting a mass of 35.0 kg at a constant speed of 6.00 m/s.  The power developed by the motor to do this lifting is

   a.   740 watts.
   b.   $1.5 \times 10^3$ watts.
   c.   $2.1 \times 10^3$ watts.
   d.   59 watts.
   e.   43 watts.

0644   **6-6   Power,   Numerical,   a**

An object with a mass of  3.45 kg is pulled up a slope AB, which is 36 m long whereas the height BC is 3.00 m.  There is no friction and the acceleration is constant.  The speed $v_1$ at A is 3.5 m/s, whereas the speed $v_2$ at B is 5.5 m/s.  The average power developed by the motor pulling the object is

   a.   17 watts.
   b.   3.9 watts.
   c.   13 watts.
   d.   130 watts.
   e.   43 watts.

0645   **6-6   Power,   Conceptual,   c**

A power $P$ is required to lift a body a distance $d$ at a constant speed $V$.  What power is required to lift the body a distance $2d$  at constant speed $3V$ ?

   a.   $P$
   b.   $2P$
   c.   $3P$
   d.   $6P$
   e.   $3P/2$

0646    **6-6   Power,   Conceptual,   e**

A power $P$ is required to do work $W$ in a time interval $T$. What power is required to do work $3W$ in a time interval $5T$ ?

   a.   $P$
   b.   $3P$
   c.   $5P$
   d.   $5P/3$
   e.   $3P/5$

0647    **6-6   Power,   Numerical,   b**

What is the power output needed from the motor of an elevator of mass $1.5 \times 10^4$ kg to lift the elevator 25 m in 6.0 seconds at a constant speed?

   a.  $2.0 \times 10^6$ W
   b.  $6.1 \times 10^5$ W
   c.  $2.2 \times 10^4$ W
   d.  $8.3 \times 10^5$ W
   e.  $3.1 \times 10^5$ W

0648    **6-7   Thermal Energy and Metabolic Rate,   Numerical,   b**

A bullet with a mass of 28 g is fired with a speed of 425 m/s into a fixed block of wood of mass 2.8 kg. The thermal energy produced in the wood is

   a.  2.8 cal
   b.  600 cal
   c.  6.0 cal
   d.  1.2 kcal
   e.  128 kcal

CHAPTER 7     Impulse, Momentum, and
Center of Mass

**0701     7-1 Impulse and Momentum,  Numerical,  c**

An arrow with a mass of 0.54 kg is shot from a bow at 45° above the horizontal.  The bow exerts a force of 125 N for a period of 0.65 s.  Neglecting air resistance the maximum height the arrow reaches is

a.   1200 m
b.   5.4 m
c.   570 m
d.   290 m
e.   610 m

**0702     7-1 Impulse and Momentum,  Conceptual,  a**

A golfball and a ping-pong ball are dropped in a vacuum chamber.  When they have fallen halfway down, they have the same

a.   speed.
b.   potential energy.
c.   kinetic energy.
d.   momentum.
e.   All of these are correct.

**0703     7-1 Impulse and Momentum,  Numerical,  b**

An automobile of mass 1300 kg has an initial velocity of 7.20 m/s toward the north and a final velocity of 6.50 m/s toward the west.  The magnitude and direction of the <u>change</u> in momentum of the car is

a.   $1.26 \times 10^4$ kg·m/s at 48° S of E.
b.   $1.26 \times 10^4$ kg·m/s at 48° S of W.
c.   $1.26 \times 10^4$ kg·m/s at 48° N of W.
d.   $1.78 \times 10^4$ kg·m/s at 48° N of W.
e.   910 kg·m/s at 48° S of E.

**0704     7-1 Impulse and Momentum,  Factual,  e**

The SI units of momentum are

a.   kg·m·s
b.   $m^2/s$
c.   kg/m/s
d.   kg/J
e.   kg·m/s

**0705**   **7-1   Impulse   and   Momentum,   Numerical,   c**

An arrow with a mass of 0.54 kg is shot from a bow.  The bow exerts a force of 125 N for a period of 0.65 s.  The speed of the arrow as it leaves the bow is

a.   230 m/s
b.   100 m/s
c.   150 m/s
d.   300 m/s
e.   270 m/s

**0706**   **7-1   Impulse   and   Momentum,   Numerical,   a**

A car having a total mass of 2250 kg and traveling at 72.0 km/h smashes into a tree.  The car is stopped in 0.250 s.  The average force acting on the car during the collision is

a.   $1.80 \times 10^5$ N
b.   80.0 N
c.   $1.80 \times 10^2$ N
d.   zero
e.   $2.2 \times 10^4$ N

**0707**   **7-1   Impulse   and   Momentum,   Conceptual,   b**

A car having a total mass of 2250 kg and traveling at 72 km/h smashes into a tree.  The car is stopped in 0.25 s.  The driver of the car is not held in place by a seat belt or any other restraining device.  After the impact but before the driver hits any part of the car, the acceleration of the driver is

a.   $80$ m/s$^2$ toward the tree.
b.   zero with respect to the tree.
c.   $80$ m/s$^2$ away from the tree.
d.   $1.8 \times 10^2$ m/s$^2$ with respect to the car.
e.   $37$ m/s$^2$ away from the tree.

**0708**   **7-1   Impulse   and   Momentum,   Numerical,   e**

A ball with a mass of 50 g is dropped from 5.41 m above a sidewalk.  The ball is in contact with the sidewalk for $8.1 \times 10^{-3}$ s.  The magnitude of the average force exerted on the ball

a.   is 120 N.
b.   is 89 N.
c.   is 9.2 N.
d.   is 0.49 N.
e.   cannot be determined without knowing how high the ball bounces.

**0709**   **7-1   Impulse   and   Momentum,   Conceptual,   e**

A ball of mass $m$ strikes a wall perpendicular to it at speed $+v$ and rebounds in the opposite direction with a speed $-v$.  The impulse exerted on the ball is

a.   $2mv$
b.   $mv$
c.   zero
d.   $-mv$
e.   $-2mv$

**0710    7-1   Impulse and Momentum,   Conceptual,   d**

Two balls are dropped from a height of 6 m. Ball A bounces back up to a height of 4 m whereas ball B bounces back up to 2 m.  Which ball experiences the larger impulse during its collision with the floor?

a.  Ball A
b.  Ball B
c.  They both experience the same impulse.
d.  It is impossible to tell without knowing the masses of the balls.
e.  It is impossible to tell without knowing the length of time of the collisions.

**0711    7-1   Impulse and Momentum,   Numerical,   b**

A particle whose mass is not known has a momentum of 73 SI units.  At a time 7.3 s later, the momentum of the particle is 38 SI units.  The magnitude of the force acting on the particle during the interval, assuming the motion is in a straight line,

a.  cannot be determined because the mass of the particle is not given.
b.  is 4.8 N
c.  is 10 N
d.  is 5.3 N
e.  9.4 N

**0712    7-2   Conservation of Momentum,   Numerical,   d**

A bullet with a mass of 20 g and a speed of 960 m/s strikes a block of wood of mass 4.5 kg resting on a horizontal surface.  The bullet gets embedded in the block.  The speed of the block immediately after the collision

a.  cannot be found since we don't know whether the surface is frictionless.
b.  is 210 m/s
c.  is 65 m/s
d.  is 4.2 m/s
e.  None of these is correct.

**0713    7-2   Conservation of Momentum,   Conceptual,   a**

Two masses $M$ and $5M$ rest on a horizontal frictionless table with a compressed spring of negligible mass between them.  When the spring is released, the energy of the spring is shared between the two masses such that

a.  $M$ gets 5/6 of the energy.
b.  $M$ gets 1/6 of the energy.
c.  $M$ gets 1/5 of the energy.
d.  $M$ gets 4/5 of the energy.
e.  None of these is correct.

0714   **7-2   Conservation of Momentum,   Numerical,   d**

For this question, assume that all velocities are horizontal and that there is no friction. Two skaters A and B are on an ice surface. A and B have the same mass $M = 90.5$ kg. A throws a ball with mass $m = 200$ g toward B with a speed $v = 21.5$ m/s relative to the ice. B catches the ball and throws it back to A with the same speed. After catching the ball, the speed of A with respect to the ice is

a.   $4.3 \times 10^3$ m/s
b.   4.3 m/s
c.   $4.8 \times 10^{-2}$ m/s
d.   $9.5 \times 10^{-2}$ m/s
e.   0.34 m/s

0715   **7-2   Conservation of Momentum,   Conceptual,   c**

The condition necessary for the conservation of momentum in a given system is that

a.   energy is conserved.
b.   one body is at rest.
c.   no external force acts.
d.   internal forces equal external forces.
e.   None of these is correct.

0716   **7-2   Conservation of Momentum,   Conceptual,   c**

The law of conservation of momentum is a statement of

a.   Newton's first law of motion.
b.   Newton's second law of motion.
c.   Newton's third law of motion.
d.   Newton's fourth law of motion.
e.   Newton's law of gravity.

0717   **7-2   Conservation of Momentum,   Conceptual,   b**

A boy and girl on ice skates face each other. The girl has a mass of 20 kg and the boy has a mass of 30 kg. The boy pushes the girl backwards at a speed of 3.0 m/s. As a result of the push, the speed of the boy is

a.   zero
b.   2.0 m/s
c.   3.0 m/s
d.   4.5 m/s
e.   9.0 m/s

0718   **7-3   Center of Mass,   Numerical,   a**

A projectile with a mass $6M$ is fired at a speed of 400 m/s at an angle of 60° above the horizontal. At the highest point of the its trajectory, the projectile is broken into two equal pieces by an internal explosion. Just after the explosion, one of the two pieces is known to be traveling vertically downward at a speed of 300 m/s. The magnitude of the velocity of the other half of the projectile is

a.   500 m/s
b.   1500 m/s
c.   400 m/s
d.   710 m/s
e.   123 m/s

**0719    7-3   Center of Mass,   Numerical,   b**

A boy is standing at the stern (back) of a boat that is 8.0 m long.  There is no friction between the boat and the water.  The boy has a mass of 63 kg and the boat has a mass of 780 kg.  The bow (front) of the boat is touching a dock and the axis of the boat is at right angles to the dock.  The boy walks from the stern of the boat to the bow .  When the boy reaches the bow, his distance from the dock is

a.   7.6 m
b.   0.60 m
c.   0.51 m
d.   0.56 m
e.   1.3 m


**0720    7-3   Center of Mass,   Numerical,   a**

The earth has mass $5.89 \times 10^{24}$ kg, and the moon has mass $7.36 \times 10^{22}$ kg and is $3.84 \times 10^5$ km from the earth.  How far from the center of the earth is the center of mass of the earth-moon system?

a.   $4.7 \times 10^3$ km
b.   $7.4 \times 10^3$ km
c.   $1.9 \times 10^5$ km
d.   $2.1 \times 10^5$ km
e.   $3.8 \times 10^3$ km


**0721    7-3   Center of Mass,   Numerical,   b**

A car of mass $3.0 \times 10^3$ kg traveling at a speed of 20 m/s is passing a truck of mass $7.5 \times 10^3$ kg traveling at a speed of 16 m/s in the same direction.  What is the speed of the center of mass of this system?

a.   16 m/s
b.   17 m/s
c.   18 m/s
d.   19 m/s
e.   20 m/s


**0722    7-3   Center of Mass,   Conceptual,   b**

A uniform horizontal bar is in a region of space where the acceleration due to gravity $g$ varies, increasing from left to right.  Where is the location of the center of mass relative to the center of gravity?

a.   They are at the same location.
b.   The center of mass is to the left of the center of gravity.
c.   The center of gravity is to the left of the center of mass.
d.   It depends on the shape of the bar.
e.   It depends on how much $g$ changes.

**0723    7-3   Center of Mass,   Conceptual,   c**

A particle of mass $2m$ is moving to the right in projectile motion.  At the top of its trajectory there is an explosion that breaks the particle into two equal parts.  After the explosion, one part falls straight down with no horizontal motion.  What is the direction of the motion of the other part just after the explosion?

a.   Up and to the left
b.   It stops moving
c.   To the right
d.   Straight up
e.   Down and to the right


**0724    7-4   Collisions,   Numerical,   d**

An object of mass $M_1$ is moving with a speed $v$  on a straight, level, frictionless track when it collides with another mass $M_2$ that is at rest on the track.  After the collision, $M_1$ and $M_2$ stick together and move with a speed

a.   $v$
b.   $M_1 v$
c.   $\dfrac{(M_1 + M_2)v}{M_1}$
d.   $\dfrac{M_1 v}{M_1 + M_2}$
e.   $\dfrac{M_1 v}{M_2}$


**0725    7-4   Collisions,   Numerical,   b**

Two identical cars approach an intersection.  One is traveling east at 18 m/s.  The second is traveling north at 24 m/s.  They collide violently, sticking together.  Immediately after the crash they are moving

a.   30 m/s, 37° N of E.
b.   30 m/s, 37° E of N.
c.   15 m/s, 37° N of E.
d.   15 m/s, 37° E of N.
e.   42 m/s, 37° N of E.


**0726    7-4   Collisions,   Conceptual,   e**

Momentum is conserved

a.     in elastic collisions.
b.     in inelastic collisions.
c.     in explosions.
d.     Two of the above answers are correct.
e.     All of the above answers are correct.

**0727    7-4   Collisions,   Conceptual,   d**

A 40-kg girl on ice pushes a 60-kg boy also on ice.  Both are initially at rest.  After the push, the boy is moving backwards at 2.0 m/s.  The girl's speed is

    a.    zero
    b.    1.3 m/s
    c.    2.0 m/s
    d.    3.0 m/s
    e.    6.0 m/s

**0728    7-4   Collisions,   Conceptual,   c**

In an elastic collision of two objects,

    a.    momentum is conserved.
    b.    the total kinetic energy remains constant.
    c.    Both a and b are true.
    d.    Neither a nor b is true.
    e.    The answer depends on the masses of the objects.

**0729    7-4   Collisions,   Numerical,   c**

A railway car having a total mass of $5.8 \times 10^5$ kg and moving with a speed of 9.1 km/h strikes another car that has a mass of $8.7 \times 10^5$ kg and is initially at rest.  The speed of the coupled cars after the collision is

    a.    9.1 km/h
    b.    7.2 km/h
    c.    3.6 km/h
    d.    1.8 km/h
    e.    4.2 km/h

**0730    7-4   Collisions,   Numerical,   a**

A block that has a mass $M = 4.25$ kg is hanging at rest on a light string.  A projectile with a mass $m = 250$ g moving horizontally strikes $M$ and sticks to it.  $M$ swings back and its center of mass rises a distance $h = 12.0$ cm.  The speed of the projectile is

    a.    28 m/s
    b.    42 m/s
    c.    280 m/s
    d.    26 m/s
    e.    14 m/s

**0731    7-4   Collisions,   Numerical,   a**

A block of wood with a mass $M = 4.65$ kg is resting on a horizontal surface when a bullet with a mass $m = 18$ g and moving with a speed $v = 725$ m/s strikes it.  The coefficient of friction between the block and the surface is $\mu = 0.35$.  The distance the block moves across the surface is

    a.    1.1 m
    b.    3.3 m
    c.    0.41 m
    d.    11 m
    e.    None of these is correct.

**0732   7-4   Collisions,   Numerical,   d**

A particle with speed $v_1 = 2.64 \times 10^6$ m/s makes a glancing elastic collision with another particle that is at rest.  Both particles have the same mass.  After the collision, the struck particle moves off at 45° to $v_1$.  The speed of the struck particle after the collision is

a.  $3.4 \times 10^6$ m/s
b.  $1.3 \times 10^6$ m/s
c.  $0.53 \times 10^6$ m/s
d.  $1.9 \times 10^6$ m/s
e.  $6.4 \times 10^6$ m/s

**0733   7-4   Collisions,   Conceptual, b**

Two identical masses are hung on strings of the same length.  One mass is released from a height $h$ above its free-hanging position and strikes the second mass; the two stick together and move off.  They rise to a height $H$ given by

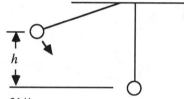
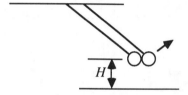

a.  $3h/4$
b.  $h/4$
c.  $h/2$
d.  $h$
e.  None of these is correct.

**0734   7-4   Collisions,   Numerical,   a**

A particle of mass $m$ moving at 5 m/s in the positive $x$ direction makes a glancing elastic collision with a particle of mass $2m$ that is at rest before the collision.  After the collision, $m$ moves off at an angle of 45° to the $x$ axis while $2m$ moves off at 60° to the $x$ axis.  The speed of $m$ after the collision is

a.  4.5 m/s
b.  2.5 m/s
c.  3.3 m/s
d.  1.8 m/s
e.  1.1 m/s

**0735   7-4   Collisions,   Numerical,   b**

A mass $m_1 = 2.5$ kg is connected to another mass $m_2 = 4.0$ kg by a compressed spring.  Both masses are at rest on a frictionless surface.  When the spring is released, the masses are pushed apart and a total energy of 16.8 J is given to the two masses.  The speed of mass $m_1$ is

a.  3.2 m/s
b.  2.9 m/s
c.  1.8 m/s
d.  8.3 m/s
e.  5.4 m/s

0736    **7-4   Collisions,   Numerical,   b**

A car having a mass of 1850 kg is traveling in a straight line with a speed of 22.5 m/s.  A truck having a mass of 3170 kg has the same momentum as this car.  The speed of the truck is

a.   38 m/s
b.   13 m/s
c.   10 m/s
d.   40 m/s
e.   27 m/s

0737    **7-4   Collisions,   Numerical,   c**

A 7000-kg flatcar of a train coasts at 7.0 m/s on a frictionless track when a 3000-kg load of coal is dropped vertically onto the car.  The flatcar's speed after the coal is added is

a.   2.1 m/s
b.   3.0 m/s
c.   4.9 m/s
d.   7.0 m/s
e.   16 m/s

0738    **7-4   Collisions,   Conceptual,   a**

Two cars of equal mass travel in opposite directions with equal speeds.  They collide in a perfectly inelastic collision.  After the collision, their velocities are

a.   zero.
b.   equal to their original velocities.
c.   equal in magnitude but opposite in direction to their original velocities.
d.   less in magnitude and in the same direction as their original velocities.
e.   less in magnitude and opposite in direction to their original velocities.

0739    **7-4   Collisions,   Conceptual,   c**

Two cars of equal mass travel in opposite directions with equal speeds.  They collide in a perfectly elastic collision.  After the collision, their velocities are

a.   zero.
b.   equal to their original velocities.
c.   equal in magnitude but opposite in direction to their original velocities.
d.   less in magnitude and in the same direction as their original velocities.
e.   less in magnitude and opposite in direction to their original velocities.

0740    **7-4   Collisions,   Conceptual,   e**

Two cars of equal mass travel in opposite directions with equal speeds.  They collide in a collision that is between elastic and inelastic.  After the collision, their velocities are

a.   zero.
b.   equal to their original velocities.
c.   equal in magnitude but opposite in direction to their original velocities.
d.   less in magnitude and in the same direction as their original velocities.
e.   less in magnitude and opposite in direction to their original velocities.

**0741   7-4   Collisions,   Conceptual,   b**

In a <u>real</u> collision,

a.  kinetic energy is conserved.
b.  linear momentum is conserved.
c.  both momentum and kinetic energy are conserved.
d.  neither momentum nor kinetic energy are conserved.
e.  the extent to which momentum and kinetic energy are conserved depends on the coefficient of restitution.

CHAPTER 8   **Rotation**

0801   **8-1   Angular Velocity and Angular Acceleration,   Conceptual,   d**

Two points are on a disk that rotates about an axis.  Point A is closer to the axis than Point B.  Which of the following is <u>not</u> true?

a.   Point B has the greater speed.
b.   Point A has the lesser centripetal acceleration.
c.   Points A and B have the same angular acceleration.
d.   Point B has the greater angular speed.
e.   Point A has the lesser tangential acceleration.

0802   **8-1   Angular Velocity and Angular Acceleration,   Conceptual,   b**

Two points are on a disk that rotates about an axis.  Point A is three times as far from the axis as Point B.  If the speed of point B is $V$, then what is the speed of point A?

a.   $V$
b.   $3V$
c.   $V/3$
d.   $9V$
e.   $V/9$

0803   **8-1   Angular Velocity and Angular Acceleration,   Conceptual,   c**

Starting from rest, a disk rotates with constant angular acceleration.  If it takes 10 revolutions to reach an angular velocity $\omega$ , then how many additional revolutions are required to reach an angular velocity $2\omega$?

a.   10 rev
b.   20 rev
c.   30 rev
d.   40 rev
e.   50 rev

0804   **8-1   Angular Velocity and Angular Acceleration,   Conceptual,   d**

A record turntable rotates through 5.0 radians in 2.8 seconds as it is accelerated uniformly from rest .  The angular velocity at the end of that time is

a.   0.6 rad/s
b.   0.9 rad/s
c.   1.8 rad/s
d.   3.6 rad/s
e.   14. rad/s

**0805** **8-1** **Angular Velocity and Angular Acceleration, Conceptual, e**

I have a friend who lives in the southern part of the United States. As the earth rotates, my linear velocity in the northern part of the country is _____ hers and my angular velocity is _____ hers.

a. greater than; equal to
b. equal to; greater than
c. greater than; less than
d. less than; greater than
e. less than; equal to

**0806** **8-1** **Angular Velocity and Angular Acceleration, Conceptual, d**

A wheel rotates through 5.0 radians in 2.8 seconds as it is uniformly brought to rest. The initial angular velocity of the wheel before the braking began was

a. 0.6 rad/s
b. 0.9 rad/s
c. 1.8 rad/s
d. 3.6 rad/s
e. 7.2 rad/s

**0807** **8-1** **Angular Velocity and Angular Acceleration, Numerical, b**

A stone on the end of a string is being whirled in a horizontal circle of radius $R = 0.65$ m with a frequency of 4 revolutions per second when the string breaks. Just after the string breaks, the velocity of the stone is

a. straight down.
b. 16 m/s along a tangent to the circle.
c. 16 m/s along the radius away from the center.
d. 1.0 m/s along the radius toward the center.
e. None of these are correct.

**0808** **8-1** **Angular Velocity and Angular Acceleration, Numerical, d**

A bicycle is moving at 9.8 m/s. The radius of the wheels of the bicycle is 51.9 cm. The angular velocity of rotation of the wheels is

a. 19 rad/s
b. 2.5 rad/s
c. 4.5 rad/s
d. 3.0 rad/s
e. 6.3 rad/s

**0809** **8-1** **Angular Velocity and Angular Acceleration, Numerical, b**

The Empire's space station is a long way from any star. It is circular and has a radius of 5.10 km. The angular velocity that is needed to give the station an artificial gravity of 9.80 m/s$^2$ at its circumference is

a. $4.4 \times 10^{-2}$ rad/s
b. $7.0 \times 10^{-3}$ rad/s
c. 0.28 rad/s
d. -0.22 rad/s
e. 1300 rad/s

**0810    8-1   Angular Velocity and Angular Acceleration,  Numerical, e**

A wheel is rotating at 30 revolutions per minute.  The angular velocity of the wheel is

   a.  $2\pi^2$ rad/s
   b.  $2\pi$ rad/s
   c.  2 rad/s
   d.  $\pi/2$ rad/s
   e.  $\pi$ rad/s

**0811    8-1   Angular Velocity and Angular Acceleration,  Numerical, c**

A particle moves uniformly around the circumference of a circle whose radius is 8 cm  with a periodic time of  $\pi/20$ s.  The angular velocity $\omega$ of the particle is

   a.  2.5 rad/s
   b.  320 rad/s
   c.  40 rad/s
   d.  7.9 rad/s
   e.  0.96 rad/s

**0812    8-1   Angular Velocity and Angular Acceleration,  Numerical, c**

A particle is moving uniformly in a circle that has a radius of 50 cm.  Its angular velocity is 96 rad/s.  The linear speed of the particle is

   a.  100 cm/s
   b.  96 cm/s
   c.  4800 cm/s
   d.  zero
   e.  1500 cm/s

**0813    8-2  Torque and Moment of Inertia,  Conceptual, b**

A disk is free to rotate  about an axis.  A force applied a distance $d$ from the axis causes an angular acceleration $\alpha$.  What angular acceleration is produced if the same force is applied a distance $2d$  from the axis?

   a.  $\alpha$
   b.  $2\alpha$
   c.  $\alpha/2$
   d.  $4\alpha$
   e.  $\alpha/4$

**0814    8-2  Torque and Moment of Inertia,  Conceptual,  a**

A bicycle wheel, a hollow sphere, and a solid sphere all have the same mass and radius. They all rotate about an axis through their centers.  Which has the greatest moment of inertia and which has the least?

   a.  The wheel has the greatest; the solid sphere has the least.
   b.  The wheel has the greatest; the hollow sphere has the least.
   c.  The hollow sphere has the greatest; the solid sphere has the least.
   d.  The hollow sphere has the greatest; the wheel has the least.
   e.  The solid sphere has the greatest; the hollow sphere has the least.

**0815   8-2  Torque and Moment of Inertia,  Numerical,  b**

Four 50-g masses are at the corners of a square with 20-cm sides.  What is the moment of inertia of this system about an axis perpendicular to the plane of the square and passing through its center?

a.  10 kg·m$^2$
b.  40 kg·m$^2$
c.  20 kg·m$^2$
d.  80 kg·m$^2$
e.  2.8 kg·m$^2$

**0816   8-2  Torque and Moment of Inertia,  Numerical,  a**

Water is drawn from a well with a bucket tied to the end of a rope whose other end wraps around a cylinder of mass 50 kg and diameter 25 cm.  As this cylinder is turned with a crank, the rope pulls the bucket up.  If the mass of the bucket filled with water is 20 kg, what torque must be applied to the crank to bring the bucket up at a constant speed?

a.  24 N·m
b.  2.5 N·m
c.  80 N·m
d.  2.4 x 10$^3$ N·m
e.  49 N·m

**0817   8-2  Torque and Moment of Inertia,  Numerical,  c**

Water is drawn from a well with a bucket tied to the end of a rope whose other end wraps around a cylinder of mass 50 kg and diameter 25 cm.  As this cylinder is turned with a crank, the rope pulls the bucket up.  The mass of the bucket filled with water is 20 kg. Someone cranks the bucket up and then lets go of the crank, and the bucket of water falls back down to the bottom of the well.  Assuming no friction or air resistance, what will be the angular acceleration of the 50-kg cylinder?

a.  110 rad/s$^2$
b.  3.6 rad/s$^2$
c.  35 rad/s$^2$
d.  63 rad/s$^2$
e.  17 rad/s$^2$

**0818   8-2  Torque and Moment of Inertia,  Numerical,  e**

A disk-shaped grindstone of mass 3.0 kg and radius 8.0 cm is spinning at 600 rev/min. After the power is shut off, a man continues to sharpen his axe by holding it against the grindstone till it stops 10 seconds later.  What is the torque exerted by the axe on the grindstone?

a.  0.0096 N·m
b.  0.12 N·m
c.  0.75 N·m
d.  603 N·m
e.  0.060 N·m

**0819    8-2  Torque and Moment of Inertia,   Conceptual,   a**

The torque exerted on the earth by the gravitational pull of the sun is

a.  zero.
b.  directed along the earth's axis to the north pole.
c.  directed along the earth's axis to the south pole.
d.  in the direction of the earth's orbit.
e.  directed toward the sun.


**0820    8-2  Torque and Moment of Inertia,   Numerical,   c**

A uniform metrestick is placed horizontally on the ground along an east-west axis.  A force of 1.0 N is applied to the center of the stick at a direction 30° west of north.  The torque exerted by the force relative to the east end of the stick is

a.  zero.
b.  0.25 m, clockwise
c.  0.43 m, clockwise.
d.  0.25 m, counterclockwise
e.  0.43 m, counterclockwise


**0821    8-2  Torque and Moment of Inertia,   Conceptual,   c**

Two wheels with identical moments of inertia are rotating about the same axle.  The first is rotating clockwise at 2.0 rad/s and the second is rotating counterclockwise at 6.0 rad/s. When they are brought together the final angular velocity will be

a.  2.0 rad/s, counterclockwise.
b.  3.0 rad/s, clockwise.
c.  4.0 rad/s, counterclockwise.
d.  5.0 rad/s, clockwise.
e.  6.0 rad/s, clockwise.


**0822    8-2  Torque and Moment of Inertia,   Conceptual,   e**

The torque exerted on an orbiting communications satellite by the gravitational pull of the earth is

a.  directed toward the earth.
b.  directed parallel to the earth's axis and toward the north pole.
c.  directed parallel to the earth's axis and toward the south pole.
d.  directed toward the satellite.
e.  zero.


**0823    8-3  Kinetic Energy and Angular Momentum,   Conceptual,   e**

If the angular momentum of a system is constant, which of the following statements must be true?

a.  No torque acts on any part of the system.
b.  A constant torque acts on each part of the system.
c.  Zero net torque acts on each part of the system.
d.  A constant external torque acts on the system.
e.  Zero net torque acts on the system.

0824    **8-3  Kinetic Energy and Angular Momentum,  Conceptual,  b**

A woman sits on a spinning piano stool with her arms folded.  When she then extends her arms,  which of the following statements is true?

a.  She increases her moment of inertia, thereby increasing her angular speed.
b.  She increases her moment of inertia, thereby decreasing her angular speed.
c.  She decreases her moment of inertia, thereby increasing her angular speed.
d.  She decreases her moment of inertia, thereby decreasing her angular speed.
e.  Both her moment of inertia and her angular speed remain constant.


0825    **8-3  Kinetic Energy and Angular Momentum,  Conceptual,  e**

Two identical cylindrical disks have a common axis.  Initially one of the disks is spinning.  When the two disks are brought into contact they stick together.  Which of the following statements is true?

a.  The total kinetic energy and the total angular momentum are unchanged from their initial values.
b.  Both the total kinetic energy and the total angular momentum are reduced to half of their original values.
c.  The total angular momentum is unchanged, but the total kinetic energy is reduced to half its original value.
d.  The total angular momentum is reduced to one-half of its original value, but the total kinetic energy is unchanged.
e.  The total angular momentum is unchanged, and the total kinetic energy is reduced to one-quarter of its original value.


0826    **8-3 Kinetic Energy and Angular Momentum,  Numerical, a**

A disk-shaped grindstone of mass 3.0 kg and radius 8.0 cm is spinning at 600 rev/min.  After the power is shut off, a man continues to sharpen his axe by holding it against the grindstone till it stops 10 seconds later.  What was its initial kinetic energy when the power was turned off?

a.  19 J
b.  $3.8 \times 10^{-3}$ J
c.  $4.8 \times 10^{-5}$ J
d.  $1.9 \times 10^{-3}$ J
e.  $2.4 \times 10^{-2}$ J


0827    **8-3  Kinetic Energy and Angular Momentum,  Numerical, a**

In a playground there is a small merry-go-round of radius 1.25 m and mass 175 kg.  The merry-go-round can be assumed to be a uniform disk.  A child of mass 45 kg runs at a speed of 3.0 m/s tangent to the rim of the merry-go-round (initially at rest) and jumps on.  Neglecting friction, what is the angular speed of the merry-go-round after the child has jumped on?

a.  0.82 rad/s
b.  2.4 rad/s
c.  0.49 rad/s
d.  1.2 rad/s
e.  0.41 rad/s

**0828    8-4   Rolling Bodies,   Conceptual,   e**

Two solid balls (one large, the other small) and a cylinder roll down a hill.  Which has the greatest speed at the bottom and which the least?

a.   The large ball has the greatest, the small ball has the least.
b.   The small ball has the greatest, the large ball has the least.
c.   The cylinder has the greatest, the small ball has the least.
d.   The cylinder has the greatest, both balls have the same lesser speed.
e.   Both balls have the same greater speed, the cylinder has the least.

**0829    8-4   Rolling Bodies,   Numerical,   c**

A bicycle wheel can be assumed to have all of its mass concentrated at its rim.  Such a wheel of mass 1.2 kg and radius 30 cm starts from rest at the top of a hill 100 m long and inclined at 20° to the horizontal.  What will be the speed of the wheel at the bottom of the hill if it rolls without slipping?

a.   21 m/s$^2$
b.   26 m/s$^2$
c.   18 m/s$^2$
d.   33 m/s$^2$
e.   37 m/s$^2$

**0830    8-4   Rolling Bodies,   Conceptual,   b**

Starting from rest at the same time, a coin and a ring roll down an incline without slipping.  Which reaches the bottom first?

a.   The ring reaches the bottom first.
b.   The coin reaches the bottom first.
c.   They arrive at the bottom simultaneously.
d.   The winner depends on the relative masses of the two.
e.   The winner depends on the relative diameters of the two.

**0831    8-4   Rolling Bodies,   Conceptual,   c**

Which is larger for a hoop (ring) of mass $M$ and radius $R$ that is rolling without slipping:  its translational or its rotational kinetic energy?

a.   Its translational kinetic energy.
b.   Its rotational kinetic energy.
c.   Both are the same size.
d.   The answer depends on the radius.
e.   The answer depends on the mass.

**0832    8-4   Rolling Bodies,   Conceptual,   a**

Which is larger for a disk of mass $M$ and radius $R$ that is rolling without slipping:  its translational or its rotational kinetic energy?

a.   Its translational kinetic energy.
b.   Its rotational kinetic energy.
c.   Both are the same size.
d.   The answer depends on the radius.
e.   The answer depends on the mass.

**0833    8-4    Rolling Bodies,    Conceptual,    a**

A sphere of radius $R$ is rolling <u>and</u> slipping down an incline.  The velocity of the center of mass is

a.  greater than $R\omega$.
b.  equal to $R\omega$.
c.  less than $R\omega$.
d.  Any of the above could be true.


**0834    8-4    Rolling Bodies,    Conceptual,    c**

A wheel on a car is rolling without slipping along level ground.  The speed of car is 36 m/s.  The wheel has an outer diameter of 50 cm.  The speed of the top of the wheel is

a.  36 m/s
b.  3.6 m/s
c.  72 m/s
d.  18 m/s
e.  98 m/s


**0835    8-4    Rolling Bodies,    Numerical,    a**

A bicycle is moving at a speed $v = 12.6$ m/s.  A small stone is stuck to one of the tires.  At the instant the stone is at point A in the figure, it comes free.  The velocity of the stone, magnitude and direction, relative to the earth just after release is

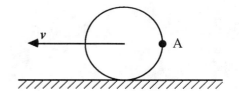

a.  17.8 m/s at 45° above the horizontal, toward the front of the bicycle.
b.  12.6 m/s at 45° above the horizontal, away from the bicycle.
c.  12.6 m/s at 37° below the horizontal.
d.  12.6 m/s straight up.
e.  17.8 m/s at 45° above the horizontal, toward the back of the bicycle.


**0836    8-4    Rolling Bodies,    Conceptual,    c**

A wheel of radius $R$ is rolling without slipping.  The velocity of the point on the rim that is in contact with the surface, relative to the surface, is

a.  equal to $R\omega$ in the direction of motion of the center of mass.
b.  equal to $R\omega$ opposite the direction of motion of the center of mass.
c.  zero.
d.  equal to the velocity of the center of mass and in the same direction.
e.  equal to the velocity of the center of mass but in the opposite direction.

**0837**    **8-5  Motion of a Gyroscope,  Conceptual,  c**

A disk rotates clockwise in the plane of the page.  What is the direction of the angular momentum vector?

a.  clockwise
b.  counterclockwise
c.  into the page
d.  out of the page
e.  angular momentum has no direction.

**0838**    **8-5  Motion of a Gyroscope,  Conceptual,  a**

The angular momentum vector for a spinning wheel lies along its axle and is pointed east. In order to make this vector point south, it is necessary to exert a force on the east end of the axle in which direction?

a.  up
b.  down
c.  north
d.  south
e.  east

**0839**    **8-5  Motion of a Gyroscope,  Conceptual,  c**

A man is walking north carrying a suitcase that contains a spinning gyroscope mounted on an axle attached to the front and back of the case.  The angular velocity of the gyroscope points north.  The man now begins to turn to walk east.  As a result, the front end of the suitcase will

a.  resist his attempt to turn and will try to remain pointed north.
b.  fight his attempt to turn and will pull to the west.
c.  raise upward.
d.  dip downward.
e.  cause no effect whatsoever.

CHAPTER 9    Gravity

0901    9-1   Kepler's Laws,  Numerical,  c

Halley's comet returns to the vicinity of the sun (and the earth) about once every 76 years. Its last appearance was in 1986. What is the average distance from Halley's comet to the sun, given that the average distance from the earth to the sun is $1.50 \times 10^{11}$ m?

a.  $6.4 \times 10^{11}$ m
b.  $1.8 \times 10^{12}$ m
c.  $2.7 \times 10^{12}$ m
d.  $1.1 \times 10^{13}$ m
e.  $9.9 \times 10^{13}$ m

0902    9-1   Kepler's Laws,  Numerical,  b

The moon has a period of 27.3 days and is an average distance of $3.84 \times 10^5$ km from the earth.  A communications satellite is placed in an earth orbit at $4.23 \times 10^4$ km from the center of the earth.  What is the period of this satellite?

a.  0.87 hours
b.  1.0 day
c.  3.0 days
d.  6.3 days
e.  8.0 hours

0903    9-1 Kepler's Laws,  Numerical,  c

A planet orbits about a distant sun at a distance of $1.8 \times 10^{12}$ m with a period of $10^8$ s.  A second planet orbits the same sun at a distance of $9 \times 10^{11}$ m.  What is the period of the second planet?

a.    $5 \times 10^7$ s
b.    $2 \times 10^8$ s
c.    $0.35 \times 10^8$ s
d.    $2.8 \times 10^8$ s
e.    $5 \times 10^8$ s

**0904   9-1 Kepler's Laws, Conceptual, c**

If the mass of a satellite is doubled while the radius of its orbit remains constant, the speed of the satellite is

a.   increased by a factor of 8.
b.   increased by a factor of 2.
c.   not changed.
d.   reduced by a factor of 8.
e.   reduced by a factor of 2.

**0905   9-2 Newton's Law of Gravity, Conceptual, a**

If the mass of a planet is doubled while its radius and the radius of orbit of its moon remain constant, the speed of the moon is

a.   increased by a factor of 1.4.
b.   increased by a factor of 2.
c.   not changed.
d.   reduced by a factor of 1.4.
e.   reduced by a factor of 2.

**0906   9-2  Newton's Law of Gravity,  Numerical,  a**

What is the difference in the force of gravity on a 1.0-kg mass at the bottom of the deepest ocean trench and that at the top of the highest mountain?  Assume the mass of the earth is concentrated at the center of the earth and that $g = 9.8$ m/s$^2$ at sea level . The radius of the earth at sea level is $6.37 \times 10^6$ m.  The deepest trench is the Marinas Trench, south of Guam, which has a depth $d = 1.103 \times 10^4$ m below sea level.  The highest mountain is Everest in Nepal, which has a height of $h = 8.847 \times 10^3$ m above sea level.  The difference is:

a.   0.061 N
b.   0.0067 N
c.   0.027 N
d.   0.034 N
e.   0.0062 N

**0907   9-2  Newton's Law of Gravity,  Numerical,  d**

What is the force of gravity between the proton and electron in a hydrogen atom?  GIVEN: $G = 6.67 \times 10^{-11}$ N·m$^2$/kg$^2$; the mass of a proton = $1.67 \times 10^{-27}$ kg; the mass of an electron = $9.1 \times 10^{-31}$ kg; and the average radius of the electron's orbit in the hydrogen atom $a_n = 0.0529$ nm.

a.   $1.9 \times 10^{-57}$ N
b.   $1.9 \times 10^{-54}$ N
c.   $3.6 \times 10^{-53}$ N
d.   $3.6 \times 10^{-47}$ N
e.   $3.6 \times 10^{-41}$ N

0908    **9-2  Newton's Law of Gravity,  Conceptual,  e**

A woman whose weight on earth is 500 N is lifted to a height two earth radii <u>above the surface</u> of the earth.  Her weight will

a.  decrease to one-half of the original amount.
b.  decrease to one-quarter of the original amount.
c.  decrease to one-quarter of the original amount.
d.  decrease to one-third of the original amount.
e.  decrease to one-ninth of the original amount.

0909    **9-2  Newton's Law of Gravity,  Numerical,  a**

A physics student is in a spaceship that has a mass of $13 \times 10^4$ kg and is $2.2 \times 10^{12}$ m from a black hole near the center of the galaxy.  The gravitational force exerted by the black hole on the spaceship is 46 N.  The force on the ship when it has moved to one-third of its original distance from the black hole is

a.  410 N
b.  140 N
c.  150 N
d.  5.0 N
e.  730 N

0910    **9-2  Newton's Law of Gravity,  Conceptual,  a**

Two planets have masses $M$ and $m$ and the ratio $M/m = 25$.

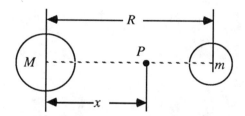

The distance between the planets is $R$.  The point $P$ is between the planets as shown and the distance $M$ to $P$ is $x$.  At $P$ the gravitational forces on an object due to $M$ and $m$ are equal in magnitude.  The value of $x$ is

a.  $5R/6$
b.  $25R/36$
c.  $R/25$
d.  $6R/5$
e.  None of these are correct.

0911    **9-2  Newton's Law of Gravity,  Conceptual,  d**

The acceleration due to gravity at the surface of the earth is $g$.  The radius of the earth is $R_E$.  The distance from the center of the earth to a point where the acceleration due to gravity is $g/9$ is

a.  $R_E$
b.  $9R_E$
c.  $(1/3)R_E$
d.  $3R_E$
e.  None of these is correct.

0912    **9-2   Newton's Law of Gravity,   Conceptual,   d**

At the surface of the moon, the acceleration due to the gravity of the moon is $a$. At a distance from the center of the moon equal to three times the radius of the moon, the acceleration due to the gravity of the moon is

a.   $9a$
b.   $a/3$
c.   $a/4$
d.   $a/9$
e.   None of these is correct.


0913    **9-2   Newton's Law of Gravity,   Conceptual,   a**

Suppose a planet exists that has half the mass of earth and half its radius.  On the surface of that planet, the acceleration due to gravity is

a.   twice that on earth.
b.   the same as that on earth.
c.   half that on earth.
d.   one-fourth that on earth.
e.   None of these is correct.


0914    **9-2   Newton's Law of Gravity,   Factual,   b**

In the SI system the units for gravitational field intensity are

a.   $kg \cdot m/s^2$
b.   $m/s^2$
c.   $kg^2/m^2$
d.   $N/m$
e.   None of these is correct.


0915    **9-2   Newton's Law of Gravity,   Conceptual,   c**

Newton's law of gravity is $F = GMm/r^2$. The SI units of the gravitational constant $G$ are

a.   $G$ has no dimensions.
b.   $N \cdot kg^2/m^2$
c.   $N \cdot m^2/kg^2$
d.   $kg^2/N \cdot m^2$
e.   None of these is correct.


0916    **9-5   Escaping the Earth,   Conceptual,   a**

If the mass of a planet is doubled with no increase in its size, the escape speed for that planet will

a.   be increased by a factor of 1.4.
b.   be increased by a factor of 2.
c.   not be changed.
d.   be reduced by a factor of 1.4.
e.   be reduced by a factor of 2.

**0917**  **9-5  Escaping the Earth,  Numerical,  b**

Suppose a rocket is fired vertically upward from the surface of the earth with one-half of the escape speed.  How far from the center of the earth will it reach before it begins to fall back?  (Let $g = 9.8$ m/s$^2$ and $R_E = 6370$ km.)

a.  $1.3 \times 10^4$ km
b.  $8.5 \times 10^3$ km
c.  $9.6 \times 10^3$ km
d.  $2.6 \times 10^4$ km
e.  $1.9 \times 10^4$ km

**0918**  **9-5  Escaping the Earth,  Numerical,  c**

What is the escape speed from the sun, beginning (from rest relative to the sun) at the orbit of the earth,  $R = 1.50 \times 10^8$ km.  (GIVEN:  $G = 6.67 \times 10^{-11}$ N·m$^2$/kg$^2$; mass of the sun = $2.0 \times 10^{30}$ kg.)

a.  $3.0 \times 10^4$ m/s
b.  $2.1 \times 10^4$ m/s
c.  $1.3 \times 10^6$ m/s
d.  $9.4 \times 10^5$ m/s
e.  $4.2 \times 10^4$ m/s

**0919**  **9-6  Potential Energy, Total Energy, and Orbits,  Numerical,  b**

An earth satellite, the mass of which is 1000 kg, is in a circlar orbit 1000 km above the surface of the earth.  It is desired to transfer it to a circular orbit 1500 km above the surface.  The amount of work that must be done to accomplish this is

a.  $3.43 \times 10^9$ J
b.  $1.71 \times 10^9$ J
c.  $-1.71 \times 10^9$ J
d.  $6.65 \times 10^{10}$ J
e.  $-3.43 \times 10^9$ J

**0920**  **9-6  Potential Energy, Total Energy, and Orbits,  Numerical,  d**

A satellite with a mass $m$ is in a stable circular orbit about a planet with a mass $M$.  The universal gravitational constant is $G$.  The radius of the orbit is $R$.  The ratio of the potential energy of the satellite to its kinetic energy is

a.  $-2R$
b.  $+2G$
c.  $-2G/R$
d.  $-2$
e.  None of these is correct.

**0921**   **9-6   Potential Energy, Total Energy, and Orbits,   Numerical,   d**

The radius of the moon is $R$.  A satellite orbiting the moon in a circular orbit has an acceleration due to the moon's gravity of 0.14 m/s$^2$.  The acceleration due to gravity at the moon's surface is 1.62 m/s$^2$.  The height of the satellite above the moon's surface is

a.   3.4$R$.
b.   0.42$R$.
c.   11$R$.
d.   2.4$R$.
e.   1.7$R$.

**0922**   **9-6   Potential Energy, Total Energy, and Orbits,   Conceptual,   c**

Four identical masses, each of mass $M$, are placed at the corners of a square of side $L$.  The total potential energy of the masses is equal to $-GM^2/L$ x $N$ where $N$ equals

a.   4
b.   $4 + 2\sqrt{2}$
c.   $4 + \sqrt{2}$
d.   $4 + 1/\sqrt{2}$
e.   $2 + 2\sqrt{2}$

CHAPTER 10    Solids and Fluids

**1001    10-1   Density,   Factual,   b**

Which of the following is the density of a material?

a.   The material's weight per unit volume.
b.   The material's mass per unit volume.
c.   The material's specific gravity.
d.   The material's volume per unit weight.
e.   The material's volume per unit mass.

**1002    10-1   Density,   Numerical,   d**

A piece of wood is floating at the surface of some water as illustrated.  The wood has a circular cross-section and a height $h = 3.0$ cm.  The density of the wood is 0.41 g/cm$^3$.  The distance $y$ from the surface of the water to the bottom of the wood is

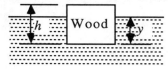

a.   impossible to determine because the area of the cross section is not given.
b.   0.81 cm
c.   3.2 cm
d.   1.2 cm
e.   None of these is correct.

**1003    10-1   Density,   Factual,   e**

Which of the following are the SI units for specific gravity?

a.   kg/m$^3$
b.   g/cm$^3$
c.   lb/ft$^3$
d.   slug/ft$^3$
e.   Specific gravity has no units.

**1004   10-1   Density,   Conceptual,   b**

A block of material has a density $\rho$.  A second block of equal volume has three times the mass of the first.  What is the density of the second block?

a.   $\rho$
b.   $3\rho$
c.   $\rho/3$
d.   $9\rho$
e.   $\rho/9$

**1005   10-1   Density,   Conceptual,   c**

A block of material has a density $\rho$.  A second block of equal mass has twice the volume of the first.  What is the density of the second block?

a.   $\rho$
b.   $2\rho$
c.   $\rho/2$
d.   $4\rho$
e.   $\rho/4$

**1006   10-1   Density,   Numerical,   d**

A penny has a mass of 3.0 g, a diameter of 1.9 cm, and a thickness of 0.15 cm.  What is the density of the metal of which it is made?

a.   1.8 g/cm$^3$
b.   3.4 g/cm$^3$
c.   3.5 g/cm$^3$
d.   7.1 g/cm$^3$
e.   4.5 g/cm$^3$

**1007   10-2   Stress and Strain,   Conceptual,   e**

Which of the following could not have units of N/m$^2$?

a.   Young's modulus
b.   Shear modulus
c.   Bulk modulus
d.   Stress
e.   Strain

**1008   10-2   Stress and Strain,   Numerical,   a**

A wire 2.5 m long has a cross-sectional area of 2.5 mm$^2$.  It is hung vertically and a 4.5-kg mass is hung from it.  By how much will the wire stretch if Young's modulus for that material is 2.0 x 10$^{11}$ N/m$^2$?

a.   0.22 mm
b.   2.2 mm
c.   0.022 mm
d.   0.72 mm
e.   0.072 mm

**1009**    **10-2  Stress and Strain,  Numerical,  b**

The bulk modulus of water is $2.0 \times 10^9$ N/m$^2$.  By how much must the pressure be increased to reduce the volume of 1.0 kg of water from 1.00 L to 0.998 L?

a.  $2.0 \times 10^6$ N/m$^2$
b.  $4.0 \times 10^6$ N/m$^2$
c.  $20 \times 10^6$ N/m$^2$
d.  $40 \times 10^6$ N/m$^2$
e.  $8.0 \times 10^6$ N/m$^2$

**1010**    **10-3  Pressure in a Fluid,  Conceptual,  c**

A glass is filled with water.  The pressure at the top of the glass is zero and the pressure at the bottom is $P$.  A second glass having three times the height and twice the diameter is also filled with water.  What is the pressure at the bottom of the second glass?

a.  $P$
b.  $2P$
c.  $3P$
d.  $3P/2$
e.  $3P/4$

**1011**    **10-3  Pressure in a Fluid,  Numerical,  a**

What is the gauge pressure at a depth of 6 cm in a glass filled with 4 cm of mercury and 4 cm of water?  Water has a density of 1000 kg/m$^3$ and mercury has a density 13.6 times as great.

a.  3.1 kPa
b.  5.6 kPa
c.  5.8 kP
d.  310 kPa
e.  560 kPa

**1012**    **10-3  Pressure in a Fluid,  Numerical,  d**

A blood pressure is reported as 50 mm Hg.  The density of mercury is 13.6 g/cm$^3$.  This pressure is equivalent to

a.    $6.7 \times 10^6$ Pa
b.    6.8 Pa
c.    $6.8 \times 10^2$ Pa
d.    $6.7 \times 10^3$ Pa
e.    $3.2 \times 10^2$ Pa

**1013    10-3   Pressure in a Fluid,   Conceptual,   a**

A U-tube has water to a height $h$ on both sides, as shown in the figure. The cross-sectional area of the left-hand tube is $A_1 = 1.50$ cm$^2$, whereas the right-hand tube has an area $A_2 = 0.50$ cm$^2$. A light oil with a density of 0.83 g/cm$^3$, which does not mix with water, is added to the right-hand side. When equilibrium is reached

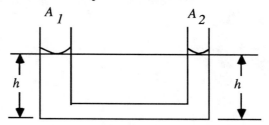

a.   the level on the right-hand side is higher than that on the left.
b.   the level on the right-hand side is lower than that on the left.
c.   the levels of the two sides are the same.
d.   the difference in the heights depends on $A_1$ and $A_2$.
e.   None of these is correct.

**1014    10-3   Pressure in a Fluid,   Numerical,   a**

The left-hand side of a U-tube has a radius $r_1 = 0.82$ cm and the right-hand side has a radius $r_2 = 0.41$ cm. Mercury and oil are poured into the U-tube. The density of mercury is 13.6 g/cm$^3$. The heights shown in the diagram are $h_1 = 3.50$ cm and $h_2 = 27.6$ cm. The density of the oil is

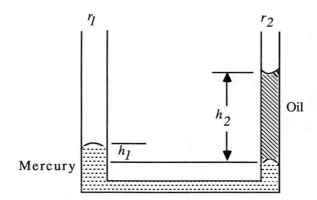

a.   1.7 g/cm$^3$
b.   110 g/cm$^3$
c.   7.9 g/cm$^3$
d.   6.9 g/cm$^3$
e.   0.82 g/cm$^3$

**1015  10-3  Pressure in a Fluid,  Numerical,  b**

A tube with a radius of 4.2 cm is holding oil with a density of 0.92 g/cm$^3$.  The pressure in the oil at a depth of 64 cm from the top of the surface is

a.  $5.8 \times 10^2$ Pa
b.  $5.8 \times 10^3$ Pa
c.  $1.0 \times 10^2$ Pa
d.  $1.0 \times 10^6$ Pa
e.  $1.7 \times 10^3$ Pa

**1016  10-3  Pressure in a Fluid,  Numerical,  a**

A small sphere of wood with a density $\rho = 0.40$ g/cm$^3$ is held at rest well under the surface of a pool of water.  The magnitude of the initial acceleration of the sphere when it is released is

a.  15 m/s$^2$
b.  9.8 m/s$^2$
c.  33 m/s$^2$
d.  23 m/s$^2$
e.  3.4 m/s$^2$

**1017  10-3  Pressure in a Fluid,  Conceptual,  e**

A flat plate with a negligible mass and an area of 1.0 cm$^2$ is placed in a horizontal position in a liquid that is not moving.  The pressure at the location of the plate is $P$  Pa.  The total force that arises from the pressure of the fluid acting on this plate is

a.  $P$ N, directed down.
b.  $P \times 10^{-4}$ N, directed down.
c.  $P$ N, directed up.
d.  $P \times 10^{-4}$ N, directed up.
e.  zero.

**1018  10-3  Pressure in a Fluid,  Conceptual,  e**

If the gauge pressure is doubled, the absolute pressure will be

a.  halved.
b.  doubled.
c.  unchanged.
d.  squared.
e.  Not enough information is given to determine the effect.

**1019  10-3  Pressure in a Fluid,  Numerical,  a**

Two pistons of a hydraulic lift have radii of 2.67 cm and 20.0 cm.  The downward force on the 2.67–cm piston that is required to lift a mass of 2000 kg supported by the 20-cm piston is

a.  350 N
b.  270 N
c.  36 N
d.  $1.5 \times 10^3$ N
e.  $2.6 \times 10^3$ N

**1020    10-3   Pressure in a Fluid,   Numerical,   a**

A ball bearing that has a density of 5.16 g/cm$^3$ is held at rest under the surface of a liquid that  has a density of 2.50 g/cm$^3$. The magnitude of the acceleration of the ball bearing just after it is released is

a.  5.0 m/s$^2$
b.  14 m/s$^2$
c.  10. m/s$^2$
d.  6.5 m/s$^2$
e.  1.6 m/s$^2$


**1021    10-4   Buoyancy and Archimedes' Principle,   Conceptual,   c**

A rock of mass $M$ with a density twice that of water is sitting on the bottom of an aquarium tank filled with water.  The normal force exerted on the rock by the bottom of the tank is

a.  $2Mg$
b.  $Mg$
c.  $Mg/2$
d.  zero
e.  impossible to determine from the given information.


**1022    10-4   Buoyancy and Archimedes' Principle,   Conceptual,   b**

A large tub is half full of water.  A mass $M = 25.0$ kg, which has a specific gravity of 2.5, is attached at $A$ on the right-hand side of the tub, out of the water.  The entire apparatus is balanced on a fulcrum at $C$.  The tub is clamped in place and $M$ is lowered to $B$, where it is on the bottom and completely submerged.  When the clamps are removed, the tub

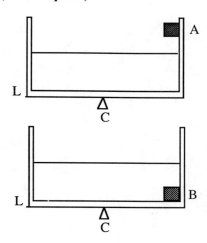

a.    remains balanced.
b.    tips, with point $L$ going down.
c.    tips, with point $L$ going up.
d.    There is not sufficient information to solve the problem.
e.    None of these is correct.

**1023    10-4   Buoyancy and Archimedes' Principle, Conceptual,  a**

A student is floating in a boat in a swimming pool. There are some large stones, with a density of 2.5 g/cm³, in the boat. The student throws the stones out of the boat such that they sink to the bottom of the pool. The water level $h$, measured vertically at the end of the pool,_____ as the stones are thrown out.

   a.  decreases
   b.  increases
   c.  There is not enough information to solve the problem.
   d.  stays the same
   e.  None of these is correct.

**1024    10-4   Buoyancy and Archimedes' Principle, Numerical,  a**

A block of wood of length $l = 21.0$ cm, width $w = 9.53$ cm, and height $h = 5.92$ cm is just barely immersed in water by placing a mass $m$ on the top of the block. The density of the wood is $\rho = 0.390$ g/cm³. The value of $m$ is

   a.   0.72 kg
   b.   7.1 kg
   c.   1.2 kg
   d.   1.6 kg
   e.   0.36 kg

**1025    10-4   Buoyancy and Archimedes' Principle,  Numerical,  b**

A cylindrical piece of wood has a mass $M = 0.235$ kg.  A small piece of lead with a mass $m = 0.021$ kg is fixed in the wood at the bottom of the cylinder so that the cylinder floats in water in a stable position, as shown.  The radius of the cylinder is 1.65 cm.  The depth $x$ of the cylinder below the surface of the water is

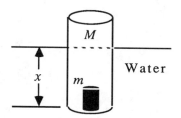

   a.  0.32 m
   b.  0.30 m
   c.  0.22 m
   d.  0.42 m
   e.  None of these is correct.

**1026    10-4   Buoyancy and Archimedes' Principle,  Conceptual,  d**

A rock is thrown into a swimming pool filled with water at a uniform temperature.  Which of the following statements is true?

   a.  The buoyant force on the rock is zero as it sinks.
   b.  The buoyant force on the rock increases as it sinks.
   c.  The buoyant force on the rock decreases as it sinks.
   d.  The buoyant force on the rock is constant as it sinks.
   e.  The buoyant force on the rock as it sinks is nonzero at first but becomes zero once the terminal velocity is reached.

1027    **10-4   Buoyancy and Archimedes' Principle,  Conceptual,  c**

A rock of mass $M$, which has a density twice that of water, is suspended in water by a thin, massless cord.  The tension in the cord is

a.   $2Mg$
b.   $Mg$
c.   $Mg/2$
d.   zero
e.   impossible to determine from the given information.

1028    **10-4   Buoyancy and Archimedes' Principle,  Numerical,  c**

A metal block suspended from a spring balance is submerged under water.  It is observed that the block displaces 55 cm$^3$ of water and that the spring balance reads 4.3 N.  What is the density of the block?

a.   7.0 g/cm$^3$
b.   8.0 g/cm$^3$
c.   9.0 g/cm$^3$
d.   1.1 g/cm$^3$
e.   1.2 g/cm$^3$

1029    **10-4   Bouyancy and Archimedes' Principle,  Conceptual,  b**

A physics student is floating in a boat in a swimming pool.  The boat contains some blocks of wood.  The specific gravity of the wood is 0.66.  The student throws the wood blocks into the pool.  When the waves settle, the depth of the water in the pool

a.   has increased.
b.   is the same as before.
c.   has decreased.
d.   cannot be determined with the given information.
e.   None of these is correct.

1030    **10-5   Surface Tension and Capillarity,  Numerical,  c**

When a thin capillary tube of radius 0.25 mm is inserted in a dish of water as shown, water is drawn up into the tube to a height $h = 6$ cm. If another tube is inserted and the height of water is observed to be 20 cm, the radius of this tube must be

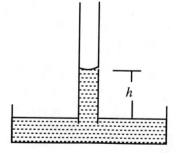

a.   0.83 mm
b.   0.46 mm
c.   0.075 mm
d.   0.14 mm
e.   0.061 mm

**1031**   **10-5   Surface Tension and Capillarity,   Numerical,  b**

In this problem, consider only the forces arising from surface tension. The U-shaped frame in the diagram has a soap film. The coefficient of surface tension is 2.7 x 10⁻² N/m. The force F that is required to keep the vertical bar *AB* at rest is

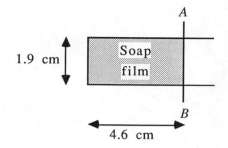

a.  4.7 x 10⁻³ N
b.  1.0 x 10⁻³ N
c.  2.5 x 10⁻³ N
d.  5.2 x 10⁻⁴ N
e.  8.7 x 10⁻⁴ N


**1032**   **10-5   Surface Tension and Capillarity,   Conceptual,  b**

A capillary tube is placed in a shallow dish of water.  The water rises to a height *h* in the tube.  How high will the water rise in a second tube  with a radius one-third that of the first tube?

a.  *h*
b.  3*h*
c.  *h*/3
d.  9*h*
e.  *h*/9


**1033**   **10-5   Surface Tension and Capillarity,   Numerical,  d**

A water beetle stands on the surface of water on four legs.  Each leg has a pad that is 2.1 mm by 1.0 mm.  The coefficient of surface tension for water is 73 dynes/cm.  The maximum mass of the beetle is

a.  6.1 g
b.  0.16 g
c.  0.63 g
d.  0.18 g
e.  0.041 g


**1034**   **10-5   Surface Tension and Capillarity,   Conceptual,  d**

An extremely light piece of wire is bent into the shape of a circle and carefully placed on a water surface.  The force then required to lift the wire off the water surface is *F*.  A second piece of wire is bent so as to enclose four times the area of the first.  What force is required to lift this second piece of wire off the water surface?

a.  *F*
b.  4*F*
c.  *F*/4
d.  2*F*
e.  *F*/2

1035    **10-6  Fluids in Motion and Bernoulli's Equation,  Numerical,  a**

Bernoulli's equation can be stated as

$$P_1 + \rho g y_1 + \frac{1}{2}\rho v_1^2 = P_2 + \rho g y_2 + \frac{1}{2}\rho v_2^2$$

A fluid is flowing through a horizontal tube that changes in cross-sectional area from $A_1 = 0.75$ cm$^2$ to $A_2 = 0.030$ cm$^2$.

When $v_1 = 3.5$ cm/s and $\rho = 1.4$ g/cm$^3$, the difference between pressure $P_2$ at $A_2$ and $P_1$ at $A_1$ is

a.  $5.4 \times 10^3$ dyn/cm$^2$, with $P_1$ higher.
b.  59 dyn/cm$^2$, with $P_2$ higher.
c.  59 dyn/cm$^2$, with $P_1$ higher.
d.  $8.3 \times 10^2$ dyn/cm$^2$, with $P_2$ higher.
e.  None of these is correct.

1036    **10-6  Fluids in Motion and Bernoulli's Equation,  Conceptual,  b**

Water from a tap is flowing at a uniform rate of 24.0 cm$^3$/s into a cylindrical container.  An exit tube is mounted on the side of the container at height $h/2$ from the base.  The height, $h$, of the water remains constant.  The volume flow rate at which the water leaves the container is

a.  12 cm$^3$/s
b.  24 cm$^3$/s
c.  36 cm$^3$/s
d.  48 cm$^3$/s
e.  72 cm$^3$/s

1037    **10-6  Fluids in Motion and Bernoulli's Equation,  Conceptual,  b**

A horizontal pipe narrows from a diameter of 10 cm to 5 cm.  For a fluid flowing from the larger diameter to the smaller,

a.  the velocity and pressure both increase.
b.  the velocity increases and the pressure decreases.
c.  the velocity decreases and the pressure increases.
d.  the velocity and pressure both decrease.
e.  either the velocity or the pressure changes but not both.

**1038    10-6   Fluids in Motion and Bernoulli's Equation,  Numerical,  d**

A tank of water is filled to a height $H$.
A small hole is punched in one of the
walls at a depth $h$ below the water's
surface. The water leaves the hole in a
horizontal direction. The stream of
water strikes the floor at a distance $x$ as
shown. The value of $x$ can be
calculated from

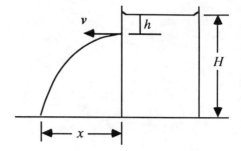

a.   $x = H - h$
b.   $x = \sqrt{2h\ (H - h)}$
c.   $x = h$
d.   $x = 2\sqrt{h\ (H - h)}$
e.   None of these is correct.

**1039    10-6   Fluids in Motion and Bernoulli's Equation,  Conceptual,  e**

Water flows at speed $v$ in a pipe of radius $r$. At what speed does the water flow through a
constriction where the radius of the pipe is $r/3$?

a.   $v/9$
b.   $v/3$
c.   $v$
d.   $3v$
e.   $9v$

**1040    10-6   Fluids in Motion and Bernoulli's Equation,  Conceptual,  a**

Water flows through the pipe shown in the figure.  The pressure

a.   is greater at $A$ than at $B$.
b.   at $A$ equals that at $B$.
c.   is less at $A$ than at $B$.
d.   at $A$ is unrelated to that at $B$.
e.   at $A$ may be greater or less than that at $B$ depending on the rate of flow.

**1041    10-6   Fluids in Motion and Bernoulli's Equation,  Numerical,  a**

A wind with speed 45 m/s blows across a roof 20 m long and 12 m wide.  What is the net
force on this roof due to the pressure difference inside and outside the roof?  (The density of
air = 1.3 kg/m$^3$.)

a.   3.2 x $10^5$ N
b.   2.4 x $10^7$ N
c.   6.3 x $10^5$ N
d.   7.0 x $10^3$ N
e.   3.2 x $10^8$ N

1042    10-7   Viscous  Flow,   Conceptual,  b

A liquid with a low viscosity, such as water, is flowing with no turbulence through the horizontal tube shown in the figure. The cross-sectional area at $A$ is equal to that at $C$ and is 5 times that at $B$. Choose the following statement that best describes the pressures that would be observed.

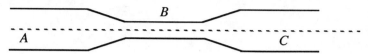

a.  The pressure at $A$ is the same as the pressure at $C$, and this pressure is smaller than the pressure at $B$.
b.  The pressure at $A$ is somewhat larger than that at $C$, and the pressures at both $A$ and $C$ are larger than the pressure at $B$.
c.  The pressures at $A$ and $C$ are the same, and this pressure is larger than the pressure at $B$.
d.  The pressure at $A$ is larger than the pressure at $B$, which is larger than the pressure at $C$.
e.  None of these is correct.


1043    10-7   Viscous  Flow,   Conceptual,   b

For the streamlined flow of a viscous liquid, such as water, in a capillary tube,

a.  the coefficient of viscosity is dependent on the radius of the inside of the tube raised to the fourth power.
b.  the velocity of the liquid is essentially zero at the tube walls and increases toward the center of the tube.
c.  there is no pressure difference as one moves along the tube provided the tube is less than 10 cm in length.
d.  the volume flow rate through the tube can never be constant.
e.  None of these is correct.


1044    10-7   Viscous  Flow,   Numerical,   c

A smooth stone is falling with its constant terminal velocity in a viscous liquid. The density of the stone is $2.89 \times 10^3$ kg/m$^3$ and the density of the liquid is $1.34 \times 10^3$ kg/m$^3$. The volume of the stone is $2.15 \times 10^{-6}$ m$^3$. The drag force $F$ of the liquid on the stone is given by $F = 3.52v$ in SI units, where $v$ is the terminal velocity. The value of $v$ is

a.  $8.5 \times 10^{-3}$ m/s
b.  $1.1 \times 10^{-2}$ m/s
c.  $9.3 \times 10^{-3}$ m/s
d.  $1.7 \times 10^{-2}$ m/s
e.  $1.7 \times 10^{-3}$ m/s


1045    10-7   Viscous  Flow,   Numerical,   c

Poiseuille's law states that the volume per second flowing through a tube with streamlined motion is given by the equation $V = (P_1 - P_2)(R^4)/(8\eta L)$, where $R$ is the tube radius, $L$ is its length, $\eta$ is the coefficient of viscosity, and $P_1 - P_2$ is the pressure difference along the tube. A pressure difference due to a 0.850-m height of water is driving water through a tube with a radius of 0.520 cm. The radius of the tube is changed to 0.360 cm and no other changes are made. The volume of water per second delivered through the new tube is

a.  $0.35V_1$
b.  $0.14V_1$
c.  $0.23V_1$
d.  $0.69V_1$
e.  $0.11V_1$

# CHAPTER 11    Temperature

**1101    11-1   The Celsius and Fahrenheit Temperature Scales,   Numerical,   a**

The temperature in January in Winnipeg, Canada, has been known to go down to -40°C.
What is this temperature on the Fahrenheit scale?

a.   -40°F
b.   -104°F
c.   +9.8°F
d.   -72°F
e.   -32°F

**1102    11-1   The Celsius and Fahrenheit Temperature Scales,   Numerical,   d**

Normal human body temperature is 98.6°F.  What is the corresponding Celsius  temperature

a.   54.8°C
b.   72.6°C
c.   40.0°C
d.   37.0°C
e.   35.5°C

**1103    11-1   The Celsius and Fahrenheit Temperature Scales,   Conceptual,   d**

If one were to plot a graph with Fahrenheit temperatures along the horizontal axis and the
corresponding Celsius temperatures along the vertical axis, the slope of the line would be

a.   -40 F°/C°
b.   32 F°/C°
c.   1.8 F°/C°
d.   0.56 F°/C°
e.   0 F°/C°

**1104    11-1   The Celsius and Fahrenheit Temperature Scales,   Factual,   c**

A temperature difference of 5 C° is the same as a difference of

a.   41 F°
b.   14 F°
c.   9 F°
d.   5 F°
e.   -15 F°

**1105**   **11-2   The Absolute Temperature Scale,   Numerical,   b**

The highest and lowest temperatures ever recorded in the United States are 134°F (California, 1913) and -80°F (Alaska, 1971).  What are these temperatures in kelvins?

    a.   407 K and 193 K
    b.   330 K and 211 K
    c.   347 K and 228 K
    d.   340 K and 300 K
    e.   365 K and 246 K


**1106**   **11-2   The Absolute Temperature Scale,   Numerical,   c**

A constant-volume gas thermometer reads 6.66 kPa at the triple point of water.  What will the pressure reading be at the normal boiling point of water?

    a.   2.44 kPa
    b.   18.2 kPa
    c.   9.10 kPa
    d.   11.8 kPa
    e.   4.87 kPa


**1107**   **11-3   The Ideal-Gas Law,   Conceptual,   d**

The pressure and volume of an ideal gas can both be doubled, by the temperature of the gas

    a.   being reduced to one-quarter of its original value.
    b.   being doubled.
    c.   being reduced to one-half of its original value.
    d.   being quadrupled.
    e.   None of these is correct.


**1108**   **11-3   The Ideal-Gas Law,   Numerical,   d**

The air in a balloon occupies a volume of 0.10 $m^3$ when at a temperature of 27°C and a pressure of 1.2 atm.  What is the balloon's volume at 7°C and 1.0 atm?  (The amount of gas remains constant.)

    a.   0.022 $m^3$
    b.   0.078 $m^3$
    c.   0.089 $m^3$
    d.   0.11 $m^3$
    e.   0.13 $m^3$


**1109**   **11-3   The Ideal Gas Law,   Numerical,   a**

In a vacuum system, a container is pumped down to a pressure of 1.33 x $10^{-6}$ Pa at 20°C. How many molecules of gas are there in 1 $cm^3$ of this container?  (Boltzmann's constant $k$ = 1.38 x $10^{-23}$ J/K.)

    a.   3.3 x $10^8$
    b.   4.8 x $10^9$
    c.   3.3 x.$10^{14}$
    d.   7.9 x $10^{12}$
    e.   4.8 x $10^{12}$

**1110    11-3   The Ideal-Gas Law,   Numerical,   c**

A rigid container of air is at atmospheric pressure and 27°C.  To double the pressure in the container, it should be heated to

a.   54°C
b.   300°C
c.   327°C
d.   600°C
e.   327 K

**1111    11-3   The Ideal-Gas Law,   Conceptual,   d**

If a certain mass of oxygen gas occupies a volume of 8 L at standard temperature and pressure,  what will be the change in the volume if the temperature is decreased to 136 K and the pressure remains constant?

a.   It will increase 8 L.
b.   It will decrease 8 L.
c.   It will increase 16 L.
d.   It will decrease 4 L.
e.   It will increase 4 L.

**1112    11-3   The Ideal-Gas Law,   Conceptual,   d**

If a certain mass of oxygen gas occupies a volume of 8 L at standard temperature and pressure,  what will be the change in the volume if the temperature is reduced by one half and the pressure is doubled?

a.   It will increase 4 L.
b.   It will decrease 2 L.
c.   It will increase 16 L.
d.   It will decrease 6 L.
e.   It will not change.

**1113    11-3   The Ideal-Gas Law,   Conceptual,   b**

A certain mass of oxygen gas occupies a volume $V$ at standard temperature and pressure. What will be the new volume if the mass is doubled and the pressure is tripled?

a.   $V$
b.   $(2/3)V$
c.   $(3/2)V$
d.   $6V$
e.   $(5/9)V$

**1114    11-3   The Ideal-Gas Law,   Conceptual,   e**

If the pressure and volume of an ideal gas are both reduced to half their original value, the absolute temperature of the gas will be

a.   unchanged.
b.   doubled.
c.   halved.
d.   quadrupled.
e.   quartered.

**1115**   **11-3   The Ideal-Gas Law,   Conceptual,   c**

If both the temperature and the volume of an ideal gas are doubled, the pressure will be

a.   increased by a factor of 4.
b.   doubled also .
c.   unchanged.
d.   diminished by a factor of 1/4.
e.   None of these is correct.

**1116**   **11-3   The Ideal-Gas Law,   Numerical,   b**

Assume that helium is a perfect gas and that the volume of the cylinder that contains the helium is independent of temperature.  A cylinder of helium at +85°C has a pressure of 208 atm.  The pressure of the helium when it is cooled to -55°C is

a.   -132 atm
b.   127 atm
c.   335 atm
d.   132 atm
e.   204 atm

**1117**   **11-3   The Ideal-Gas Law,   Numerical,   a**

When jam is preserved in glass jars, the jar is nearly filled with the jam, leaving an air space of only about 10 cm³.  The jar is closed with a rubber-gasketed cover 6 cm in diameter that allows gas to escape but prevents gas from entering the jar.  The jar is then placed into boiling water for half an hour.  How much force is needed to lift the cover off this jar after it has cooled to room temperature, 20°C?  (Neglect thermal expansion of the jam and the jar. Assume air is an ideal gas.)

a.   61 N
b.   250 N
c.   290 N
d.   220 N
e.   132 N

**1118**   **11-3   The Ideal-Gas Law,   Numerical,   c**

Bottles of homemade beer are capped at a temperature of 27°C and a pressure of 1.3 atm. The cap will pop off if the pressure inside the bottle exceeds 1.5 atm.  Assume the gas at the top of the bottle is an ideal gas and that the change in the volume of the beer and the bottle is negligible.  What temperature must the gas inside the bottle reach in order to pop the cap?

a.   -31°C
b.   31°C
c.   73°C
d.   83°C
e.   102°C

**1119   11-3   The Ideal-Gas Law,   Conceptual,   d**

The relationship between the pressure and the volume of a gas expressed by Boyle's law holds true

a.   for some gases under any conditions.
b.   if the density is constant.
c.   if the container of the gas can expand with increasing pressure.
d.   if the temperature is constant.
e.   for all gases under any conditions.

**1120   11-4   The Molecular Interpretation of Temperature,   Conceptual,   b**

The oxygen (molar mass = 32 g/mol) and nitrogen (molar mass = 28 g/mol) molecules in this room have equal average

a.   kinetic energies, but the oxygen molecules are faster.
b.   kinetic energies, but the oxygen molecules are slower.
c.   kinetic energies and speeds.
d.   speeds, but the oxygen molecules have a higher average kinetic energy.
e.   speeds, but the oxygen molecules have a lower average kinetic energy.
f.   None of these is correct.

**1121   11-4   The Molecular Interpretation of Temperature,   Conceptual,   a**

Doubling the Kelvin temperature of a gas will increase which of the following measures of its molecular velocity by a factor of 1.4?

a.   The rms speed.
b.   The average speed.
c.   The most probable speed.
d.   All three of these speeds.
e.   None of these speeds.

**1122   11-4   The Molecular Interpretation of Temperature,   Conceptual,   c**

Ethyl chloride ($C_2H_5Cl$) is used as a refrigerant under certain circumstances.  One mole of this substance contains Avogadro's number of

a.   carbon atoms.
b.   hydrogen atoms.
c.   chlorine atoms.
d.   All of the above are correct.
e.   None of the above is correct.

**1123   11-4   The Molecular Interpretation of Temperature,   Numerical,   b**

A hailstorm causes an average pressure of 1.4 $N/m^2$ on the 200-$m^2$ flat roof of a house. The hailstones, each of mass 7.0 x $10^{-3}$ kg, have an average velocity of 10 m/s perpendicular to the roof and rebound after hitting the roof with the same speed.  How many hailstones hit the roof each second?

a.   4000
b.   2000
c.   1000
d.   10
e.   800

**1124   11-4   The Molecular Interpretation of Temperature,   Conceptual,   e**

At room temperature, which of the following diatomic molecules has the greater average kinetic energy:  carbon monoxide (molar mass = 28 g/mol), nitrogen (molar mass = 28 g/mol ), or oxygen (molar mass = 32 g/mol)?

a.   Carbon monoxide
b.   Nitrogen
c.   Oxygen
d.   Both a and b are correct.
e.   All three have the same average kinetic energy.

**1125   11-4   The Molecular Interpretation of Temperature,   Numerical,   c**

At what Kelvin temperature does the root-mean-square speed of the oxygen ($O_2$) molecules in the air near the surface of the earth become equal to the escape speed from the earth?  ($R$ = 8.31 J/mol·K; molar mass of $O_2$ gas = 32 g/mol; radius of the earth $R_E$ = 6.37 x $10^6$ m; the escape speed from the earth = 11.2 km/s.)

a.   4.8 x $10^5$ K
b.   8.0 x $10^4$ K
c.   1.6 x $10^5$ K
d.   1.1 x $10^4$ K
e.   3.6 x $10^5$ K

**1126   11-4   The Molecular Interpretation of Temperature,   Conceptual,   b**

If the absolute temperature of a gas is doubled, what is the change in the average kinetic energy of its molecules?

a.   There is no change.
b.   It increases by a factor of 2.
c.   It decreases by a factor of 2.
d.   It increases by a factor of 1.4.
e.   It decreases by a factor of 1.4.

**1127   11-4   The Molecular Interpretation of Temperature,   Conceptual,   d**

If the absolute temperature of a gas is doubled, what is the change in the rms speed of its molecules?

a.   There is no change.
b.   It increases by a factor of 2.
c.   It decreases by a factor of 2.
d.   It increases by a factor of 1.4.
e.   It decreases by a factor of 1.4.

**1128   11-4   The Molecular Interpretation of Temperature,   Conceptual,   a**

If the average kinetic energy of a gas is doubled, what is the change in the average mass of its molecules?

a.   There is no change.
b.   It increases by a factor of 2.
c.   It decreases by a factor of 2.
d.   It increases by a factor of 1.4.
e.   It decreases by a factor of 1.4.

CHAPTER 12  # Heat and the First Law of Thermodynamics

**1201    12-1  Heat Capacity and Specific Heat,  Numerical,  d**

The quantity of heat absorbed by a body is given by the formula $Q = cm(T_f - T_0)$. A certain metal has a specific heat $c = 0.21$ cal/g·C°, and a mass $m = 25.6$ g. The final temperature $T_f$ = 54. 6°C and the initial temperature $T_0 = 34.6$°C. The quantity of heat absorbed is

a.   + 23 cal
b.   + 0.23 cal
c.   + 14 cal
d.   + 110 cal
e.   + 207 cal

**1202    12-1  Heat Capacity and Specific Heat,  Conceptual,  c**

Aluminum has a specific heat more than twice that of copper. Identical masses of aluminum and copper, both at 0°C, are dropped together into a can of hot water. When the system has come to equilibrium

a.   the aluminum is at a higher temperature than the copper.
b.   the copper is at a higher temperature than the aluminum.
c.   the aluminum and copper are at the same temperature.
d.   the difference in temperature between the aluminum and the copper depends on the amount of water in the can.
e.   the difference in temperature between the aluminum and the copper depends on the initial temperature of the water in the can.

**1203    12-1  Heat Capacity and Specific Heat,  Numerical,  b**

A lake with $8.0 \times 10^9$ kg of water, which has a specific heat of 4180 J/kg·C° warms from 10°C to 15°C. The heat transferred to the lake is

a.   $2.5 \times 10^3$ J
b.   $1.7 \times 10^{14}$ J
c.   $4.0 \times 10^{15}$ J
d.   $1.7 \times 10^{16}$ J
e.   $2.8 \times 10^{16}$ J

**1204    12-1  Heat Capacity and Specific Heat,  Conceptual,  d**

Body $A$ has twice the mass and three times the specific heat of body $B$. They are supplied with equal amounts of heat. Body $A$ experiences a temperature change $\Delta T$. What change in temperature is experienced by body $B$?

a.  $\Delta T$
b.  $3\,\Delta T/2$
c.  $2\,\Delta T/3$
d.  $6\,\Delta T$
e.  $\Delta T/2$

**1205    12-1  Heat Capacity and Specific Heat,  Numerical,  a**

In raising the temperature of a 2.0-kg piece of metal (without doing any work) from 20°C to 100°C, 61.8 kJ of heat is added.  What is the specific heat of this metal?

a.  0.39 kJ/kg·K
b.  0.31 kJ/kg·K
c.  1.6 kJ/kg·K
d.  1.2 kJ/kg·K
e.  0.77 kJ/kg·K

**1206    12-1  Heat Capacity and Specific Heat,  Numerical,  b**

A 250-g piece of lead is heated to 100°C and is then placed in a 400-g  copper container containing 500 g of water. The specific heat of copper is $c = 0.386$ kJ/kg·K. The container and water had an initial temperature of 18.0°C.  When thermal equilibrium is reached, the final temperature of the system is 19.15°C.  Assuming no heat is lost from the system, what is the specific heat of the lead?  (The specific heat of water is 4180 J/kg·K.)

a.  0.119 kJ/kg·K
b.  0.128 kJ/kg·K
c.  0.110 kJ/kg·K
d.  0.0866 kJ/kg·K
e.  0.0372 kJ/kg·K

**1207   12-1   Heat Capacity and Specific Heat,   Conceptual,   c**

Heat is added to a substance at a constant rate. The substance starts as a solid and is melted; the liquid is heated and vaporized; finally, the vapor is heated. This process is shown in the diagram. The specific heat of the solid can be found by

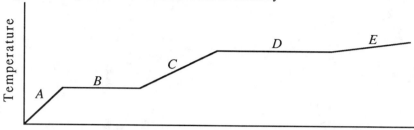

a.   multiplying the length of B (in seconds) times the rate at which the heat is added and dividing by the mass of the substance.
b.   multiplying the length of D (in seconds) times the rate at which the heat is added and dividing by the mass of the substance.
c.   dividing the rate at which the heat is added by the product of the slope of A  times the mass of the substance.
d.   dividing the rate at which the heat is added by the product of the slope of C  times the mass of the substance.
e.   dividing the rate at which the heat is added by the product of the slope of E  times the mass of the substance.

**1208   12-1   Heat Capacity and Specific Heat,   Conceptual,   d**

Heat is added to a substance at a constant rate. The substance starts as a solid and is melted; the liquid is heated and vaporized; finally, the vapor is heated. This process is shown in the diagram. The specific heat of the liquid can be found by

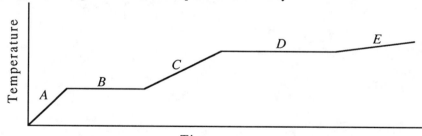

a.   multiplying the length of B (in seconds) times the rate at which the heat is added and dividing by the mass of the substance.
b.   multiplying the length of D (in seconds) times the rate at which the heat is added and dividing by the mass of the substance.
c.   dividing the rate at which the heat is added by the product of the slope of A  times the mass of the substance.
d.   dividing the rate at which the heat is added by the product of the slope of C  times the mass of the substance.
e.   dividing the rate at which the heat is added by the product of the slope of E  times the mass of the substance.

**1209    12-1   Heat Capacity and Specific Heat,   Conceptual,   e**

Heat is added to a substance at a constant rate.  The substance starts as a solid and is melted; the liquid is heated and vaporized; finally, the vapor is heated.  This process is shown in the diagram.  The specific heat of the vapor can be found by

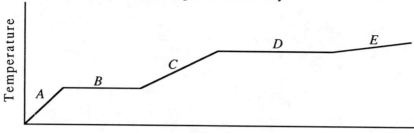

a.  multiplying the length of $B$ (in seconds) times the rate at which the heat is added and dividing by the mass of the substance.
b.  multiplying the length of $D$ (in seconds) times the rate at which the heat is added and dividing by the mass of the substance.
c.  dividing the rate at which the heat is added by the product of the slope of $A$ times the mass of the substance.
d.  dividing the rate at which the heat is added by the product of the slope of $C$ times the mass of the substance.
e.  dividing the rate at which the heat is added by the product of the slope of $E$ times the mass of the substance.

**1210    12-2   The First Law of Thermodynamics,   Numerical,   b**

A 6.0-g lead bullet traveling at 300 m/s penetrates a wooden block and stops.  If 50% of the initial kinetic energy of the bullet is converted into thermal energy in the bullet, by how much does the bullet's temperature increase?  (The specific heat of lead is 128 J/kg·K.)

a.  0.17 C°
b.  180 C°
c.  17 C°
d.  350 C°
e.  35 C°

**1211    12-2   The First Law of Thermodynamics,   Conceptual,   b**

A system absorbs heat $Q$ and has an equal amount of positive work done on it.  What is the change in the internal energy of the system?

a.  $Q$
b.  $2Q$
c.  $-2Q$
d.  Zero
e.  $Q/2$

**1212    12-2   The First Law of Thermodynamics,  Numerical,  a**

Besides Joule's classic experiment, another way of demonstrating the equivalence between mechanical energy and of heat would be the following:  Put some lead shot into a glass tube, seal off both ends of the tube, invert the tube quickly several times, and measure the temperature of the shot.  Assuming that all the mechanical energy is converted into heat in the lead shot and that no heat is lost, what would be the change in the temperature of the shot if the tube is 1.0 m long, there are 100 g of shot, and the tube is inverted 10 times?  (The specific heat of lead is 0.128 kJ/kg·K.)

a.   0.77 C°
b.   0.077 C°
c.   2.5 C°
d.   7.7 C°
e.   0.25 C°


**1213    12-2   The First Law of Thermodynamics,  Conceptual,  a**

The percentage of mechanical energy that can theoretically be turned into heat energy according to the first law of thermodynamics is

a.   100%
b.   90%
c.   75%
d.   50%
e.   0%


**1214    12-3   Work and the *PV* Diagram for a Gas,  Conceptual,  a**

An ideal gas undergoes a cyclic process in which total (positive) work $W$ is done by the gas. What total heat is added to the gas in one cycle?

a.   $W$
b.   $-W$
c.   zero
d.   $2W$
e.   $W/2$


**1215    12-3   Work and the *PV* Diagram for a Gas,  Conceptual,  d**

An ideal gas is heated such that it expands at constant pressure.  The gas does work $W$. What heat is added to the gas?

a.   $W$
b.   $-W$
c.   zero
d.   more than $W$
e.   less than $W$


**1216    12-3   Work and the *PV* Diagram for a Gas,  Conceptual,  b**

An isobaric expansion is one in which the pressure remains constant.  In such an expansion

a.   no work is done.
b.   work is done by the gas.
c.   work is done on the gas.
d.   isobaric and expansion are contradictory terms.
e.   work may or may not be done depending on whether the temperature of the gas changes.

**1217**  **12-3  Work and the *PV* Diagram for a Gas,  Numerical,  d**

A balloon contains a gas at a pressure 1.2 atm (1 atm = 101.3 kPa) and has a volume of 0.10 m$^3$.  More gas is pumped into the balloon at constant pressure until the volume is doubled.  How much work is done by the pump?

a.  12 J
b.  2.4 x 10$^4$ J
c.  24 J
d.  1.2 x 10$^4$ J
e.  6.1 x 10$^3$ J

**1218**  **12-3  Work and the *PV* Diagram for a Gas,  Numerical,  e**

The work done by an ideal gas in an isothermal expansion from volume $V_1$ to volume $V_2$ is given by the formula:

$$W = nRT \ln(V_2/V_1)$$

Standard atmospheric pressure (1 atm) is 101.3 kPa.  If 1.0 L of He gas at room temperature (20°C) and 1.0 atm of pressure is compressed isothermally to a volume of 100 mL, how much work is done on the gas?

a.  5.6 x 10$^3$ J
b.  470 J
c.  4.7 x 10$^5$ J
d.  2.3 x 10$^5$ J
e.  230 J

**1219**  **12-4  Heat Capacities and the Equipartition Theorem,  Conceptual,  a**

An ideal monatomic gas has a molar heat capacity $C_{mp}$ at constant pressure.  What is the molar heat capacity at constant volume of an ideal diatomic gas?

a.  $C_{mp}$
b.  $C_{mp} + R$
c.  $C_{mp} - R$
d.  $C_{mp} + 3R/2$
e.  $C_{mp} - 3R/2$

**1220**  **12-4  Heat Capacities and the Equipartition Theorem,  Numerical,  b**

The molar heat capacity at constant volume of a certain gas is found to be 20.74 J/mol·K. What is the molar heat capacity at constant pressure of this gas?  (The ideal-gas law constant is $R$ = 8.31 J/mol·K.)

a.  12.4 J/mol·K
b.  29.0 J/mol·K
c.  33.2 J/mol·K
d.  41.5 J/mol·K
e.  8.28 J/mol·K

**1221    12-4  Heat Capacities and the Equipartition Theorem,  Numerical,  e**

A certain gas has molar heat capacity at constant volume of 28.39 J/mol·K.  Assuming the equipartition theorem to be valid, how many degrees of freedom (including translational) are there for the molecules of this gas?  (The ideal-gas law constant is $R = 8.31$ J/mol·K.)

a.  1
b.  3
c.  4
d.  5
e.  7

CHAPTER 13 Thermal Properties and Processes

**1301**  **13-1 Thermal Expansion, Conceptual, b**

If the linear thermal-expansion coefficient of a material is $\alpha$ at 0°C, the volume thermal-expansion coefficient $\beta$ of this material at 0°C is

a.  $\alpha$.
b.  $3\alpha$.
c.  $\alpha^3$.
d.  $\alpha^{1/3}$.
e.  None of these is correct.

**1302**  **13-1 Thermal Expansion, Numerical, a**

A pendulum made of aluminum, which has a coefficient of linear expansion of 24 x $10^{-6}$/K, has a period of exactly one second at 20°C.  Before a homeowner leaves town for one week, he turns the thermostat down to 10°C.  When he returns, the clock will be

a.  fast by about 73 seconds.
b.  fast by about 7.6 minutes.
c.  exactly on time.
d.  slow by about 7.6 minutes.
e.  slow by about 73 seconds.

**1303**  **13-1 Thermal Expansion, Factual, a**

The coefficient of linear expansion for most materials

a.  is less than 1 $K^{-1}$.
b.  is greater than 1 $K^{-1}$.
c.  is approximately 1 $K^{-1}$.
d.  may be less than, greater than, or about equal to 1 $K^{-1}$.

**1304**  **13-1 Thermal Expansion, Conceptual, b**

The amount of linear expansion of a long rod does NOT depend on

a.  the original length of the rod.
b.  the specific heat of the rod.
c.  the change in the absolute temperature of the rod.
d.  the coefficient of linear expansion.
e.  the material out of which the rod is made.

**1305    13-1   Thermal Expansion,   Conceptual,   b**

A large sheet of metal has a hole cut in the middle of it.  When the sheet is heated, the area of the hole will

a.   not change.
b.   always increase.
c.   always decrease.
d.   increase if the hole is not in the exact center of the sheet.
e.   decrease only if the hole is in the exact center of the sheet.


**1306    13-1   Thermal Expansion,   Numerical,   b**

The volume thermal-expansion coefficient of water at 20°C is 0.207 x $10^{-3}$ $K^{-1}$.  A thin glass tube contains a 0.750-m long column of water at 20°C.  Assuming that the thermal expansion of the glass tube is negligible, by how much will the length of the column of water expand when it is heated to 80°C?

a.   3.1 mm
b.   9.3 mm
c.   12.4 mm
d.   4.1 mm
e.   28 mm


**1307    13-1   Thermal Expansion,   Numerical,   b**

Modern railway tracks consist of continuous welded-steel rails of 1.0-km lengths.  If the linear expansion coefficient of steel is 11 x $10^{-6}$ $K^{-1}$, by how much would such a rail change in length between the highest summer temperature (40°C) and the lowest winter temperature (-40°C)?

a.   44 cm
b.   88 cm
c.   8.8 x $10^{-4}$ m
d.   1.8 x $10^{-3}$ m
e.   4.4 cm


**1308    13-2   Change of Phase and Latent Heat,   Numerical,   d**

A group of explorers in the Antarctic can obtain the water they need only by melting snow. How much heat does it take for them to make a cup of coffee (100 g water at 100°C)? Assume that the snow has an initial temperature of -40°C; that the latent heats of fusion and vaporization of water are, respectively, 333.5 kJ/kg and 2257 kJ/kg; and that the specific heats of ice (snow) and water are, respectively, 2.05 kJ/kg·K and 4.18 kJ/kg·K.

a.   33 kJ
b.   50 kJ
c.   75 kJ
d.   83 kJ
e.   310 kJ

**1309    13-2  Change of Phase and Latent Heat,  Numerical,  c**

Fifty grams of ice cubes are put into 125 g of water that is initially at 20°C in a calorimeter of negligible heat capacity.  When the system has reached equilibrium, how much of the ice remains? (Latent heat of fusion of water = 333.5 kJ/kg, specific heat of water = 4.18 kJ/kg·K.)

a.  31 g
b.  48 g
c.  19 g
d.  47 g
e.  All of the ice melts.

**1310    13-2  Change of Phase and Latent Heat,  Conceptual,  b**

Heat is added to a substance at a constant rate.  The substance starts as a solid and is melted; the liquid is heated and vaporized; finally, the vapor is heated.  This process is shown in the diagram.  Which of the following statements is correct?

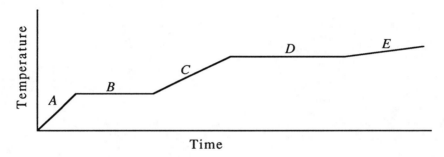

a.  The latent heat of fusion is greater than the latent heat of vaporization.
b.  The latent heat of vaporization is greater than the latent heat of fusion.
c.  The latent heat of vaporization is equal to the latent heat of fusion.
d.  The mass of the substance must be known before any statements about the latent heats can be made.
e.  The relative sizes of the latent heats depend on the rate at which the heat is being added.

**1311    13-2  Change of Phase and Latent Heat,  Factual,  d**

When a substance goes directly from a solid state to a gaseous form, the process is known as

a.  vaporization.
b.  evaporation.
c.  condensation.
d.  sublimation.
e.  deposition.

**1312 13-2 Change of Phase and Latent Heat, Conceptual, a**

Heat is added to a substance at a constant rate. The substance starts as a solid and is melted; the liquid is heated and vaporized; finally, the vapor is heated. This process is shown in the diagram. The latent heat of fusion can be found by

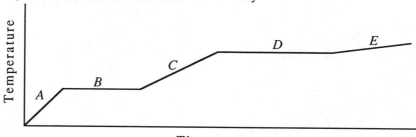

a. multiplying the length of B (in seconds) times the rate at which the heat is added and dividing by the mass of the substance.
b. multiplying the length of D (in seconds) times the rate at which the heat is added and dividing by the mass of the substance.
c. multiplying the slope of A by the rate at which the heat is added and dividing by the mass of the substance.
d. multiplying the slope of C by the rate at which the heat is added and dividing by the mass of the substance.
e. multiplying the slope of E by the rate at which the heat is added and dividing by the mass of the substance.

**1313 13-2 Change of Phase and Latent Heat, Conceptual, b**

Heat is added to a substance at a constant rate. The substance starts as a solid and is melted; the liquid is heated and vaporized; finally, the vapor is heated. This process is shown in the diagram. The latent heat of vaporization can be found by

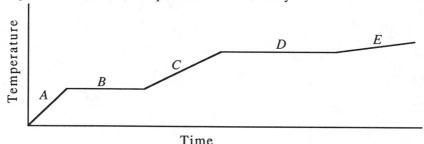

a. multiplying the length of B (in seconds) times the rate at which the heat is added and dividing by the mass of the substance.
b. multiplying the length of D (in seconds) times the rate at which the heat is added and dividing by the mass of the substance.
c. multiplying the slope of A by the rate at which the heat is added and dividing by the mass of the substance.
d. multiplying the slope of C by the rate at which the heat is added and dividing by the mass of the substance.
e. multiplying the slope of E by the rate at which the heat is added and dividing by the mass of the substance.

1314   **13-3  The van der Waals Equation and Liquid-Vapor Isotherms,  Factual, d**

The axes on a phase diagram are

a.  temperature and volume.
b.  pressure and volume.
c.  isotherms and pressure.
d.  temperature and pressure.
e.  solid, liquid, and vapor.

1315   **13-3  The van der Waals Equation and Liquid-Vapor Isotherms,  Factual, c**

Mountaineers say that you cannot hard boil an egg on the top of Mount Rainier.  This is true because

a.  the air is too cold to boil water.
b.  the air pressure is too low for stoves to burn.
c.  boiling water is not hot enough to hard boil the egg.
d.  the oxygen content of the air is too low.
e.  eggs always break in their backpacks.

1316   **13-4  Humidity,  Numerical,  b**

[This problem requires that the students be given Table 13-3 (p. 301) from the text or the equivalent.]

On a day when the temperature outside is 0°C and the relative humidity outside is 100%, what is the relative humidity inside a house at 20°C, assuming that the partial pressure of water vapor inside and outside the house is the same?

a.  100%
b.  26%
c.  74%
d.  0.26%
e.  50%

1317   **13-4  Humidity,  Numerical,  c**

[This problem requires that the students be given Table 13-3 (p. 301) from the text or the equivalent.]

If the temperature is 30°C and the dew point is 10°C, what is the relative humidity?

a.  53%
b.  71%
c.  29%
d.  3.4%
e.  33%

1318   **13-4  Humidity,  Conceptual,  b**

During the evening the partial pressure of water vapor in the air remains constant.  As the temperature decreases, the relative humidity

a.  will stay the same.
b.  will increase.
c.  will decrease.
d.  may increase or decrease depending on the temperature.

**1319    13-5  The Transfer of Heat,  Numerical,  a**

An outer wall of a house consists of three layers:  a wooden outer wall with an $R$ factor of 1.0; a 3-in layer of fiberglass insulation with an $R$ factor of 11; and a gypsum-board inner wall with an $R$ factor of 0.33.  What would be the rate of heat loss through an 8-ft x 15-ft section of this wall when the temperature is 68°F inside the house and -4.0°F outside?  All $R$ factors are in h·ft$^2$·F°/Btu.

a.  700 Btu/h
b.  780 Btu/h
c.  5.8 Btu/h
d.  130 BTU/h
e.  350 Btu/h

**1320    13-5  The Transfer of Heat,  Factual,  c**

The earth receives approximately $1.7 \times 10^{17}$ J of energy from the sun each second through a process called

a.  conduction.
b.  convection.
c.  radiation.
d.  sublimation.
e.  evaporation.

**1321    13-5  The Transfer of Heat,  Numerical,  d**

A certain blackbody radiates 100 watts at a temperature of 2000 K.  How much power would this body radiate at 3000 K?

a.  150 W
b.  225 W
c.  338 W
d.  506 W
e.  759 W

**1322    13-5  The Transfer of Heat,  Conceptual,  d**

If the thickness of a uniform wall is doubled, the rate at which heat is conducted through the wall is

a.  doubled.
b.  increased by a factor of four.
c.  decreased by a factor of four.
d.  cut in half.
e.  unchanged.

**1323    13-5  The Transfer of Heat,  Conceptual,  c**

Two types of walls separate a refrigerated room from the rest of a building.  Wall one has half the thermal conductivity of wall two.  Wall two is half as thick as wall one.  The two walls have the same area.  The rate of heat flow through wall two compared to the rate of heat flow through wall one is

a.  four times greater.
b.  twice as great.
c.  the same.
d.  half as great.
e.  one-quarter as great.

1324   **13-5  The Transfer of Heat,  Conceptual,  e**

Which of the following processes of heat transfer is INDEPENDENT of the area exposed?

a.   Conduction
b.   Convection
c.   Radiation
d.   All of the above are independent of the area exposed.
e.   None of the above is independent of the area exposed.

1325   **13-5  The Transfer of Heat,  Conceptual,  e**

If the absolute temperature of the filament of a lamp were doubled, the energy radiated per second by the filament would

a.   remain the same.
b.   increase by a factor of 2.
c.   increase by a factor of 4.
d.   increase by a factor of 8.
e.   increase by a factor of 16.

1326   **13-5  The Transfer of Heat,  Conceptual,  e**

If the temperature on the warmer side of a wall is doubled, the rate at which heat is conducted through the wall

a.   is doubled.
b.   is increased by a factor of 4.
c.   is decreased by a factor of 4.
d.   is cut in half.
e.   will increase but the rate cannot be determined.

1327   **13-5  The Transfer of Heat,  Conceptual,  d**

If the absolute temperature of an object is tripled, the rate at which it radiates thermal energy

a.   is tripled.
b.   is increased by a factor of 9.
c.   is increased by a factor of 27.
d.   is increased by a factor of 81.
e.   depends on whether the absolute temperature is above or below zero.

1328   **13-5  The Transfer of Heat,  Conceptual,  c**

The main process by which heat is transferred to your home when it is heated by solar energy is

a.   conduction.
b.   convection.
c.   radiation.
d.   latent heat transfer.
e.   insulation.

CHAPTER 14    The Availability of Energy

1401    **14-1  Heat Engines and the Kelvin-Planck Statement of the Second Law of Thermodynamics,  Conceptual,  c**

A heat engine absorbs heat $Q$ from a hot reservoir.  The amount of work done by the engine

a.  is $Q$.
b.  must be greater than $Q$.
c.  must be less than $Q$.
d.  could be greater than $Q$.
e.  is zero.

1402    **14-1  Heat Engines and the Kelvin-Planck Statement of the Second Law of Thermodynamics,  Conceptual,  d**

A heat engine exhausts heat $Q$ to a cold reservoir.  The amount of work done by the engine

a.  is $Q$.
b.  must be greater than $Q$.
c.  must be less than $Q$.
d.  could be greater than $Q$.
e.  is zero.

1403    **14-1  Heat Engines and the Kelvin-Planck Statement of the Second Law of Thermodynamics,  Conceptual,  a**

If you run a refrigerator in a closed room with the door to the refrigerator open, the temperature of the room will

a.  increase.
b.  remain the same.
c.  decrease.
d.  Any of the above could happen depending on how efficient the refrigerator is.
e.  Any of the above could happen depending on the relative sizes of the room and the refrigerator.

1404    **14-1  Heat Engines and the Kelvin-Planck Statement of the Second Law of Thermodynamics,  Numerical,  b**

A heat engine absorbs 150 J of heat from a hot reservoir and rejects 90 J to a cold reservoir. What is the efficiency of this engine?

a.  20%
b.  40%
c.  60%
d.  67%
e.  90%

1405    **14-1  Heat Engines and the Kelvin-Planck Statement of the Second Law of Thermodynamics,  Numerical,  d**

A heat engine with an output of 300 W has an efficiency of 25% and works at 10 cycles/s. How much heat is absorbed ($Q_h$) and how much rejected ($Q_c$) in each cycle?

a.  $Q_h = 150$ J,  $Q_c = 120$ J
b.  $Q_h = 1500$ J, $Q_c = 1200$ J
c.  $Q_h = 40$ J,   $Q_c = 10$ J
d.  $Q_h = 120$ J,  $Q_c = 90$ J
e.  $Q_h = 1200$ J, $Q_c = 900$ J

1406    **14-2  Refrigerators and the Clausius Statement of the Second Law of Thermodynamics,  Numerical,  a**

A refrigerator extracts 25 kJ from a cold reservoir and rejects 35 kJ to a hot reservoir. What is the coefficient of performance of this refrigerator?

a.  2.5
b.  3.5
c.  1.4
d.  5.0
e.  4.0

1407    **14-2  Refrigerators and the Clausius Statement of the Second Law of Thermodynamics,  Factual,  e**

For which of the following is COP the abbreviation?

a.  Clausius or Planck
b.  Cycle of pressure
c.  Coefficients of pressure
d.  Carnot ordered performance
e.  Coefficient of performance

1408    **14-2  Refrigerators and the Clausius Statement of the Second Law of Thermodynamics,  Conceptual,  b**

A refrigerator extracts heat $Q$ from a cold reservoir. The heat exhausted to the hot reservoir

a.  is $Q$.
b.  must be greater than $Q$.
c.  must be less than $Q$.
d.  could be greater than $Q$.
e.  is zero.

1409    **14-2  Refrigerators and the Clausius Statement of the Second Law of Thermodynamics,  Numerical,  d**

A refrigerator with a coefficient of performance 5.0 removes 25 kJ of heat from a cold reservoir. If this refrigerator is reversible and is run backwards as a heat engine, what would be the efficiency of the heat engine?

a.  50%
b.  80%
c.  83%
d.  17%
e.  20%

**1410**   **14-3  Equivalence of the Kelvin-Planck and Clausius Statements, Conceptual,  d**

You wish to construct a perfect refrigerator from a perfect heat engine.  What else do you need?

a.  You need a second perfect heat engine.
b.  You need a  non-perfect heat engine.
c.  You need a  non-perfect refrigerator.
d.  You will need nothing else.  A perfect refrigerator is just a perfect heat engine run backwards.
e.  A perfect refrigerator cannot be constructed even if you have a perfect heat engine.


**1411**   **14-4  The Carnot Engine,  Numerical,  c**

The Carnot efficiency for a heat engine operating between the temperatures of 227°C and 27°C is

a.  20%
b.  25%
c.  40%
d.  88%
e.  100%


**1412**   **14-4  The Carnot Engine,  Conceptual,  d**

A reversible engine absorbs heat $Q$ from a hot reservoir at 127° C and exhausts heat to a cold reservoir at 27ºC.  How much heat is exhausted to the cold reservoir?

a.  $Q$
b.  $27Q/127$
c.  $127Q/27$
d.  $3Q/4$
e.  $4Q/3$


**1413**   **14-4  The Carnot Engine,  Conceptual,  b**

The second-law efficiency of an engine

a.  is the same as the actual efficiency.
b.  is greater than the actual efficiency.
c.  is less than the actual efficiency.
d.  could be greater or less than the actual efficiency.
e.  has no relation to the actual efficiency.

**1414  14-4  The Carnot Engine,  Numerical,  c**

In a nuclear power plant, heat is taken from the reactor core at 300°C, work is done to drive an electric generator, and heat is rejected to the environment at 40°C.  What is the maximum possible efficiency of this system?

a.  13%
b.  27%
c.  45%
d.  55%
e.  87%

**1415  14-4  The Carnot Engine,  Numerical,  e**

The ideal efficiency of a Carnot engine operating between 300°C and 250°C is about

a.  83%
b.  17%
c.  57%
d.  43%
e.  9%

**1416  14-4  The Carnot Engine,  Numerical,  c**

A steam power plant with a second-law efficiency of 65% operates between 250°C and 40°C.  How much heat is rejected to the cold reservoir in doing 1.0 kJ of work?

a.  3.8 kJ
b.  0.83 kJ
c.  2.8 kJ
d.  1.8 kJ
e.  0.67 kJ

**1417  14-5  The Heat Pump,  Numerical,  e**

What is the maximum possible coefficient of performance of a heat pump that is capable of maintaining the interior of a house at +20°C when the temperature outside is -40°C?

a.  2.0
b.  5.2
c.  11.6
d.  4.9
e.  3.9

**1418  14-5  The Heat Pump,  Conceptual,  c**

A heat pump with COP = 5 uses electrical energy $W$ to heat a house.  How much heat is pumped into the house?

a.  $W$
b.  $5W$
c.  $6W$
d.  $4W$
e.  $1.2W$

**1419    14-6   Entropy and Disorder,   Conceptual,   a**

When you make ice cubes, the entropy of the water

a.   decreases.
b.   remains unchanged.
c.   increases.
d.   is unchanged as the water cools but decreases as the water freezes.
e.   decreases while the water is cooling but doesn't change as it turns to ice.


**1420    14-6   Entropy and Disorder,   Conceptual,   a**

The change in the entropy of the universe due to an operating Carnot engine

a.   is zero.
b.   must be positive.
c.   must be negative.
d.   could be positive or negative.
e.   is meaningless to consider, since a Carnot engine has no connection to entropy.


**1421    14-6   Entropy and Disorder,   Conceptual,   e**

Heat is removed from a hot reservoir at absolute temperature $T$ and added to a cold reservoir at absolute temperature $T/2$.  The cold reservoir experiences an entropy increase $S$.  What is the change in the entropy of the universe?

a.   $S$
b.   Zero
c.   $-S$
d.   $2S$
e.   $S/2$


**1422    14-6   Entropy and Disorder,   Numerical,   a**

A car of mass 2000 kg is traveling at 22.0 m/s on a day when the temperature is 20.0°C. The driver steps on the brakes and stops the car.  By how much does the entropy of the universe increase?

a.   $1.6 \times 10^3$ J/K
b.   $2.4 \times 10^4$ J/K
c.   $4.8 \times 10^5$ J/K
d.   150 J/K
e.   $3.3 \times 10^3$ J/K


**1423    14-6   Entropy and Disorder,   Numerical,   b**

A steam power plant operates with second-law efficiency of 65% between 250°C and 40°C. What is the change in the entropy of the universe when this plant does 1.0 kJ of work?

a.   16 J/K
b.   1.7 J/K
c.   55 J/K
d.   $1.7 \times 10^{-3}$ J/K
e.   0.85 J/K

**1424**   **14-7  Entropy and Probability,  Conceptual,  c**

Which of the following statements is true of an isolated system consisting of 15 gas molecules?

a.  According to the second law, the entropy of the gas cannot decrease.
b.  According to the second law, the entropy of the gas cannot increase.
c.  According to the second law, the entropy of the gas is not likely to decrease.
d.  According to the second law, the entropy of the gas is not likely to increase.
e.  According to the second law, the entropy of the gas must stay the same.

CHAPTER 15     Oscillations

**1501    15-1  Simple Harmonic Motion: A Mass on a Spring,  Conceptual,  c**

When an object has simple harmonic motion in the vertical direction,  its maximum speed occurs when the object

a.  is at its highest point.
b.  is at its lowest point.
c.  is at the equilibrium point.
d.  has the maximum net force exerted on it.
e.  has a position equal to its amplitude.

**1502    15-1  Simple Harmonic Motion: A Mass on a Spring,  Conceptual,  c**

A mass $m$ hanging on a spring with a spring constant $k$ has simple harmonic motion with a period $T$.  If the mass is doubled to $2m$, the period of oscillation will

a.  be increased by a factor of 2.
b.  be decreased by a factor of 2.
c.  be increased by a factor of $\sqrt{2}$.
d.  be decreased by a factor of $\sqrt{2}$.
e.  not be affected.

**1503    15-1  Simple Harmonic Motion:  A Mass on a Spring,  Conceptual,  a**

If the period of a simple harmonic oscillator is doubled,  the amplitude will be

a.  unaffected.
b.  7/10 as large.
c.  half as large.
d.  doubled.
e.  None of these is correct.

**1504    15-1  Simple Harmonic Motion:  A Mass on a Spring,  Factual,  a**

If $F$ is the force, $x$ is the displacement, and $k$ is a particular constant, for simple harmonic motion we MUST have

a.  $F = -kx$
b.  $F = k/x$
c.  $F = \sqrt{k/x^2}$
d.  $F = -kx^2$
e.  None of these is correct.

**1505    15-1  Simple Harmonic Motion:  A Mass on a Spring,  Numerical,  a**

A particle with a mass of $1.56 \times 10^{-25}$ kg is moving with simple harmonic motion. The frequency of the motion is $2.4 \times 10^5$ s$^{-1}$ and the amplitude is $A = 1.25 \times 10^{-9}$ m. The motion starts when the particle is at its extreme positive displacement. At a time $t = 4.0 \times 10^{-5}$ s later, the force that is acting on the particle is

a.  $+3.6 \times 10^{-22}$ N
b.  $-2.3 \times 10^4$ N
c.  $+2.2 \times 10^{-21}$ N
d.  $+2.9 \times 10^{-13}$ N
e.  $+1.8 \times 10^{-11}$ N

**1506    15-1  Simple Harmonic Motion:  A Mass on a Spring,  Numerical,  b**

The frequency of a simple harmonic motion is $2.6 \times 10^4$ s$^{-1}$. The oscillation starts ($t = 0$) when the displacement has its maximum positive value of $6.5 \times 10^{-3}$ cm. The shortest possible time for the simple harmonic motion to have a displacement of $x = -2.6 \times 10^{-3}$ cm is

a.  $7.1 \times 10^{-6}$ s
b.  $1.2 \times 10^{-5}$ s
c.  $1.1 \times 10^{-4}$ s
d.  $1.1 \times 10^{-3}$ s
e.  $4.2 \times 10^{-3}$ s

**1507    15-1  Simple Harmonic Motion:  A Mass on a Spring,  Numerical,  d**

A particle moving with a simple harmonic motion has its maximum displacement of +18 cm at time $t = 0$. The frequency of the motion is 10 s$^{-1}$. At a time $t = 0.65$ s, the position of the particle is

a.  +18 cm
b.  zero
c.  -13 cm
d.  -18.0 cm
e.  +7.3 cm

**1508    15-1  Simple Harmonic Motion:  A Mass on a Spring,  Conceptual,  d**

A mass $m$ hanging on a spring with a spring constant $k$ has simple harmonic motion with a period $T$. If the same mass is hung from a spring with a spring constant of $2k$, the period of oscillation will

a.  be increased by a factor of 2.
b.  be decreased by a factor of 2.
c.  be increased by a factor of $\sqrt{2}$.
d.  be decreased by a factor of $\sqrt{2}$.
e.  not be affected.

**1509**   **15-1   Simple Harmonic Motion: A Mass on a Spring,   Conceptual,   d**

It is desired to have a mass hanging on the end of a spring oscillate with a period of one second.  If the spring has a spring constant of 10 N/m, the mass should be

a.   10 kg
b.   $\sqrt{10}$ kg
c.   $4\pi^2(10)$ kg
d.   $\dfrac{1}{4\pi^2}(10)$ kg
e.   None of the above are correct.

**1510**   **15-1   Simple Harmonic Motion: A Mass on a Spring,   Factual,   e**

The instantaneous speed of a mass undergoing simple harmonic motion on the end of a spring depends on

a.   the amplitude of oscillation.
b.   the frequency of oscillation.
c.   the period of oscillation.
d.   the time at which the speed is measured.
e.   All of the above are correct.

**1511**   **15-1   Simple Harmonic Motion:  A Mass on a Spring,   Numerical,   c**

A particle moving in  simple harmonic motion with a period $T = 1.5$ s passes through the equilibrium point at time $t_0 = 0$ with a velocity of 1.00 m/s to the right.  A time $t$ later, the particle is observed to move to the left with a velocity of 0.50 m/s.  (Note the change in direction of the velocity.)  The smallest possible value of the time $t$ is

a.   0.17 s
b.   0.33 s
c.   0.50 s
d.   0.25 s
e.   0.82 s

**1512**   **15-1   Simple Harmonic Motion:  A Mass on a Spring,   Numerical,   c**

A particle moving with simple harmonic motion has a maximum displacement of +12.0 cm. The particle moves from its maximum positive to its maximum negative displacement in 2.25 s.  The motion starts when the displacement is $x = +12.0$ cm.  The time for the particle to move to $x = -6.0$ cm is

a.   1.7 s
b.   0.75 s
c.   1.5 s
d.   2.2 s
e.   0.98 s

**1513    15-1   Simple Harmonic Motion:   A Mass on a Spring,   Numerical,   d**

The force constant of a massless spring is 25.0 N/m.  A mass of 0.45 kg is oscillating in simple harmonic motion at the end of the spring with an amplitude of 0.32 m.  The maximum speed of the mass is

   a.   5.7 m/s
   b.   56 m/s
   c.   7.4 m/s
   d.   2.4 m/s
   e.   10 m/s

**1514    15-1   Simple Harmonic Motion:   A Mass on a Spring,   Numerical,   b**

The equation for the period $T$ of a mass $m$ oscillating with simple harmonic motion at the end of a spring with a force constant $k$ is $T = 2\pi\sqrt{m/k}$.  A mass $m$ that is oscillating on a spring with a force constant of 0.52 N/m has a period of 2.1 s.  On a second spring the same mass has a period of 3.5 s.  The force constant of the second spring is

   a.   impossible to determine because the mass is not given.
   b.   0.19 N/m
   c.   1.4 N/m
   d.   0.31 N/m
   e.   0.75 N/m

**1515    15-1   Simple Harmonic Motion:   A Mass on a Spring,   Numerical,   a**

A particle with a mass of 65 g is moving with simple harmonic motion.  At time $t = 0$ the particle is at its extreme positive displacement of 18.0 cm.  The period of the motion is 0.600 s.  At a time $t = 1.35$ s, the velocity of the particle is

   a.   -1.9 m/s
   b.   zero
   c.   0.84 m/s
   d.   +1.9 m/s
   e.   - 0.84 m/s

**1516    15-1   Simple Harmonic Motion:   A Mass on a Spring,   Numerical,   d**

A particle is oscillating with simple harmonic motion.  The frequency of the motion is 10 Hz and the amplitude of the motion is 5.0 cm.  As the particle passes its central equilibrium position, the acceleration of the particle is

   a.   100 cm/s$^2$
   b.   1.6 x 10$^5$ cm/s$^2$
   c.   4 x 10$^6$ cm/s$^2$
   d.   zero
   e.   3.2 x 10$^6$ cm/s$^2$

**1517    15-2  Simple Harmonic Motion and Circular Motion,  Numerical,  d**

In simple harmonic motion, the displacement $x = A \cos \omega t$ and the acceleration $a = -\omega^2 x$. If $A = 0.25$ m and the period is 0.32 s,  the acceleration when t = 0.12 s is

   a.   zero
   b.   +390 m/s$^2$
   c.   -390 m/s$^2$
   d.   +68 m/s$^2$
   e.   -68 m/s$^2$

**1518    15-2  Simple Harmonic Motion and Circular Motion,  Numerical,  a**

A particle moving in a circle of radius 15 cm makes 33.3 revolutions per minute.  Assuming the particle starts on the positive $x$ axis at time $t = 0$, what is the $x$ component of the particle's velocity at time $t = 1.2$ s?

   a.   45 cm/s
   b.   -3.8 cm/s
   c.   26 cm/s
   d.   -45 cm/s
   e.   13 cm/s

**1519    15-2  Simple Harmonic Motion and Circular Motion,  Conceptual,  d**

The object in the diagram is in circular motion.  The $y$ component of its position is given by

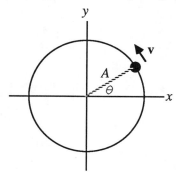

   a.   $y = y_0 + v_{0y}t + \frac{1}{2}at^2$
   b.   $y = A \cos 2\pi f t$
   c.   $y = A \sin 2\pi v t$
   d.   $y = A \sin 2\pi f t$
   e.   $y = A \cos 2\pi v t$

**1520    15-2   Simple Harmonic Motion and Circular Motion,   Conceptual,   b**

The object in the diagram is in circular motion.  The $y$ component of its velocity is given by

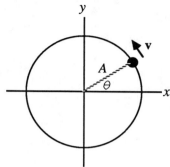

a.   $v_y{}^2 = v_{0y}{}^2 + 2a(y - y_0)$
b.   $v_y = 2\pi f A \cos 2\pi f t$
c.   $v_y = 2\pi v A \sin 2\pi v t$
d.   $v_y = 2\pi f A \sin 2\pi f t$
e.   $v_y = 2\pi v A \cos 2\pi v t$

**1521    15-2   Simple Harmonic Motion and Circular Motion,   Conceptual,   d**

The object in the diagram is in circular motion.  The $y$ component of its acceleration is given by

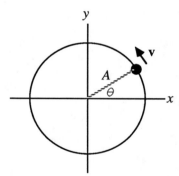

a.   $a_y = (v_y - v_{0y})/t$
b.   $a_y = - (2\pi f)^2 A \cos 2\pi f t$
c.   $a_y = - (2\pi v)^2 A \sin 2\pi v t$
d.   $a_y = - (2\pi f)^2 A \sin 2\pi f t$
e.   $a_y = - (2\pi v)^2 A \cos 2\pi v t$

**1522    15-3   Energy in Simple Harmonic Motion,   Numerical,   b**

A 2.50-kg object is attached to a spring of force constant $k = 4.50$ kN/m.  The spring is stretched 10.0 cm from equilibrium and released.  What is the maximum kinetic energy of this system?

a.   45 J
b.   $2.2 \times 10^{-2}$ J
c.   56 J
d.   $2.2 \times 10^5$ J
e.   4.5 J

1523    **15-3   Energy in Simple Harmonic Motion,   Numerical, a**

A mass of 0.50 kg is attached to a massless spring with a spring constant $k = 600$ N/m (see diagram).  The system rests on a level, friction-free surface and is initially at rest.  A second mass of 0.20 kg makes an elastic head-on collision with the mass attached to the spring; thereafter, the oscillating system vibrates with an amplitude of 0.25 m.  What was the incident speed of the second mass?

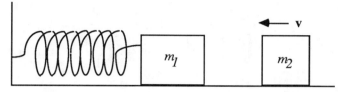

a.   15 m/s
b.   8.7 m/s
c.   6.1 m/s
d.   11 m/s
e.   5.3 m/s

1524    **15-3   Energy in Simple Harmonic Motion,   Conceptual,  a**

A mass attached to a spring has simple harmonic motion with an amplitude of 4.0 cm. When the mass is 2.0 cm from the equilibrium position, what fraction of its total energy is potential energy?

a.   One-quarter
b.   One-third
c.   One-half
d.   Two-thirds
e.   Three-quarters

1525    **15-3   Energy in Simple Harmonic Motion,   Conceptual,  d**

When the compression of a spring is doubled, the potential energy stored in the spring is

a.   still the same as before.
b.   doubled.
c.   tripled.
d.   quadrupled.
e.   None of these is correct.

1526    **15-3   Energy in Simple Harmonic Motion,   Conceptual,  c**

The energy of a simple harmonic oscillator could be doubled by increasing the amplitude by a factor of

a.   0.7
b.   1.0
c.   1.4
d.   2.0
e.   4.0

1527    **15-3   Energy in Simple Harmonic Motion,  Numerical,  c**

A 2.50-kg object is attached to a spring of force constant $k = 4.50$ kN/m.  The spring is stretched 10.0 cm from equilibrium and released.  What is the kinetic energy of the mass-spring system when the mass is 5.00 cm from its equilibrium position?

   a.  5.6 J
   b.  11 J
   c.  17 J
   d.  14 J
   e.  42 J

1528    **15-3   Energy in Simple Harmonic Motion,  Conceptual,  b**

The force constant for a simple harmonic motion is $k$ N/m and the amplitude of the motion is $A$ m.  The maximum value of the potential energy of a mass of $m$ kg oscillating with simple harmonic motion is

   a.  $2\sqrt{m/k}$ J
   b.  $(1/2)kA^2$ J
   c.  $kA^2$ J
   d.  $kA$ J
   e.  None of these is correct.

1529    **15-3   Energy in Simple Harmonic Motion,  Conceptual,  c**

In simple harmonic motion, when the displacement of the object is one-quarter of the amplitude $A$, the potential energy is what fraction of the total energy?

   a.  1/4
   b.  1/2
   c.  1/16
   d.  Too little information is given to answer correctly.
   e.  None of these is correct.

1530    **15-3   Energy in Simple Harmonic Motion,  Conceptual,  e**

If the amplitude of a simple harmonic oscillator is doubled, the total energy is

   a.  unchanged.
   b.  one-fourth as large.
   c.  half as large.
   d.  doubled.
   e.  quadrupled.

1531    **15-3   Energy in Simple Harmonic Motion,  Numerical,  d**

A mass on a spring oscillates with an amplitude of 5.0 cm.  What is the position of the mass when the kinetic and potential energies are equal?

   a.  There is not enough information given to answer this question.
   b.  1.2 cm
   c.  2.5 cm
   d.  3.5 cm
   e.  3.8 cm

**1532    15-4  The Simple Pendulum,  Conceptual,  c**

Clocks with basic time-keeping mechanisms consisting of a mass on a spring and a simple pendulum are taken to the top of a mountain.  At the base of the mountain, they both keep perfect time.  At the top of the mountain,

a.   neither keeps correct time.
b.   only the pendulum clock keeps correct time.
c.   only the mass-spring clock keeps correct time.
d.   both keep correct time.

**1533    15-4  The Simple Pendulum,  Conceptual,  a**

A mass-spring system and a simple pendulum each have a period of one second.  Both are taken to the moon in a lunar landing module.  While they are inside the module on the surface of the moon,

a.   the pendulum has a period longer than one second.
b.   the mass-spring system has a period longer than one second.
c.   Both answers a and b are true.
d.   the periods of both are unchanged.
e.   one of them has a period shorter than one second.

**1534    15-4  The Simple Pendulum,  Conceptual,  b**

If the length of a simple pendulum with a period $T$ is reduced to half of its original value, the new period $T$ is

a.   $0.5T$
b.   $0.7T$
c.   $T$ (unchanged)
d.   $1.4T$
e.   $2T$

**1535    15-4  The Simple Pendulum,  Conceptual,  d**

To double the period of a pendulum, the length

a.   must be increased by a factor of 2.
b.   must be decreased by a factor of 2.
c.   must be increased by a factor of $\sqrt{2}$.
d.   must be increased by a factor of 4.
e.   need not be affected.

**1536    15-4  The Simple Pendulum,  Conceptual,  a**

A simple-pendulum clock keeps accurate time when its length is $L$.  If the length is increased a small amount, the clock will

a.   lose time.
b.   gain time.
c.   continue to keep accurate time.
d.   The answer cannot be determined without knowing the original length of the pendulum.
e.   The answer cannot be determined without knowing the percent increase in the length of the pendulum.

**1537**    **15-4   The Simple Pendulum,   Conceptual,   c**

A pendulum does not have simple harmonic motion if its angular amplitude $\theta_0$ is not small. For large angular amplitudes, the period is given by:

$$T = T_0 \left( 1 + \frac{1}{2^2} \sin^2 \theta_0 + \frac{1}{2^2}\frac{3}{4^2} \sin^4 \frac{1}{2} \theta_0 + \dots \right)$$

As the angular amplitude of the pendulum gets larger, the frequency of the pendulum will

a.  not change.
b.  increase.
c.  decrease.
d.  do whatever the period does.
e.  change in proportion to $T_0$.

**1538**    **15-4   The Simple Pendulum,   Numerical,   a**

What must be the length of a simple pendulum with a period of 2.0 s if $g = 9.8$ m/s$^2$?

a.  99 cm
b.  97 m
c.  6.2 cm
d.  3.1 m
e.  2.0 m

**1539**    **15-4   The Simple Pendulum,   Factual,   d**

A pendulum has simple harmonic motion provided that

a.  its bob is not too heavy.
b.  the supporting string is not too long.
c.  the arc through which it swings is not too small.
d.  the arc through which it swings is not too large.
e.  None of these is correct.

**1540**    **15-4   The Simple Pendulum,   Numerical,   b**

You have landed your spaceship on the moon and wish to determine the acceleration due to gravity using a simple pendulum of length 1.0 m.  If you time the period of this pendulum to be 5.0 s, what is the value of $g$ on the moon?

a.  1.3 m/s$^2$
b.  1.6 m/s$^2$
c.  0.80 m/s$^2$
d.  0.63 m/s$^2$
e.  2.4 m/s$^2$

**1541**    **15-5   Damped and Driven Oscillations,   Numerical,   c**

An oscillator has a quality factor of 300.  By what percentage does its energy decrease in each cycle?

a.  0.33%
b.  1%
c.  2%
d.  3%
e.  4%

**1542    15-5    Damped and Driven Oscillations,   Conceptual,   d**

When pushing a child in a swing, one will most likely

a.  push with as large a force as possible.
b.  push with a periodic force as often as possible.
c.  push with a periodic force with a period that depends on the weight of the child.
d.  push with a periodic force with a period that depends on the length of the swing.
e.  push with a force equal to the weight of the child.

**1543    15-5    Damped and Driven Oscillations,   Factual,   a**

When a crystal glass is broken using an intense sound, it is an example of

a.  resonance.
b.  a $Q$ factor.
c.  critical damping.
d.  an exponential decrease.
e.  overdamping.

CHAPTER 16     Mechanical Waves: Sound

**1601    16-1    Wave Pulses,   Factual,   b**

A wave pulse travels along a light string that is attached to a heavier string in which the wave speed is smaller.  The reflected pulse is _____, and the transmitted pulse is _____.

a.   inverted; inverted
b.   inverted; not inverted
c.   not inverted; not inverted
d.   not inverted; inverted
e.   nonexistent; not inverted

**1602    16-1    Wave Pulses,   Conceptual,   d**

Two wave pulses on a string move towards one another.  One pulse is inverted relative to the other.  Which of the following statements is TRUE at the moment the pulses overlap?

a.   The pulses constructively interfere, tending to add to each other.
b.   The pulses destructively interfere, tending to add to each other.
c.   The pulses constructively interfere, tending to cancel each other.
d.   The pulses destructively interfere, tending to cancel each other.
e.   The pulses compress and reflect each other.

**1603    16-1    Wave Pulses,   Conceptual,   a**

The waves on a violin string are good examples of what kind of waves?  Sound waves are good examples of what kind of waves?  Water waves are good examples of what kind of waves?

a.   Transverse; longitudinal; both transverse and longitudinal
b.   Longitudinal; transverse; both transverse and longitudinal
c.   Transverse; both transverse and longitudinal; longitudinal
d.   Longitudinal; both transverse and longitudinal; transverse
e.   Both transverse and longitudinal; transverse; longitudinal

**1604    16-1    Wave Pulses,   Conceptual,   c**

Which of the following statements is TRUE?

a.   Waves transmit energy but not momentum.
b.   Waves transmit momentum but not energy.
c.   Waves transmit both energy and momentum.
d.   Waves transmit neither energy nor momentum.
e.   Waves can transmit either energy or momentum but not both.

**1605   16-2  Speed of Waves,  Factual,  e**

In which of the following is the speed of sound greatest?

a.  Air
b.  Water
c.  A vacuum
d.  Wood
e.  Steel

**1606   16-2  Speed of Waves,  Conceptual,  b**

A string under tension carries transverse waves traveling at speed $V$.  If the same string is under four times the tension, what will be the wave speed?

a.  $V$
b.  $2V$
c.  $V/2$
d.  $4V$
e.  $V/4$

**1607   16-2  Speed of Waves,  Numerical,  b**

A piano wire has a tension of 650 N and a mass per unit length of 0.060 g/cm.  What is the speed of waves on this wire?

a.  $1.0 \times 10^2$ m/s
b.  $3.3 \times 10^2$ m/s
c.  $1.0 \times 10^3$ m/s
d.  33 m/s
e.  52 m/s

**1608   16-2  Speed of Waves,  Numerical,  c**

The speed of sound in air at 0°C is 331 m/s.  What is the speed of sound in air at -40°C?

a.  241 m/s
b.  282 m/s
c.  306 m/s
d.  309 m/s
e.  379 m/s

**1609   16-2  Speed of Waves,  Conceptual,  b**

A general rule for estimating the distance in kilometres between you and a lightning bolt is to count the number of seconds between the time you see the flash and the time you hear the thunder and divide by

a.  2
b.  3
c.  4
d.  5
e.  None of these is correct.

**1610    16-2   Speed of Waves,   Conceptual,   a**

Sound travels at 340 m/s in air and 1500 m/s in water.  A sound of 256 Hz is made under water.  In the air,

a.   the frequency will remain the same but the wavelength will be shorter.
b.   the frequency will be higher but the wavelength will stay the same.
c.   the frequency will be lower but the wavelength will be longer.
d.   the frequency will be lower and the wavelength will be shorter.
e.   both the frequency and the wavelength will remain the same.

**1611    16-3   Harmonic Waves,   Conceptual,   a**

A wave is traveling with a speed $v$ along the $x$-axis in the positive direction.  The upper graph shows the displacement $y$ versus the distance $x$ for a given instant of time.  The lower graph shows the displacement $y$ versus the time $t$ for any given point $x$.  From the information on the graphs, the wave speed $v$ is

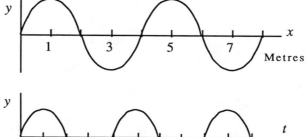

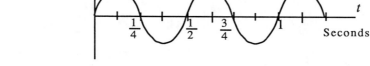

a.   8.0 m/s
b.   4.0 m/s
c.   6.0 m/s
d.   There is not enough information to solve the problem.
e.   None of these is correct.

**1612    16-3   Harmonic Waves,   Conceptual,   b**

A traveling wave passes a point of observation.  At this point, the time between successive crests is 0.2 s.

a.   The wavelength is 5 m.
b.   The frequency is 5 Hz.
c.   The velocity of propagation is 5 m/s.
d.   The wavelength is 0.2 m.
e.   There is not enough information to justify any of these statements.

**1613    16-3   Harmonic Waves,   Numerical,   b**

A set of waves has a speed of 4.2 m/s and a frequency of 2 Hz.  The wavelength is

a.  8.4 m
b.  2.1 m
c.  0.48 m
d.  0.84 m
e.  3.2 m


**1614    16-3   Harmonic Waves,   Numerical,   b**

Waves on the surface of a liquid are observed to have a wavelength of 12.9 mm and a speed of 30.9 cm/s.  The frequency of the wave motion is

a.  $1.8 \times 10^{-3}$ Hz
b.  24 Hz
c.  0.042 Hz
d.  2.4 Hz
e.  $2.4 \times 10^{-3}$ Hz


**1615    16-4   The Doppler Effect,   Conceptual,   d**

While you are standing on a corner, a police car with a 1-kHz siren drives past you at 30 m/s with its siren on.  The speed of sound is 340 m/s.  After the car passes you, the frequency you hear is about

a.  1097 Hz
b.  1088 Hz
c.  1000 Hz
d.  919 Hz
e.  912 Hz


**1616    16-4   The Doppler Effect,   Numerical,   a**

A train traveling at 90 km/h is blowing its whistle at 440 Hz as it crosses a level crossing. You are waiting at the crossing and hear the pitch of the whistle change as the train passes you by.  From what frequency to what frequency does the sound you hear change? (Take the speed of sound to be 340 m/s.)

a.  475 Hz to 410 Hz
b.  410 Hz to 475 Hz
c.  408 Hz to 472 Hz
d.  472 Hz to 408 Hz
e.  598 Hz to 348 Hz

**1617    16-4   The Doppler Effect,   Numerical,   d**

A blue line in the spectrum of the hydrogen atom has a wavelength $\lambda = 486$ nm. In the hydrogen-atom spectrum emitted by a distant galaxy, this line is observed on earth at $\lambda = 550$ nm. With what speed is this galaxy receding from us? (The speed of light is $3.0 \times 10^8$ m/s.)

a.  $1.31 \times 10^7$ m/s
b.  $1.13 \times 10^8$ m/s
c.  $2.65 \times 10^8$ m/s
d.  $3.49 \times 10^7$ m/s
e.  $3.95 \times 10^7$ m/s

**1618    16-4   The Doppler Effect,   Conceptual,   c**

Car $A$ moves at speed $V$ towards car $B$, which is at rest. The frequency of car $A$'s horn is observed by car $B$ to be $F$. What will be the frequency of car $A$'s horn as heard by an observer in car $B$ if car $A$ is at rest and car $B$ moves at speed $V$ towards car $A$? (Assume there is no wind.)

a.  $F$
b.  Greater than $F$
c.  Less than $F$
d.  It could be either greater than or less than $F$.
e.  $2F$

**1619    16-4   The Doppler Effect,   Conceptual,   a**

The frequency of a car horn is $F$. What frequency is observed if both the car and the observer are at rest, but a wind blows towards the observer?

a.  $F$
b.  Greater than $F$
c.  Less than $F$
d.  It could be either greater or less than $F$.
e.  It could be $F$ or greater than $F$, depending on how wind speed compares to speed of sound.

**1620    16-5   Energy and Intensity,   Conceptual,   d**

The intensity of a wave at a certain point is $I$. A second wave has twice the energy density and three times the speed of the first. What is the intensity of the second wave?

a.  $I$
b.  $2I$
c.  $3I$
d.  $6I$
e.  $2I/3$

**1621    16-5   Energy and Intensity,  Conceptual,  c**

The sound level of a dog's bark is 50 dB.  The intensity of a rock concert is 10,000 times that of the dog's bark.  What is the sound level of the rock concert?

    a.  10,050 dB
    b.  500,000 dB
    c.  90 dB
    d.  2000 dB
    e.  54 dB

**1622    16-5   Energy and Intensity,  Numerical,  c**

A note is played at 60 dB.  Another is played that sounds four times as loud.  The sound intensity level of the second note is

    a.  80 dB
    b.  100 dB
    c.  66 dB
    d.  64 dB
    e.  240 dB

**1623    16-5   Energy and Intensity,  Conceptual,  a**

Two sounds differ by 30 dB.  The intensity of the louder sound $I_L$ compared to the softer $I_S$ is $I_L/I_S$.  The value of the ratio is

    a.  1000
    b.  30
    c.  9
    d.  100
    e.  300

**1624    16-5   Energy and Intensity,  Conceptual,  b**

Two sounds differ by 20 dB.  This means that the louder sound is _____ times as intense and _____ times as loud.

    a.  twenty; twenty
    b.  one hundred; twenty
    c.  twenty; four
    d.  one hundred; four
    e.  two; two

**1625    16-5   Energy and Intensity,  Numerical,  c**

If a sound of intensity $I = 1.0 \times 10^{-6}$ W/m$^2$ falls on a detector of area $A = 7.0 \times 10^{-5}$ m$^2$ (about the size of your eardrum), how much power is received by the detector?

    a.  $6.2 \times 10^{-14}$ W
    b.  $1.0 \times 10^{-6}$ W
    c.  $7.0 \times 10^{-11}$ W
    d.  $1.4 \times 10^{-2}$ W
    e.  70 W

**1626**    **16-5   Energy and Intensity,   Numerical,   d**

At an outside bandstand, what would be the difference in the sound intensity levels (dB) received by a listener 5.0 m from the bandstand and one 40 m from the bandstand, assuming there is no sound reflection?  [$\beta = 10 \log(I/I_0)$.]

   a.   8.0 dB
   b.   9.0 dB
   c.   10 dB
   d.   18 dB
   e.   The answer depends on how loudly the band plays.

**1627**    **16-5   Energy and Intensity,   Numerical,   d**

A noisy workplace has a noise level of 90 dB.  It is desired to reduce this to a more comfortable 75 dB.  By what factor must the power of the noise source be reduced?  (That is, what is the ratio of the new power to the old?)

   a.   0.83
   b.   0.67
   c.   0.32
   d.   0.032
   e.   0.010

CHAPTER 17     Interference, Diffraction, and Standing Waves

**1701**    **17-1   Interference of Waves from Two Point Sources, Conceptual,   d**

Two waves of the same frequency and equal amplitude $A$ arrive at a point. The waves are out of phase by 90°. The resulting amplitude observed is

a.   $2A$
b.   zero
c.   $A$
d.   $1.4A$
e.   $0.7A$

**1702**    **17-1   Interference of Waves from Two Point Sources, Numerical,   b**

Two loudspeakers, $S_1$ and $S_2$, 3.0 m apart both emit the same single-frequency tone in phase at the speakers. A listener directly in front of one of the speakers ($S_1$) notices that the intensity is a minimum when she is 4.0 m from that speaker (see diagram). What is the lowest frequency of the emitted tone? (The speed of sound in air = 340 m/s.)

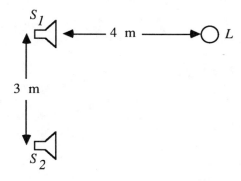

a.   85 Hz
b.   170 Hz
c.   260 Hz
d.   340 Hz
e.   510 Hz

**1703    17-1 Interference of Waves from Two Point Sources,   Numerical,   d**

Two loudspeakers, $S_1$ and $S_2$, 3.0 m apart both emit the same single-frequency tone in phase at the speakers. A listener directly in front of one of the speakers ($S_1$) notices that the intensity is a minimum when she is 4.0 m from that speaker (see diagram). The listener now walks around speaker $S_1$ in an arc of a circle, staying 4.0 m from that speaker but increasing her distance from the other speaker (see diagram). How far is she from speaker $S_2$ when she notices the first maximum in the sound intensity? (The speed of sound in air = 340 m/s.)

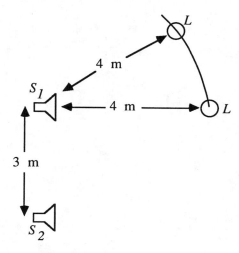

a.  4.5 m
b.  5.0 m
c.  5.5 m
d.  6.0 m
e.  6.5 m

**1704    17-1   Interference of Waves from Two Point Sources,   Factual,   b**

The interference of two harmonic waves with the same frequency, wavelength, and amplitude depends on

a.   the amplitude of the waves.
b.   the phase of the waves.
c.   the frequency of the waves.
d.   the wavelength of the waves.
e.   the synthesis of the waves.

**1705    17-1   Interference of Waves from Two Point Sources,   Conceptual,   a**

If two identical waves with the same phase are added, the resultant is

a.   a wave with the same frequency but twice the amplitude.
b.   a wave with the same amplitude but twice the frequency.
c.   a wave with zero amplitude.
d.   a wave with zero frequency.
e.   This cannot be answered without knowing the wavelengths of the two waves.

**1706**    **17-1   Interference of Waves from Two Point Sources,   Conceptual,   a**

If two identical waves with a phase difference of $6\pi$ are added, the resultant is

a.  a wave with the same frequency but twice the amplitude.
b.  a wave with the same amplitude but twice the frequency.
c.  a wave with zero amplitude.
d.  a wave with zero frequency.
e.  This cannot be answered without knowing the wavelengths of the two waves.

**1707**    **17-1   Interference of Waves from Two Point Sources,   Conceptual,   c**

If two identical waves with a phase difference of $3\pi$ are added, the resultant is

a.  a wave with the same frequency but twice the amplitude.
b.  a wave with the same amplitude but twice the frequency.
c.  a wave with zero amplitude.
d.  a wave with an intensity equal to the sum of the intensities of the two waves.
e.  This cannot be answered without knowing the wavelengths of the two waves.

**1708**    **17-1   Interference of Waves from Two Point Sources,   Conceptual,   c**

Two waves with the same frequency and wavelength but with different amplitudes are added.  If $A_1 = 2A_2$  and the waves are 180° out of phase, then the amplitude of the resultant wave will be

a.  zero.
b.  the same as $A_1$.
c.  the same as $A_2$.
d.  equal to $A_1 + A_2$.
e.  coherent.

**1709**    **17-2   Diffraction,   Conceptual,   e**

If a traveling wave passes through an opening with a width equal to the wavelength of the wave,

a.  nothing special happens.
b.  the wave will stop.  The opening must be larger than the wavelength.
c.  diffraction will occur only if the wavelength and the width of the opening are large.
d.  diffraction will occur only if the wavelength and the width of the opening are small.
e.  diffraction will always occur.

**1710**    **17-2   Diffraction,   Factual,   c**

The bending of light rays that occurs to some extent when part of the wavefront is limited is called

a.  reflection.
b.  refraction.
c.  diffraction.
d.  coherence.
e.  interference.

**1711    17-2  Diffraction,   Conceptual,   d**

Why can we hear sounds that are made around a corner but cannot see light that is made around a corner?

a.  Light travels only in straight lines, while sound can travel in a curved path.
b.  Sound has more energy than light.
c.  Sound will echo off walls of the room, while light does not.
d.  Sound has longer wavelengths than light.
e.  None of these is correct.

**1712    17-3  Beats,   Numerical,   d**

Two whistles produce sounds of wavelengths 3.4 m and 3.3 m.  What is the beat frequency produced?  (The speed of sound is 340 m/s.)

a.  0.1 Hz
b.  1.0 Hz
c.  2.0 Hz
d.  3.0 Hz
e.  4.0 Hz

**1713    17-3  Beats,   Numerical,   b**

Middle C on a piano has a frequency of 262 Hz.  Sometimes it is said that middle C is actually $2^8 = 256$ Hz, and tuning forks are made with this frequency.  How many beats per second would be heard if such a tuning fork were sounded simultaneously with the middle C of a (well-tuned) piano?

a.  3
b.  6
c.  12
d.  4
e.  8

**1714    17-3  Beats,   Numerical,   c**

A violinist is tuning the A string on her violin by listening for beats when this note is played simultaneously with a tuning fork of frequency 440 Hz.  She hears 4 beats per second.  She notices that, when she increases the tension in the string slightly, the beat frequency decreases.  What was the frequency of the mistuned A string?

a.  448 Hz
b.  444 Hz
c.  436 Hz
d.  432 Hz
e.  438 Hz

**1715    17-3   Beats,   Numerical,   a**

Two trumpet players are both playing a note with a frequency of 440 Hz, corresponding to the musical note A above middle C.  However, one of the trumpet players is marching away from you so that you hear a beat frequency of 4 Hz from the two trumpets.  With what speed is the departing trumpet player moving away from you?  (The speed of sound in air is 340 m/s.)

a.  3.12 m/s
b.  3.09 m/s
c.  3.06 m/s
d.  3.00 m/s
e.  2.95 m/s

**1716    17-3   Beats,   Conceptual,   e**

When a piano tuner strikes an A note on the piano and a 440 Hz tuning fork, he hears 4 beats each second.  The frequency of the piano's A note is

a.  440 Hz
b.  444 Hz
c.  880 Hz
d.  436 Hz
e.  either 436 Hz or 444 Hz

**1717    17-4   Standing Waves,   Conceptual,   d**

A string fixed at both ends is vibrating in a standing wave.  There are three nodes between the ends of the string, not including those on the ends.  The string is vibrating at a frequency that is its

a.  fundamental.
b.  second harmonic.
c.  third harmonic.
d.  fourth harmonic.
e.  fifth harmonic.

**1718    17-4   Standing Waves,   Conceptual,   d**

On a standing wave pattern, the distance between two consecutive nodes is $d$.  The wavelength is

a.  $d/2$
b.  $d$
c.  $3d/2$
d.  $2d$
e.  $4d$

**1719    17-4   Standing  Waves,   Numerical,  d**

One source of sound is at $A$ and another is at $B$. The two sources are in phase. The distance $AB = 10.0$ m. The frequency of the sound waves from both sources is 1000 Hz and both have the same amplitude. The speed of sound in air is 330 m/s. A receiver is at point $C$ and $AB$ is perpendicular to $AC$. The greatest distance $AC$ for which the signal at $C$ is a minimum is

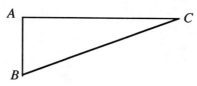

a.  0.33 m
b.  152 m
c.  330 m
d.  303 m
e.  100 m


**1720    17-4   Standing  Waves,   Conceptual,  c**

A stretched string of length $L$ that is fixed at both ends is vibrating in its third harmonic. How far from the end of the string can the blade of a screwdriver be placed against the string and not disturb the amplitude of the vibration?

a.  $L/6$
b.  $L/4$
c.  $L/3$
d.  $L/2$
e.  None of these is correct.


**1721    17-4   Standing  Waves,   Conceptual,  c**

In a resonance-tube experiment similar to the one described in the text, resonance is heard when the water level is at the 10-cm mark and again when it is at the 36-cm mark. After completing the experiment, the student notices that the zero mark on the scale is not even with the top of the tube. Based on the inaccurate experimental data, the student's BEST estimate of the wavelength of the sound is

a.  40 cm
b.  72 cm
c.  52 cm
d.  46 cm
e.  None of these choices are good estimates. The experiment must be done again.


**1722    17-4   Standing  Waves,   Conceptual,  c**

In a pipe that is open at one end and closed at the other and has a fundamental frequency of 256 Hz, which of the following frequencies CANNOT be produced?

a.  768 Hz
b.  1280 Hz
c.  5120 Hz
d.  19,712 Hz
e.  All of these can be produced.

**1723    17-4   Standing Waves,   Conceptual,   b**

The fundamental frequency for a pipe that has one end closed is 256 Hz.  When both ends of the same pipe are opened, the fundamental frequency is

a.   64 Hz
b.   128 Hz
c.   256 Hz
d.   512 Hz
e.   1024 Hz


**1724    17-4   Standing Waves,   Conceptual,   b**

The standing waves on a string of length $L$ that is fixed at both ends have a speed $v$.  The three lowest frequencies of vibration are

a.   $v/L$, $2v/L$, and $3v/L$
b.   $v/2L$, $v/L$, and $3v/2L$
c.   $\lambda/2$, $\lambda$, and $3\lambda/2$
d.   $L/v$, $2L/v$, and $3L/v$
e.   $\lambda/3$, $2\lambda/3$, and $3\lambda/3$


**1725    17-4   Standing Waves,   Conceptual,   d**

Standing waves exist in a string of length $L$ that is fixed at one end and free at the other.  The speed of the waves on the string is $v$.  The three lowest frequencies of vibration are

a.   $v/4L$, $v/2L$, and $3v/4L$
b.   $v/2L$, $v/L$, and $3v/2L$
c.   $\lambda/4$, $\lambda/2$, and $3\lambda/4$
d.   $v/4L$, $3v/4L$, and $5v/4L$
e.   $\lambda/3$, $2\lambda/3$, and $3\lambda/3$


**1726    17-4   Standing Waves,   Conceptual,   b**

The standing waves in air in a pipe of length $L$ that is open at both ends have a speed $v$.  The frequencies of the three lowest harmonics are

a.   $v/L$, $2v/L$, and $3v/L$
b.   $v/2L$, $v/L$, and $3v/2L$
c.   $\lambda/2$, $\lambda$, and $3\lambda/2$
d.   $L/v$, $2L/v$, and $3L/v$
e.   $\lambda/3$, $2\lambda/3$, and $3\lambda/3$


**1727    17-4   Standing Waves,   Conceptual,   d**

The standing waves in air in a pipe of length $L$ that is open at one end and closed at the other have a speed $v$.  The frequencies of the three lowest harmonics are

a.   $v/4L$, $v/2L$, and $3v/4L$
b.   $v/2L$, $v/L$, and $3v/2L$
c.   $\lambda/4$, $\lambda/2$, and $3\lambda/4$
d.   $v/4L$, $3v/4L$, and $5v/4L$
e.   $\lambda/3$, $2\lambda/3$, and $3\lambda/3$

1728    **17-4  Standing Waves,  Factual,  a**

A standing wave on a string is an example of

a.  resonance.
b.  beats.
c.  diffraction.
d.  polarization.
e.  harmonic analysis.

1729    **17-4  Standing Waves,  Numerical,  d**

A 1.0-m long string fixed at both ends vibrates in its fundamental mode at 440 Hz.  What is the speed of the waves on this string?

a.  220 m/s
b.  440 m/s
c.  660 m/s
d.  880 m/s
e.  $1.1 \times 10^3$ m/s

1730    **17-4  Standing Waves,  Numerical,  a**

The human vocal tract can be thought of as a tube that is open at one end. If the length of this tube is 17 cm (about average for an adult male), what are the lowest two harmonics? (The speed of sound in air = 340 m/s.)

a.  500 Hz, 1500 Hz
b.  500 Hz, 1000 Hz
c.  1000 Hz, 2000 Hz
d.  1000 Hz, 3000 Hz
e.  1500 Hz, 2500 Hz

1731    **17-4  Standing Waves,  Numerical,  d**

For a tube of length 57.0 cm that is open at both ends, what is the frequency of the fundamental mode?  (The speed of sound in air = 340 m/s.)

a.  149 Hz
b.  447 Hz
c.  596 Hz
d.  298 Hz
e.  746 Hz

1732    **17-4  Standing Waves,  Numerical,  d**

A string fixed at both ends is 50 cm long and has a tension that causes the frequency of its fundamental to be 262 Hz.  If the tension is increased by 4.0%, what does the fundamental frequency become?

a.  252 Hz
b.  257 Hz
c.  264 Hz
d.  267 Hz
e.  272 Hz

**1733** **17-4 Standing Waves, Numerical, b**

A clarinet which is essentially a tube open at one end, is properly tuned to concert A (440 Hz) indoors, where the temperature is 20°C and the speed of sound is 340 m/s. The musician then takes the instrument to play an outdoor concert, where the temperature is 0°C and the speed of sound is 331 m/s. What will be the frequency of the A played on the cold clarinet? (Ignore any thermal changes to the body of the clarinet itself.)

   a. 417 Hz
   b. 428 Hz
   c. 434 Hz
   d. 445 Hz
   e. 451 Hz

**1734** **17-5 Harmonic Analysis and Synthesis, Conceptual, d**

The reason we can tell the difference between a trumpet and a clarinet even when they both play the same note is that they have

   a. the same overtones.
   b. the same harmonics.
   c. different fundamental frequencies.
   d. different waveforms.
   e. harmonic syntheses.

**1735** **17-5 Harmonic Analysis and Synthesis, Conceptual, e**

An electronic music synthesizer is based on the ideas of

   a. harmonic synthesis.
   b. overtones.
   c. tone quality.
   d. Fourier analysis.
   e. All of these choices are correct.

CHAPTER 18    Electric Fields and Forces

**1801**    **18-1  Electric Charge,  Factual,  c**

Electrical charges of the same sign

    a.  also have the same magnitude.
    b.  attract each other.
    c.  repel each other.
    d.  exert no forces on each other.
    e.  None of these is correct.

**1802**    **18-2  Coulomb's Law,  Numerical,  a**

A positive charge of $6.3 \times 10^{-8}$ C is 15.0 cm from a negative charge of $4.5 \times 10^{-8}$ C. The force on one of the charges due to the other is

    a.  $1.13 \times 10^{-3}$ N
    b.  $1.13 \times 10^{-7}$ N
    c.  $1.02 \times 10^{7}$ N
    d.  $1.25 \times 10^{-13}$ N
    e.  $1.02 \times 10^{-6}$ N

**1803**    **18-2  Coulomb's Law,  Numerical,  b**

Two small spheres of mass $m = 5$ g and equal charges $q$ are suspended from a common point by threads of length $L = 0.3$ m.  What is the charge on each sphere if the threads make an angle $\theta = 20°$ with the vertical.

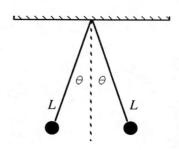

    a.  $7.9 \times 10^{-7}$ C
    b.  $1.1 \times 10^{-6}$ C
    c.  $7.5 \times 10^{-2}$ C
    d.  $6.3 \times 10^{-13}$ C
    e.  $1.8 \times 10^{-7}$ N

1804   18-2  Coulomb's Law,  Conceptual,  e

Three charges, $+q$, $+Q$, and $-Q$, are placed
at the corners of an equilateral triangle as
shown.  The net force on charge $+q$ due to
the other two charges is

$+q$
●

●                    ●
$+Q$                  $-Q$

a.  vertically up.
b.  vertically down.
c.  zero.
d.  horizontal to the left.
e.  horizontal to the right.


1805   18-2  Coulomb's Law,  Numerical,  a

Charges $q_1$ and $q_2$ exert 10-N repulsive forces on each other. What is the repulsive force
when their separation is decreased so that their final separation is 80% of their initial
separation?

a.  16 N
b.  12 N
c.  10 N
d.  8.0 N
e.  6.4 N


1806   18-2  Coulomb's Law,  Numerical,  b

Two positive charges (+8.0 mC and +2.0 mC) are separated by 300 m.  A third charge is
placed a distance $r$ from the +8.0 mC charge such that the resultant electric force on the third
charge due to the other two charges is zero. The distance $r$ is

a.  250 m
b.  200 m
c.  150 m
d.  125 m
e.  100 m


1807   18-2  Coulomb's Law,  Numerical,  a

Three charges, each separated by 100 m from adjacent charges, are located along a
horizontal line:  a -3.00-C charge on the left, a +2.00-C charge in the middle, and a +1.00-C
charge on the right.  What is the resultant force on the 1.00-C charge due to the other two?

a.  $1.1 \times 10^6$ N to the right
b.  $1.1 \times 10^6$ N to the left
c.  $2.5 \times 10^6$ N to the right
d.  $2.5 \times 10^6$ N to the left
e.  $4.5 \times 10^7$ N to the right

**1808    18-3  The Electric Field,  Factual,  b**

A proton is moving horizontally north in an electric field pointed vertically upward.  The force on the proton is

a.  zero.
b.  upward.
c.  downward.
d.  to the west.
e.  to the east.

**1809    18-3  The Electric Field,  Factual,  e**

The SI units of electric field can be expressed as

a.  $C/m^2$
b.  $C/S$
c.  $V \cdot C$
d.  N
e.  V/m

**1810    18-3  The Electric Field,  Numerical,  c**

Three charges, each separated by 100 m from adjacent charges, are located along a horizontal line:  a -3.00-C charge on the left, a +2.00-C charge in the middle, and a +1.00-C charge on the right. What is the electric field $\mathbf{E}$ on the horizontal line halfway between the -3.00-C and +2.00-C charges?

a.  $2.2 \times 10^7$ N/C to the left
b.  $1.8 \times 10^7$ N/C to the right
c.  $1.8 \times 10^7$ N/C to the left
d.  $3.2 \times 10^6$ N/C to the right
e.  $4.0 \times 10^6$ N/C to the left

**1811    18-3  The Electric Field,  Conceptual,  d**

A positive charge that is free to move but is at rest in an electric field $\mathbf{E}$ experiences a force that is

a.  perpendicular to $\mathbf{E}$ .
b.  zero because the speed is zero.
c.  in the direction opposite to $\mathbf{E}$.
d.  in the same direction as $\mathbf{E}$.
e.  None of these is correct.

**1812** **18-3 The Electric Field, Numerical, d**

Three charges $Q_1$, $Q_2$, and $Q_3$, each equal to $+6.4 \times 10^{-19}$, are in a straight line. The distance between neighboring charges is $6.0 \times 10^{-10}$ m. The magnitude of the electric field at $P$, which is $8.0 \times 10^{-10}$ m from $Q_2$ on a line at right angles to the line between $Q_1$ and $Q_3$, is

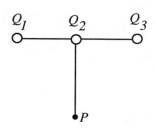

a.  $1.2 \times 10^{-8}$ N/C
b.  16 N/C
c.  2.0 N/C
d.  $1.8 \times 10^{10}$ N/C
e.  $1.2 \times 10^8$ N/C

**1813** **18-3 The Electric Field, Numerical, a**

Two charges $Q_1$ and $Q_2$ are 8.0 cm apart. Charge $Q_1 = +50 \times 10^{-9}$ C and $Q_2 = -50 \times 10^{-9}$ C. The magnitude of electric field at point $P$, 3.0 cm from the midpoint of the line joining $Q_1$ and $Q_2$ is

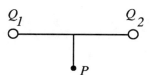

a.  $29 \times 10^4$ N/C
b.  $2.9 \times 10^4$ N/C
c.  $3.6 \times 10^5$ N/C
d.  290 N/C
e.  $36 \times 10^5$ N/C

**1814** **18-3 The Electric Field, Conceptual, b**

Two charges of the same magnitude and sign are placed 0.05 m apart. There is only one point in space near them where the electric field is zero. Which of the following statements about that point is true?

a.  It cannot be on the line joining the charges.
b.  It must be on the line joining the charges and between the charges.
c.  It must be on the line joining the charges but not between the charges.
d.  Its position will depend on the size of the charges.
e.  None of these is correct.

**1815    18-3  The Electric Field,  Numerical,  a**

Three charges, each $Q = 3.2$ x $10^{-19}$ C, are
arranged  at three of the corners of a square
of side 20 nm as shown.  The magnitude of
the electric field at $D$, the fourth corner of
the square, is

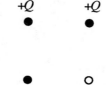

a.   14 x $10^6$ N/C
b.   10 x $10^{10}$ N/C
c.   3.6 x $10^{10}$ N/C
d.   30  N/C
e.

**1816    18-3  The Electric Field,  Conceptual,  c**

Three positive and equal charges $Q_1$, $Q_2$,
and $Q_3$ are at the corners of an equilateral
triangle as shown.  Point $P$ is at the
midpoint of the line between $Q_1$ and $Q_3$.
The electric field at $P$ is:

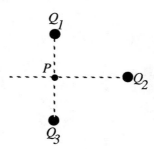

a.   zero.
b.   not zero and is directed along the line from $P$ to $Q_3$.
c.   not zero and is directed along the line from $Q_2$ to $P$.
d.   not zero and is directed along the line from $Q_1$ to $Q_2$.
e.   None of these is correct.

**1817    18-3  The Electric Field,  Numerical,  b**

An electric field with a magnitude of 6.0 x $10^4$ N/C is directed along the positive $y$ axis.  A
particle with a charge $q = +4.8$ x $10^{-19}$ C is moving along the $x$ axis with a speed $v = 3$ x
$10^6$ m/s.  The force on the charge is

a.   8.64 x $10^{-8}$ N perpendicular to the $xy$ plane.
b.   2.88 x $10^{-14}$ N along the $y$ axis.
c.   8.64 x $10^{-8}$ N along the $x$ axis.
d.   zero.
e.   2.88 x $10^{-14}$ N along the $x$ axis.

**1818**    **18-3   The Electric Field,   Numerical,   a**

In the figure, the electric field at point A is zero.  Find the charge $Q_1$.

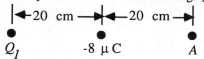

a.   +32 μC
b.   -32 μC
c.   The field cannot be zero at $A$ for any value of $Q_1$.
d.   +16 μC
e.   -16 μC

**1819**    **18-4   Lines of Force,   Factual,   d**

An electrical dipole consists of a positive charge separated from a negative charge of the same magnitude by a small distance.  The electric field lines around an electrical dipole are best represented by which of the following diagrams?

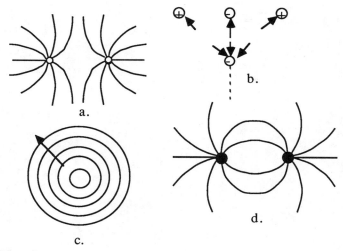

e.   None of these is correct.

**1820**    **18-4   Lines of Force,   Factual,   d**

The electric field inside a spherically symmetric shell of charge is

a.   dependent on the magnitude of the charge on the shell.
b.   dependent on whether the shell is made of a conducting or nonconducting material.
c.   dependent on the electric field outside the shell.
d.   zero.
e.   None of these is correct.

**1821    18-4  Lines of Force,  Factual,  b**

The magnitude of the electric field inside a spherically symmetric shell of charge is

a.  greater than the magnitude of the electric field outside of the shell.
b.  less than the magnitude of the electric field outside of the shell.
c.  equal to the magnitude of the electric field outside of the shell.
d.  greater than, less than, or equal to the magnitude of the electric field outside of the shell.
e.  None of these is correct.

**1822    18-4  Lines of Force,  Conceptual,  d**

Which of the following statements about electric field lines is NOT true?

a.  The number of lines leaving a positive charge or entering a negative charge is proportional to the charge.
b.  The lines begin on positive charges and end on negative charges.
c.  The density of lines (the number per unit area perpendicular to the lines) is proportional to the magnitude of the field.
d.  Electric field lines cross midway between charges that have equal magnitude and sign.

**1823    18-5  Gauss' Law,  Conceptual,  b**

A charge $+Q$ is located inside a Styrofoam ball of radius $R$ . The electric field at the surface has a magnitude $E$. What is the magnitude of the electric field at the surface if the charge inside is doubled to $2Q$?

a.  $4E$
b.  $2E$
c.  $0.5E$
d.  $0.25E$
e.  $E$

**1824    18-5  Gauss' Law,  Conceptual,  b**

A charge $+Q$ is located inside a Styrofoam ball of radius $R$ . The net electric flux at the surface is $\emptyset_{net}$. What is the value of the net electric flux at the surface if the charge inside is doubled and the radius of the ball is tripled.

a.  $\emptyset_{net}$
b.  $2\emptyset_{net}$
c.  $(9/2)\emptyset_{net}$
d.  $(2/9)\emptyset_{net}$
e.  $(4/9)\emptyset_{net}$

**1825    18-6  Electric Dipoles in Electric Fields,  Numerical,  b**

A point charge of $+3.5 \times 10^{-10}$ C is above a point charge of $-3.5 \times 10^{-10}$ C on a vertical line. The distance between the charges is 4.0 mm. What are the magnitude and direction of the dipole moment **p**?

a.  Zero
b.  $1.4 \times 10^{-12}$ C·m up
c.  $1.4 \times 10^{-12}$ C·m down
d.  $2.8 \times 10^{-12}$ C·m up
e.  $2.8 \times 10^{-12}$ C·m down

**1826    18-6   Electric Dipoles in Electric Fields,   Numerical,   d**

An electric dipole **p** of magnitude 2.50 x $10^{-10}$ C·m makes an angle of 65° with a uniform electric field **E** of magnitude 3.00 x $10^{-6}$ N/C.  What is the torque on the dipole?

a.   3.2 x $10^{-16}$ N·m
b.   6.2 x $10^{-16}$ N·m
c.   1.4 x $10^{-15}$ N·m
d.   6.8 x $10^{-16}$ N·m
e.   Zero

**1827    18-6   Electric Dipoles in Electric Fields,   Conceptual,   d**

As the distance between the charges of an electric dipole increases,

a.   the charges decrease.
b.   the dipole moment decreases.
c.   the charges increase.
d.   the dipole moment increases.
e.   None of these is correct.

CHAPTER 19    Electrostatics

**1901**    **19-1   Electric Potential and Potential Difference,   Conceptual,   b**

Charges $+Q$ and $-Q$ are arranged at the corners
of a square as shown.  When the electric field $E$
and the electric potential $V$ are determined at $P$,
the center of the square, one finds that

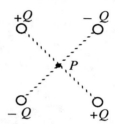

a.   $E$ is not $= 0$ and $V > 0$.
b.   $E = 0$ and $V = 0$.
c.   $E = 0$ and $V > 0$.
d.   $E$ is not $= 0$ and $V < 0$.
e.   None of these is correct.

**1902**    **19-1   Electric Potential and Potential Difference,   Numerical,   a**

The voltage between the cathode and the screen of a television set is 22 kV.  If an electron
leaves the cathode with an initial speed of zero, what is its speed just before it hits the
screen?

a    $8.8 \times 10^7$ m/s
b.   $2.8 \times 10^6$ m/s
c.   $6.2 \times 10^7$ m/s
d.   $7.7 \times 10^{15}$ m/s
e.   $5.3 \times 10^7$ m/s

**1903**    **19-1   Electric Potential and Potential Difference,   Conceptual,   b**

A lithium nucleus with a charge of $3(1.6 \times 10^{-19})$ C and a mass of $7(1.67 \times 10^{-27})$ kg, and
an alpha particle with a charge of $2(1.6 \times 10^{-19})$ C and a mass of $4(1.67 \times 10^{-27})$ kg are at
rest.  A method that could be used to accelerate them to the same kinetic energy would be to

a.   accelerate them through the same electrical potential difference.
b.   accelerate the alpha particle through $V_1$ volts and the lithium nucleus through $(2/3)V_1$
     volts.
c.   accelerate the alpha particle through $V_1$ volts and the lithium nucleus through $(7/4)V_1$
     volts.
d.   accelerate the alpha particle through $V_1$ volts and the lithium nucleus through $(2 \times$
     $7)/(3 \times 4)V_1$ volts.
e.   None of these is correct.

**1904    19-1   Electric Potential and Potential Difference,  Numerical,  b**

An electric dipole has a positive charge of $4.8 \times 10^{-19}$ C separated from a negative charge of the same magnitude by $6.4 \times 10^{-10}$ m. The electric potential at a point $9.2 \times 10^{-10}$ m from each of the two charges is

a.  9.4 V
b.  zero
c.  4.2 V
d.  $5.1 \times 10^9$ V
e.  1.7 V

**1905    19-1   Electric Potential and Potential Difference,  Numerical,  d**

An electric dipole has a positive charge of $4.80 \times 10^{-19}$ C separated from a negative charge of the same magnitude by $6.40 \times 10^{-10}$ m. The magnitude of the electric field at the midpoint of the dipole is

a.  zero
b.  27.0 N/C
c.  $4.22 \times 10^{10}$ N/C
d.  $8.44 \times 10^{10}$ N/C
e.  $12.3 \times 10^{10}$ N/C

**1906    19-1   Electric Potential and Potential Difference,  Numerical,  b**

$ABC$ is a straight line with $AB = BC = 6 \times 10^{-10}$ m. $BP$ is perpendicular to $ABC$ and $BP = 8 \times 10^{-10}$ m. Charges of $+3.2 \times 10^{-19}$ C are placed at $A$ and $C$ and a charge of $-3.2 \times 10^{-19}$ C is placed at $B$. The magnitude of the electric field at $P$ is

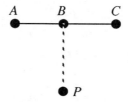

a.  $9.1 \times 10^9$ N/C
b.  $1.1 \times 10^8$ N/C
c.  $1.2 \times 10^{10}$ N/C
d.  $1.0 \times 10^{10}$ N/C
e.  $3.3 \times 10^{10}$ N/C

**1907    19-1   Electric Potential and Potential Difference,  Numerical,  a**

$ABC$ is a straight line with $AB = BC = 6 \times 10^{-10}$ m. $BP$ is perpendicular to $ABC$ and $BP = 8 \times 10^{-10}$ m. Charges of $+3.2 \times 10^{-19}$ C are placed at $A$ and $C$ and a charge of $-3.2 \times 10^{-19}$ C is placed at $B$. The potential at P is:

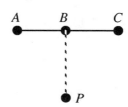

a.  2.2 V
b.  9.4 V
c.  29 V
d.  $4.3 \times 10^{-10}$ V
e.  160 V

**1908    19-2   Electric Conductors,   Factual,   c**

Electrical conductors contain

a.   only free electrons.
b.   only bound electrons.
c.   both free and bound electrons.
d.   neither bound nor free electrons.
e.   only protons and neutrons.


**1909    19-2   Electric Conductors,   Conceptual,   b**

A positively charged insulator is brought near two metallic spheres that are in contact.  When separated, the metallic ball on the right will have

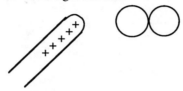

a.   no net charge.
b.   a positive charge.
c.   a negative charge.
d.   either a positive or negative charge.
e.   None of these is correct.


**1910    19-2   Electric Conductors,   Conceptual,   e**

The electric field at the surface of a conductor

a.   is parallel to the surface.
b.   depends only on the total charge on the conductor.
c.   depends only on the area of the conductor.
d.   depends only on the curvature of the surface.
e.   depends on both the area of and the charge on the conductor.


**1911    19-2   Electric Conductors,   Numerical,   c**

A large, flat conducting plate has a surface charge density $\sigma = 8.0 \times 10^{-9}$ C/m$^2$.  What is the magnitude of the electric field 0.01 mm from this plate?

a.   72 N/C
b.   230 N/C
c.   900 N/C
d.   9.0 x $10^7$ N/C
e.   9.0 x $10^{12}$ N/C

**1912**    **19-2   Electric Conductors,   Numerical,   d**

A solid spherical conductor has a radius of 15 cm.  The electric field 30 cm from the center of this sphere has a magnitude of 800 N/C.  What is the surface charge density $\sigma$ on the sphere?

    a.   $7.1 \times 10^{-9}$ C/m$^2$
    b.   $1.0 \times 10^{-8}$ C/m$^2$
    c.   $1.4 \times 10^{-8}$ C/m$^2$
    d.   $2.8 \times 10^{-8}$ C/m$^2$
    e.   $1.1 \times 10^{-7}$ C/m$^2$

**1913**    **19-3   Equipotential Surfaces, Charge Sharing, and Dielectric Breakdown, Conceptual,   e**

In the region around an array of charges,

    a.   there may be lines of force in the electric field or on the equipotential surfaces, but not in both.
    b.   the lines of force must lie on the equipotential surfaces.
    c.   the lines of force are everywhere normal (at right angles) to the equipotential surfaces and the positive direction is from lower to higher potential.
    d.   there is no relation between the lines of force and the equipotential surfaces.
    e.   None of these is correct.

**1914**    **19-3   Equipotential Surfaces, Charge Sharing, and Dielectric Breakdown, Numerical,   a**

A solid spherical conductor of radius 15 cm has a charge $Q = 6.5$ nC on it.  A second spherical conductor of radius 10 cm is brought up to the first until they touch and is then moved far away from it.  How much charge is there on the second sphere after the two spheres have been separated?

    a.   2.6 nC
    b.   2.2 nC
    c.   3.2 nC
    d.   3.9 nC
    e.   4.3 nC

**1915**    **19-3   Equipotential Surfaces, Charge Sharing, and Dielectric Breakdown, Numerical,   e**

The metal sphere at the top of a small Van de Graaf generator has a diameter of 20 cm.  How much charge can be accumulated on this sphere before dielectric breakdown of the air around it occurs?  (the dielectric strength of air = 3 MV/m.)

    a.   $6.7 \times 10^{-5}$ C
    b.   $3.3 \times 10^{-5}$ C
    c.   $1.3 \times 10^{-5}$ C
    d.   $6.7 \times 10^{-6}$ C
    e.   $3.3 \times 10^{-6}$ C

**1916**  **19-3  Equipotential Surfaces, Charge Sharing, and Dielectric Breakdown, Factual,  d**

The dielectric strength of the atmosphere is of the order of

a.  1 V/m
b.  $10^2$ V/m
c.  $10^4$ V/m
d.  $10^6$ V/m
e.  $10^8$ V/m

**1917**  **19-3  Equipotential Surfaces, Charge Sharing, and Dielectric Breakdown, Conceptual,  c**

Two charged metal spheres are connected by a wire.  Sphere $A$ is larger than sphere $B$ as shown.  The magnitude of the electric potential of sphere $A$

a.  is greater than that at the surface of sphere $B$.
b.  is less than that at the surface of sphere $B$.
c.  is the same as that at the surface of sphere $B$.
d.  could be greater than or less than that at the surface of sphere $B$, depending on the radii of the spheres.
e.  could be greater than or less than that at the surface of sphere $B$, depending on the charge on the spheres.

**1918**  **19-3  Equipotential Surfaces, Charge Sharing, and Dielectric Breakdown, Conceptual,  b**

Two charged metal spheres are connected by a wire.  Sphere $A$ is larger than sphere $B$ as shown.  The magnitude of the electric field of sphere $A$

a.  is greater than that at the surface of sphere $B$.
b.  is less than that at the surface of sphere $B$.
c.  is the same as that at the surface of sphere $B$.
d.  could be greater than or less than that at the surface of sphere $B$, depending on the radii of the spheres.
e.  could be greater than or less than that at the surface of sphere $B$, depending on the charge on the spheres.

**1919    19-4   Capacitance,  Numerical,  a**

Two flat, parallel plates have radii $r = 0.10$
m and are $d = 0.40$ cm apart.  The potential
difference between the plates is 360 V.
The electric field at the point $P$ at the center
is

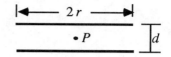

a.  $9.0 \times 10^4$ N/C
b.  3600 N/C
c.  900 N/C
d.  zero
e.  $3.6 \times 10^5$ N/C

**1920    19-4   Capacitance,  Conceptual,  b**

Two large metallic plates are parallel to each other and charged.  The distance between the
plates is $d$ metres.  The potential difference between the plates is $V$ volts.  The magnitude of
the electric field $E$ in the region between the plates and away from the edges is given by

a.  $d/V$
b.  $V/d$
c.  $dV$
d.  $V/d^2$
e.  None of these is correct.

**1921    19-4   Capacitance,  Factual,  a**

When a piece of wax paper is inserted between the plates of a capacitor, the capacitance

a.  increases.
b.  decreases.
c.  does not change.
d.  could increase, decrease, or not change depending on the dielectric constant of the wax
    paper.
e.  None of these is correct.

**1922    19-4   Capacitance,  Conceptual,  c**

As the voltage in the circuit is increased (but not to the breakdown voltage), the capacitance

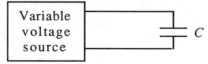

a.  increases.
b.  decreases.
c.  does not change.
d.  will increase, decrease, or not change depending on the charge on the plates of the
    capacitor.
e.  None of these is correct.

1923    **19-4   Capacitance,   Conceptual,   e**

A capacitor is connected to a battery as shown.  When a dielectric is inserted between the plates of the capacitor,

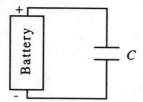

a.   only the capacitance changes.
b.   only the voltage across the capacitor changes.
c.   only the charge on the capacitor changes.
d.   both the capacitance and the voltage change.
e.   both the capacitance and the charge change.

1924    **19-4   Capacitance,   Conceptual,   b**

If the area of the plates of a parallel-plate capacitor is doubled, the capacitance is

a.   not changed.
b.   doubled.
c.   halved.
d.   increased by a factor of 4.
e.   decreased by 1/4.

1925    **19-4   Capacitance,   Numerical,   b**

A 0.080-$\mu$F capacitor is charged to a potential of 500 V.  How much charge is accumulated on each plate of the capacitor?

a.   $4.0 \times 10^{-4}$ C
b.   $4.0 \times 10^{-5}$ C
c.   $4.0 \times 10^{-10}$ C
d.   $1.6 \times 10^{-10}$ C
e.   $1.6 \times 10^{-7}$ C

1926    **19-4   Capacitance,   Numerical,   c**

It is desired to store $10^{10}$ excess electrons on the negative plate of a capacitor at 9.00 V. How large a capacitance must be used?

a.   0.014 $\mu$F
b.   0.18 $\mu$F
c.   180 pF
d.   14 pF
e.   5.6 pF

**1927    19-4    Capacitance,    Numerical,    c**

A capacitor is made with two strips of metal foil, 2.5 cm wide by 50 cm long, with a 0.70-μm thick strip of paper (dielectric constant $K = 3.7$) sandwiched between them. The capacitor is rolled up to save space. What is the capacitance of this device? (The permittivity of free space $\epsilon_0 = 8.85 \times 10^{-12}$ F/m.)

a.  0.043 μF
b.  0.16 μF
c.  0.58 μF
d.  2.0 μF
e.  7.3 μF

**1928    19-5    Combinations of Capacitors,    Numerical,    b**

Three capacitors are connected together as shown in the diagram. What is the effective capacitance of this combination when $C_1 = 5.0$ μF, $C_2 = 4.0$ μF, and $C_3 = 3.0$ μF?

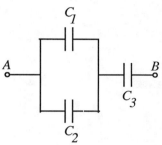

a.  0.44 μF
b.  2.25 μF
c.  3.45 μF
d.  5.2 μF
e.  12 μF

**1929    19-5    Combinations of Capacitors,    Numerical,    c**

Three capacitors are connected together as in the diagram. $C_1 = C_3 = 2.5$ μF, $C_2 = 5.0$ μF. A potential difference $V = 9.0$ V is maintained between the terminals $A$ and $B$. What is the magnitude of the charge on capacitor $C_3$?

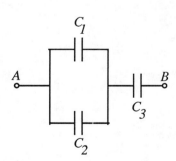

a.  4.2 μC
b.  4.8 μC
c.  17 μC
d.  37 μC
e.  90 μC

**1930    19-5   Combinations of Capacitors,   Numerical,   a**

For a set of capacitors in parallel, the charge on each capacitor is

a.   directly proportional to its capacitance.
b.   inversely proportional to its capacitance.
c.   independent of its capacitance.
d.   the same.
e.   None of these is correct.

**1931    19-5   Combinations of Capacitors,   Numerical,   b**

Two capacitors, $C_1 = 15$ pF and $C_2 = 30$ pF, are connected in series to a 1.5-V battery. What is the potential difference across capacitor $C_1$?

a.   0.50 V
b.   1.0 V
c.   1.5 V
d.   0.33 V
e.   0.67 V

**1932    19-5   Combinations of Capacitors,   Conceptual,   b**

If $C_1 < C_2 < C_3 < C_4$, the equivalent capacitance for this combination of capacitors

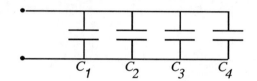

a.   is less than $C_1$.
b.   is more than $C_4$.
c.   is between $C_2$ and $C_3$.
d.   could be any value depending on the values of the four capacitances.
e.   could be any value depending on the applied voltage.

**1933    19-5   Combinations of Capacitors,   Conceptual,   a**

If $C_1 < C_2 < C_3 < C_4$, the equivalent capacitance for this combination of capacitors

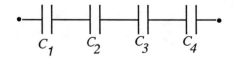

a.   is less than $C_1$.
b.   is more than $C_4$.
c.   is between $C_2$ and $C_3$.
d.   could be any value depending on the values of the four capacitances.
e.   could be any value depending on the applied voltage.

**1934    19-6   Electrical Energy Storage,   Numerical,   a**

A 30-pF capacitor is attached to a 1.5-V battery.  How much energy is stored in the capacitor?

    a.   $3.4 \times 10^{-11}$ J
    b.   $4.5 \times 10^{-11}$ J
    c.   $6.7 \times 10^{-11}$ J
    d.   $3.4 \times 10^{-8}$ J
    e.   $4.5 \times 10^{-8}$ J

**1935    19-6   Electrical Energy Storage,   Numerical,   b**

A 4.0-$\mu$F capacitor is charged to 150 V.  How much additional energy must be added to charge it to 300 V?

    a.   $6.0 \times 10^{-4}$ J
    b.   $1.4 \times 10^{-1}$ J
    c.   $1.80 \times 10^{-5}$ J
    d.   $0.30 \times 10^{-3}$ J
    e.   $2.8 \times 10^{-1}$ J

**1936    19-6   Electrical Energy Storage,   Numerical,   d**

Three capacitors are connected together as shown in the diagram.  If the potential difference between $A$ and $B$ is 24.5 V, what is the total energy stored in this system of capacitors if  $C_1 = 5.0\ \mu$F, $C_2 = 4.0\ \mu$F, and $C_3 = 3.0\ \mu$F?

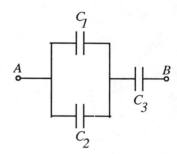

    a.   $1.7 \times 10^{-4}$ J
    b.   $1.5 \times 10^{-4}$ J
    c.   $2.2 \times 10^{-5}$ J
    d.   $6.8 \times 10^{-4}$ J
    e.   $4.0 \times 10^{-4}$ J

**1937    19-6   Electrical Energy Storage,   Conceptual,   b**

If the potential difference of a capacitor is reduced by one-half, the energy stored in that capacitor is

    a.   reduced to one-half.
    b.   reduced to one-quarter.
    c.   increased by a factor of 2.
    d.   increased by a factor of 4.
    e.   not changed.

**1938    19-6   Electrical Energy Storage,   Conceptual,   d**

The energy stored in a capacitor is directly proportional to

a.   the voltage across the capacitor.
b.   the charge on the capacitor.
c.   the reciprocal of the charge on the capacitor.
d.   the square of the voltage across the capacitor.
e.   None of these is correct.

CHAPTER 20    Electric Current and Circuits

**2001    20-1  Current and Motion of Charges,  Numerical,  d**

If $4.7 \times 10^{16}$ electrons pass a particular point in a wire every second, what is the current in the wire?

a.  $4.7 \times 10^{16}$ A
b.  7.5 A
c.  2.9 A
d.  7.5 mA
e.  0.29 A

**2002    20-2  Ohm's Law and Resistance,  Conceptual,  c**

The same potential difference is applied across two wires. Wire $A$ carries twice the current of wire $B$. If the resistance of wire $B$ is $R$, what is the resistance of wire $A$?

a.  $R$
b.  $2R$
c.  $R/2$
d.  $4R$
e.  $R/4$

**2003    20-2  Ohm's Law and Resistance,  Conceptual,  e**

Two wires of the same length and material have different diameters. Wire $A$ has twice the diameter of wire $B$. If the resistance of wire $B$ is $R$, then what is the resistance of wire $A$?

a.  $R$
b.  $2R$
c.  $R/2$
d.  $4R$
e.  $R/4$

**2004    20-2  Ohm's Law and Resistance,  Conceptual,  b**

Two wires of the same material and cross-sectional area have different lengths. Wire $A$ is twice as long as wire $B$. If the resistance of wire $B$ is $R$, then what is the resistance of wire $A$?

a.  $R$
b.  $2R$
c.  $R/2$
d.  $4R$
e.  $R/4$

**2005** **20-2 Ohm's Law and Resistance, Conceptual, c**

A metal bar is to be used as a resistor. Its dimensions are 2 by 4 by 10 units. To get the smallest resistance from this bar, one should attach leads to the opposite sides that have the dimensions of

a. 2 by 4 units.
b. 2 by 10 units.
c. 4 by 10 units.
d. All connections will give the same resistance.
e. None of these is correct.

**2006** **20-2 Ohm's Law and Resistance, Numerical, e**

Two copper wires have the same volume, but wire 2 is 20% longer than wire 1. The ratio of the resistances of the two wires $R_2/R_1$ is

a. 1.2
b. 0.83
c. 1.1
d. 0.91
e. 1.4

**2007** **20-2 Ohm's Law and Resistance, Numerical, a**

Two copper wires have the same volume, but wire 2 is 10% longer than wire 1. The ratio of the resistances of the two wires $R_2/R_1$ is

a. 1.2
b. 1.1
c. 0.82
d. 0.91
e. 1.0

**2008** **20-2 Ohm's Law and Resistance, Numerical, b**

A potential difference of 120 V produces a current of 8.0 A in the heating element of a toaster. What is the resistance of this heating element?

a. $6.7 \times 10^{-2} \ \Omega$
b. $15 \ \Omega$
c. $960 \ \Omega$
d. $67 \ \Omega$
e. $30 \ \Omega$

**2009** **20-2 Ohm's Law and Resistance, Numerical, c**

A 10-gauge copper wire (diameter = 2.588 mm, $\rho = 1.7 \times 10^{-8} \ \Omega \cdot m$) has a total resistance of 0.32 $\Omega$. How long is the wire?

a. $4.0 \times 10^2$ m
b. $1.6 \times 10^3$ m
c. 99 m
d. 31 m
e. 65 m

**2010**  **20-3  Energy in Electric Circuits,  Numerical,  b**

An immersion heater of negligible mass draws a current of 7.5 A from a source with a potential difference of 120 V.  The heater is in 0.950 m$^3$ of water.  The initial temperature of the water is 12.5°C.  Find the time it takes to increase the temperature of the water to 27.5 Neglect any heat loss.  One calorie is equivalent to 4.18 J.

a.  4.7 x 10$^4$ s
b.  6.6 x 10$^4$ s
c.  1.1 x 10$^4$ s
d.  1.6 x 10$^4$ s
e.  None of these is correct.

**2011**  **20-3  Energy in Electric Circuits,  Numerical,  d**

If electrical energy costs 10 cents per kilowatt-hour, how many cents does it cost to keep a 660-watt toaster in steady operation for 30 minutes at a voltage of 110 volts?

a.  15 cents
b.  12 cents
c.  6.9 cents
d.  3.3 cents
e.  1.7 cents

**2012**  **20-3  Energy In Electric Circuits,  Numerical,  a**

An electric motor drives a pump that lifts water from a well that is 11.9 m deep and then delivers the water through a hose at a rate of 180 L/min and a speed of 21.0 m/s.  Assuming 100% efficiency, the current drawn by the motor from a 220-volt source is

a.  4.6 A
b.  7.2 A
c.  6.0 A
d.  1.0 x 10$^3$ A
e.  None of these is correct.

**2013**  **20-3  Energy in Electric Circuits,  Numerical,  b**

A motor running from a 220-V line is lifting a mass of 35 kg at a constant speed of 6.0 m/s.  Assuming 100% efficiency, the current required is

a.  0.27 A
b.  9.4 A
c.  7.7 A
d.  3.34 A
e.  None of these is correct.

**2014    20-3   Energy in Electric Circuits,   Numerical,   c**

A heating element made of nichrome wire (resistivity at 20°C, $\rho = 1.00$ x $10^{-6}$ Ω·m, temperature coefficient of resistivity, $\propto = 0.400$ x $10^{-3}$ K$^{-1}$) is connected to a 120-V source. It dissipates 960 watts of power when it is just turned on and its temperature is 20°C. What is the power dissipated when the temperature has risen to 300°C?

a.   $1.07$ x $10^3$ W
b.   $9.60$ x $10^2$ W
c.   $8.63$ x $10^2$ W
d.   $8.57$ x $10^2$ W
e.   $1.08$ x $10^3$ W

**2015    20-3   Energy in Electric Circuits,   Conceptual,   d**

A resistor carries a current $I$. The power dissipated in the resistor is $P$. What is the power dissipated if the same resistor carries current $3I$?

a.   $P$
b.   $3P$
c.   $P/3$
d.   $9P$
e.   $P/9$

**2016    20-3   Energy in Electric Circuits,   Conceptual,   d**

Two resistors have the same power dissipated in them. The potential drop across resistor $A$ is twice that across resistor $B$. If the resistance of resistor $B$ is $R$, what is the resistance of $A$?

a.   $R$
b.   $2R$
c.   $R/2$
d.   $4R$
e.   $R/4$

**2017    20-4   Combinations of Resistors,   Conceptual,   b**

Two resistors are connected in parallel across a potential difference. The resistance of resistor $A$ is twice that of resistor $B$. If the current carried by resistor $A$ is $I$, then what is the current carried by $B$?

a.   $I$
b.   $2I$
c.   $I/2$
d.   $4I$
e.   $I/4$

**2018    20-4    Combinations of Resistors,    Conceptual,    a**

Two resistors are connected in series across a potential difference. Resistor $A$ has twice the resistance of resistor $B$. If the current carried by resistor $A$ is $I$, then what is the current carried by $B$?

a. $I$
b. $2I$
c. $I/2$
d. $4I$
e. $I/4$

**2019    20-4    Combinations of Resistors,    Numerical,    b**

In the circuit shown, the power dissipated in the 18-$\Omega$ resistor is

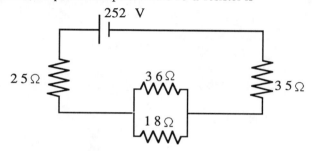

a.  150 W.
b.  98 W.
c.  33 W.
d.  160 W.
e.  None of these is correct.

**2020    20-4    Combinations of Resistors,    Numerical,    d**

Two resistors $R_1$ and $R_2$ are connected in parallel, and this combination is connected in series with a third resistor $R_3$. If $R_1 = 5.0\ \Omega$, $R_2 = 2.0\ \Omega$, $R_3 = 6.0\ \Omega$, what is the equivalent resistance of this combination?

a.  0.31 $\Omega$
b.  3.2 $\Omega$
c.  6.7 $\Omega$
d.  7.4 $\Omega$
e.  13 $\Omega$

**2021    20-4    Combinations of Resistors,    Numerical,    a**

In the accompanying circuit, the current $I$ through the battery is

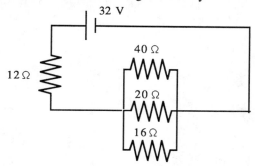

a.  1.7 A
b.  4.4 A
c.  0.36 A
d.  0.60 A
e.  None of these is correct.

**2022    20-4    Combinations of Resistors,    Numerical,    c**

In the circuit shown, the current through the 5-$\Omega$ resistor is

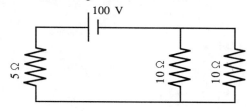

a.  4 A
b.  20 A
c.  10 A
d.  40 A
e.  None of these is correct.

**2023    20-4    Combinations of Resistors,    Numerical,    a**

When two resistors are connected in series, the equivalent resistance is $R_s = 10$ $\Omega$.  When they are connected in parallel, the equivalent resistance is $R_p = 2.4$ $\Omega$.  What are the values of the two resistances?

a.  4.0 $\Omega$ and 6.0 $\Omega$
b.  Both are 5.0 $\Omega$
c.  1.0 $\Omega$  and 1.4 $\Omega$
d.  Both are 1.2 $\Omega$
e.  2.5 $\Omega$  and 7.5 $\Omega$

**2024    20-5   Kirchhoff's Rules,   Numerical,   b**

In the illustrated circuit, two batteries, one
with a potential difference of 10 V and the
other with a potential difference of 20 V,
are connected in series across a resistance
of 90 Ω.  The current in the circuit is

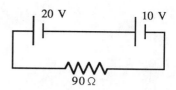

a.   3.0 A
b.   0.33 A
c.   9.0 A
d.   30 A
e.   4.5 A

**2025    20-5   Kirchhoff's Rules,   Numerical,   d**

The current through the battery in the figure
is

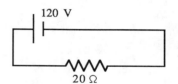

a.   10.0 A
b.   13.3 A
c.   0.67 A
d.   6.0 A
e.   None of these is correct.

**2026    20-5   Kirchhoff's Rules,   Numerical,   c**

In the adjoining circuit, the
current is

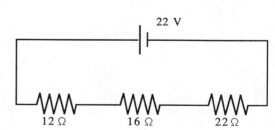

a.   1.0 A
b.   0.65 A
c.   0.44 A
d.   0.22 A
e.   None of these is correct.

**2027    20-5   Kirchhoff's Rules,   Numerical,   c**

In the circuit shown, the current *I* through the battery is

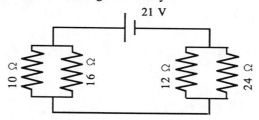

a.   0.013 A
b.   300 A
c    1.5 A
d.   0.67 A
e.   None of these is correct.

**2028    20-5   Kirchhoff's Rules,   Numerical,   c**

In the circuit shown, the power dissipated in the 21-Ω resistor is

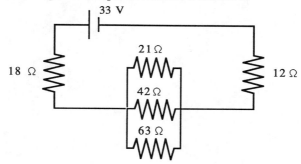

a.   14 W
b.   68 W
c.   4.0 W
d.   13 W
e.   None of these is correct.

**2029    20-5   Kirchhoff's Rules,   Numerical,   e**

When two identical resistors are connected in series across a battery, the total power dissipated by them is 20 W.  If these resistors are connected in parallel across the same battery, the total power dissipated will be

a.   5 W
b.   10 W
c.   20 W
d.   40 W
e.   80 W

**2030    20-5   Kirchhoff's Rules,   Numerical,   a**

Resistors of 2 Ω, 3 Ω, and 6 Ω are connected in parallel across a battery.  The current through the 6-Ω resistor is 3 A.  Find the currents in the other two resistors.

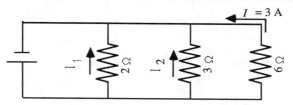

a.   $I_1 = 9$ A; $I_2 = 6$ A
b.   $I_1 = 6$ A; $I_2 = 9$ A
c.   $I_1 = 1$ A; $I_2 = 1.5$ A
d.   The answer cannot be obtained without knowing the emf of the battery.
e.   None of these is correct.

**2031    20-5   Kirchhoff's Rules,   Numerical,   c**

Calculate the current through the circuit shown in the figure.  The positive direction of conventional current is shown by the arrow on the diagram.

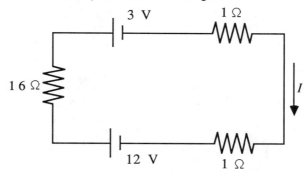

a.   +0.83 A
b.   -0.50 A
c.   +0.50 A
d.   +0.55 A
e.   None of these is correct.

**2032    20-5   Kirchhoff's Rules,   Factual,   c**

The conservation of energy in an electrical circuit is closely related to which of the following?

a.   Ohm's law
b.   Kirchhoff's junction rule
c.   Kirchhoff's loop rule
d.   Volta's rules
e.   Ampere's law

2033   **20-5   Kirchhoff's Rules,   Factual,   b**

The conservation of charge in an electrical circuit is closely related to which of the following?

a. Ohm's law
b. Kirchhoff's junction rule
c. Kirchhoff's loop rule
d. Volta's rules
e. Ampere's law

2034   **20-5   Kirchhoff's Rules,   Conceptual,   a**

Battery $A$ has a relatively high internal resistance, whereas battery $B$ has a low internal resistance. If both batteries provide the same current to some external circuitry, which of the following statements is likely to be true?

a. Battery $A$ is warmer to the touch than battery $B$.
b. Battery $B$ is warmer to the touch than battery $A$.
c. Battery $A$ is cooler to the touch than battery $B$.
d. Both batteries are equally warm to the touch.
e. The emf of each battery must be known in order to contrast the batteries' warmth to the touch.

2035   **20-5   Kirchhoff's Rules,   Conceptual,   b**

When a battery goes from "good" to "bad," which of the following is likely to be true?

a. The voltage is used up.
b. The internal resistance has increased.
c. The internal resistance has decreased.
d. The voltage is used up and the internal resistance has increased.
e. The voltage is used up and the internal resistance has decreased.

2036   **20-6   *RC* Circuits,   Conceptual,   e**

A battery is hooked to a series combination of a switch, a resistor, and an initially uncharged capacitor. The switch is closed at $t = 0$. Which of the following statements is true?

a. As the charge on the capacitor increases, the current increases.
b. As the charge on the capacitor increases, the voltage drop across the resistor increases.
c. As the charge on the capacitor increases, the current remains constant.
d. As the charge on the capacitor increases, the voltage drop across the capacitor decreases.
e. As the charge on the capacitor increases, the voltage drop across the resistor decreases.

2037   **20-6   *RC* Circuits,   Numerical,   d**

In a flash camera, a 1.2-$\mu$F capacitor is charged by a 1.5-V battery. When the camera flashes, this capacitor is discharged through a resistor with a time constant $\tau = 10$ ms. What must be the value of the resistance?

a. $8.0 \times 10^{-2}$ $\Omega$
b. $0.12$ $\Omega$
c. $12$ k$\Omega$
d. $8.3$ k$\Omega$
e. $3.1$ k$\Omega$

**2038    20-6 *RC* Circuits,   Numerical,   b**

A 6.0-μF capacitor, initially uncharged, is connected to a 10-kΩ resistor and a 9.0-V battery.  What is the initial current in this circuit?

a.  6.0 x 10$^{-2}$ A
b.  9.0 x 10$^{-4}$ A
c.  5.4 x 10$^{-5}$ A
d.  0.90 A
e.  6.0 x 10$^{-5}$ A

**2039    20-7   Ammeters, Voltmeters, and Ohmmeters,   Numerical,   a**

A galvanometer has an internal resistance of 200 Ω and requires a current of 5.0 mA for full-scale deflection.  What resistance should be connected in parallel with this galvanometer to make an ammeter that reads 10 A at full-scale deflection?

a.  0.10 Ω
b.  4.0 x 10$^5$ Ω
c.  400 Ω
d.  0.20 Ω
e.  2.0 Ω

**2040    20-7   Ammeters, Voltmeters, and Ohmmeters,   Numerical,   b**

A galvanometer has an internal resistance 200 Ω and requires a current of 5.0 mA for full-scale deflection.  What resistance should be connected in series with this galvanometer to make a voltmeter that reads 25 V at full-scale deflection?

a.  2.4 kΩ
b.  4.8 kΩ
c.  5.0 kΩ
d.  5.2 kΩ
e.  9.6 kΩ

**2041    20-7   Ammeters, Voltmeters and Ohmmeters,   Factual,   b**

Given a sensitive galvanometer *G* and a collection of resistances of various sizes, a voltmeter can be constructed by

a.  connecting a small resistance in series with *G*.
b.  connecting a large resistance in series with *G*.
c.  connecting a small resistance in parallel with *G*.
d.  connecting a large resistance in parallel with *G*.
e.  It is not possible to make a voltmeter with the given equipment.

**2042    20-7   Ammeters, Voltmeters, and Ohmmeters,   Conceptual,   c**

Which of the following statements is true concerning an ideal ammeter and an ideal voltmeter?

a.  Both have infinite resistance.
b.  Both have zero resistance.
c.  The ammeter has zero resistance, whereas the voltmeter has infinite resistance.
d.  The ammeter has infinite resistance, whereas the has voltmeter zero resistance.
e.  Both have equal, finite resistances.

**2043    20-7   Ammeters, Voltmeters, and Ohmmeters,   Conceptual,   d**

The current through and the voltage drop across a resistor are to be measured.  How should the ammeter and voltmeter be connected to the resistor?

a.   Both meters should be connected in parallel.
b.   Both meters should be connected in series.
c.   The ammeter should be connected in parallel, and the voltmeter in series.
d.   The ammeter should be connected in series, and the voltmeter in parallel.
e.   It does not matter how the meters are connected to the resistor.

**2044    20-7   Ammeters, Voltmeters, and Ohmmeters,   Numerical,   d**

A student wishes to measure a resistance of a resistor by passing a current $I$ through it, measuring this current with an ammeter connected in series with the resistor, measuring the voltage $V$ across the resistor only with a voltmeter, and then dividing the voltage by the current to get the resistance.  If the voltmeter has an internal resistance of 5.0 k$\Omega$, what will be the percent error in measuring a 1.0-k$\Omega$ resistance?

a.   0.17%
b.   1.7%
c.   2.0%
d.   17%
e.   20%

CHAPTER 21    The Magnetic Field

**2101    21-1   Definition of the Magnetic Field,   Numerical,   b**

A charged particle is moving with a velocity of $3.5 \times 10^6$ m/s horizontally westward in a region where there is a magnetic field directed vertically downwards of magnitude $5.6 \times 10^{-5}$ T.  The particle experiences a force of $7.8 \times 10^{-16}$ N northwards.  What is the charge on the particle?

a.   $+4.0 \times 10^{-18}$ C
b.   $-4.0 \times 10^{-18}$ C
c.   $+4.9 \times 10^{-5}$ C
d.   $-1.2 \times 10^{-14}$ C
e.   $+1.4 \times 10^{-11}$ C

**2102    21-1   Definition of the Magnetic Field,   Conceptual,   c**

A proton with a charge $+e$ is moving with a speed $v$ at 50° to the direction of a magnetic field **B**.  The component of the resulting force on the proton in the direction of **B** is

a.   $evB \sin 50° \cos 50°$
b.   $evB \cos 50°$
c.   zero
d.   $evB \sin 50°$
e.   None of these is correct.

**2103    21-1   Definition of the Magnetic Field,   Numerical,   d**

An electron has an instantaneous velocity of $2.5 \times 10^5$ m/s in the positive $x$ direction  in a region where there is a uniform magnetic field **B** of 0.450 T directed at 35° to the $x$ axis in the horizontal plane.  What is the magnitude and direction of the force on the electron?

a.   $1.8 \times 10^{-14}$ N up
b.   $1.5 \times 10^{-14}$ N down
c.   $1.5 \times 10^{-14}$ N up
d.   $1.0 \times 10^{-14}$ N down
e.   $1.0 \times 10^{-14}$ N up

**2104    21-1   Definition of the Magnetic Field,   Numerical,   b**

A wire 30 cm long with an east-west orientation carries a current of 3.0 A eastward. There is a uniform magnetic field perpendicular to this wire. If the force on the wire is 0.18 N upward, what is the direction and magnitude of the magnetic field?

a.  0.20 T up
b.  0.20 T north
c.  0.20 T south
d.  2.0 x  $10^{-3}$ T north
e.  2.0 x $10^{-3}$ T up

**2105    21-1   Definition of the Magnetic Field,   Conceptual,   a**

If the magnetic field vector is directed toward the north and a positively charged particle is moving toward the east, what is the direction of the magnetic force on the particle?

a.  Up
b.  West
c.  South
d.  Down
e.  East

**2106    21-1   Definition of the Magnetic Field,   Conceptual,   e**

A positively charged particle is moving northward in a magnetic field.  The magnetic force on the particle is toward the northeast.  What is the direction of the magnetic field?

a.  Up
b.  West
c.  South
d.  Down
e.  This situation cannot exist.

**2107    21-1   Definition of the Magnetic Field,   Factual,   a**

The SI unit of magnetic field is the tesla.  This is equivalent to

a.  $\dfrac{N \cdot s}{C \cdot m}$
b.  $\dfrac{N \cdot C}{s \cdot m}$
c.  $\dfrac{N \cdot m}{s^2}$
d.  $\dfrac{C}{A \cdot s}$
e.  None of these is correct.

**2108    21-2   Torques on Magnets and Current Loops,   Conceptual,   e**

A compass needle, which is a magnetic dipole, is in a magnetic field **B** with its north-seeking pole pointing in the positive direction of **B**.  The net force on the compass needle is

a.  in the negative direction of **B**.
b.  in the positive direction of **B**.
c.  at right angles to the plane of **B** and the needle.
d.  at right angles to **B**.
e.  None of these is correct

**2109    21-2  Torques on Magnets and Current Loops,  Numerical,  a**

A small permanent magnet is placed in a uniform magnetic field of magnitude 0.35 T.  If the maximum torque experienced by the magnet is 0.50 N·m, what is the magnitude of the magnetic moment of the magnet?

a.  1.4 A·m$^2$
b.  0.70 A·m$^2$
c.  0.18 A·m$^2$
d.  2.8 A·m$^2$
e.  0.35 A·m$^2$

**2110    21-2  Torques on Magnets and Current Loops,  Factual,  c**

When a compass needle is in stable equilibrium in a magnetic field **B**,

a.  the needle axis is at 45° to the **B** field.
b.  the south pole points in the positive direction of **B**.
c.  the north pole points in the positive direction of **B**.
d.  the needle axis is perpendicular to **B**.
e.  None of these is correct.

**2111    21-2  Torques on Magnets and Current Loops,  Conceptual,  a**

A compass needle, which is a magnetic dipole, is in a magnetic field **B** with its south pole pointing in the positive direction of **B**.  The net force on the compass needle is

a.  zero.
b.  in the same direction as **B**.
c.  at a right angle to **B**.
d.  at right angles to the plane of **B** and the needle.
e.  in the opposite direction of **B**.

**2112    21-2  Torques on Magnets and Current Loops,  Numerical,  c**

A circular, 20-turn coil of radius 5.0 cm is oriented such that its axis makes a 30° angle with a uniform magnetic field of 0.15 T.  What is the torque on the coil when it carries a current of 2.5 A?

a.  1.5 x 10$^{-3}$ N·m
b.  9.4 x 10$^{-3}$ N·m
c.  2.9 x 10$^{-2}$ N·m
d.  5.1 x 10$^{-2}$ N·m
e.  0.59 N·m

**2113    21-3  Motion of a Point Charge in a Magnetic Field,  Numerical,  b**

An alpha particle, the mass of which is 4(1.66 x 10$^{-27}$ kg), has a charge of +2$e$ and is moving at right angles to a magnetic field **B** = 0.27 T with a speed $v$ = 6.15 x 10$^5$ m/s.  The force acting on this charged particle is

a.  zero
b.  5.3 x 10$^{-14}$ N
c.  3.3 x 10$^5$ N
d.  2.7 x 10$^{-14}$ N
e.  None of these is correct.

**2114    21-3  Motion of a Point Charge in a Magnetic Field,  Numerical,  b**

An alpha particle with a charge = $2e$ and a mass = $4(1.66 \times 10^{-27}$ kg) is moving at right angles to a uniform  magnetic field of 1.20 T.  The radius of curvature of the track of the particle is 0.20 m.  The momentum of the alpha particle is

a.  The question cannot be worked because the speed of the particle is not given.
b.  7.7 x $10^{-20}$ kg·m/s
c.  3.1 x $10^{-19}$ kg·m/s
d.  0.77 kg·m/s
e.  None of these is correct.


**2115    21-3  Motion of a Point Charge in a Magnetic Field,  Numerical,  b**

The apparatus shown in the figure consists of a pair of parallel plates (shown on edge) and a large magnet (not shown).  The field of the magnet is uniform, perpendicular to the electric field between the plates, and directed into the plane of the paper.  The magnitude of **B** is 0.40 T.  Charged particles with speeds of 5.0 x $10^5$ m/s enter this region through the slit at the left and emerge through the exit slit at the right.  What magnitude and direction must the **E** field have so that positively charged particles entering from the left will traverse to the exit slit undeviated?

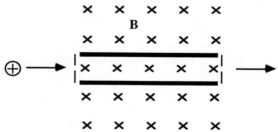

a.  2.0 x $10^5$ V/m up
b.  2.0 x $10^5$ V/m down
c.  1.2 x $10^6$ V/m down
d.  1.2 x $10^6$ V/m up
e.  None of these is correct.


**2116    21-3  Motion of a Point Charge in a Magnetic Field,  Conceptual,  a**

A $^7$Li nucleus with a charge = $+3e$ and a mass = $7(1.66 \times 10^{-27}$ kg) and a proton with charge = $+e$ and a mass = $1(1.66 \times 10^{-27}$ kg) are both moving in a plane perpendicular to a magnetic field **B**.  The two particles have the same momentum.  The ratio of the radius of curvature of the path of the proton $R_p$ to that of the $^7$Li nucleus, $R_{Li}$ is

a.  $R_p/R_{Li} = 3$
b.  $R_p/R_{Li} = 1/3$
c.  $R_p/R_{Li} = 1/7$
d.  $R_p/R_{Li} = 3/7$
e.  None of these is correct.

**2117    21-3  Motion of a Point Charge in a Magnetic Field,  Conceptual,  d**

An electron is traveling horizontally east in the magnetic field of the earth near the equator. The direction of the force on the electron is

a.   zero.
b.   north.
c.   south.
d.   upward.
e.   downward.

**2118    21-3  Motion of a Point Charge in a Magnetic Field,  Conceptual,  c**

A doubly-ionized oxygen atom $^{16}O^{++}$ is moving in the same uniform magnetic field as an alpha particle.  The  velocities of both particles are at right angles to the magnetic field.  The paths of the particles have the same radius of curvature.  The ratio of the energy of the alpha particle to that of the $^{16}O^{++}$ ion is

a.   $E_\alpha/E_o = 1/1$
b.   $E_\alpha/E_o = 1/4$
c.   $E_\alpha/E_o = 1/16$
d.   $E_\alpha/E_o = 4/1$
e.   None of these is correct.

**2119    21-3  Motion of a Point Charge in a Magnetic Field,  Numerical,  d**

An alpha particle of charge $+2e$ and mass $4(1.66 \times 10^{-27}$ kg), and an $^{16}O$ nucleus of charge $+8e$ and mass $16(1.66 \times 10^{-27}$ kg) have been accelerated from rest through the same electrical potential.  They are then injected into a uniform magnetic field **B**, where both move at right angles to the field.  The ratio of the radius of the path of the alpha particle to the radius of the path  of the nucleus $^{16}O$ is

a.   $r_\alpha/r_O = 1/1$
b.   $r_\alpha/r_O = 1/4$
c.   $r_\alpha/r_O = 1/8$
d   $r_\alpha/r_O = 1/2$
e.   None of these is correct.

**2120    21-3 Motion of a Point Charge in a Magnetic Field,  Numerical,  a**

An electron is accelerated from rest through a potential difference of 475 V.  After the acceleration, the electron is injected into a uniform magnetic field of $1.27 \times 10^{-3}$ T.  The velocity of the electron and the magnetic field lines are perpendicular to one another.  The electron remains in the magnetic field for $5.00 \times 10^{-9}$ s.  The angle between the initial electron velocity and the final electron velocity is

a.   1.1 radians.
b.   $5.8 \times 10^{-2}$ radians.
c.   $8.68 \times 10^{-2}$ radians.
d.   $6.5 \times 10^{-2}$ radians.
e.   None of these is correct.

**2121    21-3  Motion of a Point Charge in a Magnetic Field,  Numerical,  e**

An electron passes through a region where there is an electric field $E = 4.0 \times 10^5$ V/m and a magnetic field $B = 0.090$ T. The directions of the electric field, the magnetic field, and the electron velocity are mutually perpendicular.  If the electron is NOT deflected from its straight-line path through these fields, its velocity  must be

a.   $3.6 \times 10^4$ m/s
b.   $5.0 \times 10^5$ m/s
c.   $2.2 \times 10^{-7}$ m/s
d.   $1.2 \times 10^4$ m/s
e.   $4.4 \times 10^6$ m/s


**2122    21-3  Motion of a Point Charge in a Magnetic Field,  Conceptual,  c**

An electron moving with velocity $v$ to the right enters a region of uniform magnetic field that points out of the paper.  After the electron enters this region, it will be

a.   deflected out of the plane of the paper.
b.   deflected into the plane of the paper.
c.   deflected upward.
d.   deflected downward.
e.   undeviated in its motion.


**2123    21-4  Sources of the Magnetic Field,  Conceptual,  c**

Two wires lie in the plane of the paper and carry equal currents in opposite directions as shown.  At a point midway between the wires, the magnetic field is

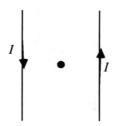

a.   zero.
b.   into the page.
c.   out of the page.
d.   toward the top or bottom of the page.
e.   toward one of the two wires.


**2124    21-4  Sources of the Magnetic Field,  Factual,  d**

What is the direction of the magnetic field around a wire carrying a current perpendicularly into this page?

a.   Parallel to and in the same direction as the current flow.
b.   Parallel to but oppositely directed to the current flow.
c.   Counterclockwise around the wire in the plane of the page.
d.   Clockwise around the wire in the plane of the page.
e.   None of these is correct.

**2125    21-4  Sources of the Magnetic Force,  Conceptual,  a**

The Biot-Savart law is similar to Coulomb's law in that both

a.  are inverse square laws.
b.  deal with forces on charged particles.
c.  deal with excess charges.
d.  include the permeability of free space.
e.  are not electrical in nature.

**2126    21-4  Sources of the Magnetic Force,  Conceptual,  c**

A wire carries an electrical current straight up.  What is the direction of the magnetic field due to the wire a distance of 2 m north of the wire?

a.  North
b.  East
c.  West
d.  South
e.  Upward

**2127    21-4  Sources of the Magnetic Force,  Conceptual,  a**

Two parallel wires carry currents $I_1$ and $I_2 = 2I_1$ in the same direction.  The forces on the wires are

a.  $F_1 = F_2$
b.  $F_1 = 2F_2$
c.  $2F_1 = F_2$
d.  $F_1 = 4F_2$
e.  $4F_1 = F_2$

**2128    21-4  Sources of the Magnetic Force,  Conceptual,  e**

Two current-carrying wires are perpendicular to each other.  The current in one flows vertically upward and the current in the other flows horizontally toward the east.  The horizontal wire is one metre south of the vertical wire.  What is the direction of the net magnetic force on the horizontal wire?

a.  North
b.  East
c.  West
d.  South
e.  There is no net magnetic force on the horizontal wire.

**2129    21-5  Ampere's Law,  Conceptual,  e**

Ampere's law is valid when

a.  there is a high degree of symmetry.
b.  there is no symmetry.
c.  the current is constant.
d.  the magnetic field is constant.
e.  It is valid in all of these situations.

**2130    21-6   Current Loops, Solenoids, and Magnets,  Numerical,  c**

What is the magnetic field at the center of a circular loop of diameter 15.0 cm carrying a current of 1.50 A?

a.  zero
b.  $6.28 \times 10^{-6}$ T
c.  $1.26 \times 10^{-5}$ T
d.  $2.51 \times 10^{-5}$ T
e.  $1.68 \times 10^{-4}$ T

**2131    21-6   Current Loops, Solenoids, and Magnets,  Conceptual,  a**

A solenoid carries a current $I$ as indicated.  An electron is injected with velocity v along the axis $AB$ of the solenoid.  When the electron is at $C$, it experiences a force that is

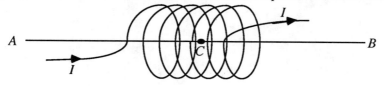

a.  zero.
b.  not zero and along $AB$.
c.  not zero and along $BA$.
d.  not zero and perpendicular to the page.
e.  None of these is correct

**2132    21-6   Current Loops, Solenoids, and Magnets,  Numerical,  a**

A 1000-turn solenoid is 50 cm long and has a radius of 2.0 cm.  It carries a current of 8.0 A.  What is the magnetic field inside the solenoid?

a.  $2.0 \times 10^{-2}$ T
b.  $3.2 \times 10^{-3}$ T
c.  $4.0 \times 10^{-4}$ T
d.  1.0 T
e.  $2.0 \times 10^{-4}$ T

**2133    21-7  Magnetism in Matter,  Conceptual,  a**

If the magnetic susceptibility is positive,

a.  paramagnetic effects must be greater than diamagnetic effects.
b.  diamagnetic effects must be greater than paramagnetic effects.
c.  diamagnetic effects must be greater than ferromagnetic effects.
d.  ferromagnetic effects must be greater than paramagnetic effects.
e.  paramagnetic effects must be greater than ferromagnetic effects.

CHAPTER 22   Magnetic Induction

**2201    22-1   Magnetic Flux and Faraday's Law,  Conceptual,  d**

A conducting loop lies in the plane of this page and carries a clockwise induced current. Which of the following statements could be true?

a.   A constant magnetic field is directed into the page.
b.   A constant magnetic field is directed out of the page.
c.   An increasing magnetic field is directed into the page.
d.   A decreasing magnetic field is directed into the page.
e.   A decreasing magnetic field is directed out of the page.

**2202    22-1   Magnetic Flux and Faraday's Law,  Conceptual,  b**

A conducting loop around a bar magnet begins to move away from the magnet.  Which of the following statements is true?

a.   The magnet and the loop repel one another.
b.   The magnet and the loop attract one another.
c.   The magnet is attracted, but the loop is repelled.
d.   The magnet is repelled, but the loop is attracted.
e.   The magnet and loop neither attract nor repel one another.

**2203    22-1   Magnetic Flux and Faraday's Law,  Numerical,  c**

A 3.0-cm by 5.0-cm rectangular coil has 100 turns.  Its axis makes an angle of 55° with a uniform magnetic field of 0.35 T.  What is the magnetic flux through this coil?

a.   $3.0 \times 10^{-4}$ Wb
b.   $4.3 \times 10^{-4}$ Wb
c.   $3.0 \times 10^{-2}$ Wb
d.   $4.3 \times 10^{-2}$ Wb
e.   $5.3 \times 10^{-2}$ Wb

**2204    22-1   Magnetic Flux and Faraday's Law,  Numerical,  d**

A 3.0-cm by 5.0-cm rectangular coil has 100 turns.  Its axis makes an angle of 55° with a uniform magnetic field of 0.35 T.  It is turned in 0.33 s until its plane is perpendicular to the magnetic field.  What is the (average) magnitude of the induced emf?

a.   0.16 V
b.   0.13 V
c.   0.091 V
d.   0.068 V
e.   0.029 V

**2205    22-1  Magnetic Flux and Faraday's Law,  Conceptual,  b**

Consider the edge of this paper to be a conducting loop of wire.  A bar magnet is thrown through the loop, south pole first.  As the magnet passes through the paper moving away from you, the current in the loop (as you look at it) will be

a.  zero.  No current will be induced.
b.  clockwise.
c.  counterclockwise.
d.  first clockwise, then counterclockwise.
e.  first counterclockwise, then clockwise.

**2206    22-1  Magnetic Flux and Faraday's Law,  Conceptual,  a**

A bar magnet is dropped through a loop of copper wire as shown in the diagram.  Recall that magnetic field lines point away from a  north pole and toward a south pole.  If the positive direction of the induced current $I$ in the loop is as shown by the arrow on the loop, the variation of $I$ with time as the bar magnet falls through the loop is illustrated qualitatively by which of the following graphs?  The time when the midpoint of the magnet passes through the loop is indicated by $C$.

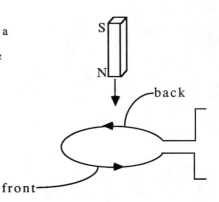

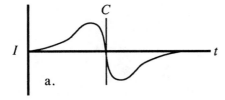

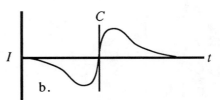

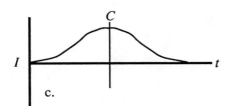

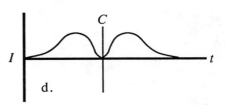

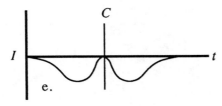

2207    **22-1  Magnetic Flux and Faraday's Law,  Factual,  b**

The emf $\mathcal{E}$ that is generated when a mechanical force moves a straight conducting wire through a uniform magnetic field **B** that sweeps out an area $A$ at right angles to **B** in a time $t$ is given by

a.  No emf is generated.
b.  $\mathcal{E} = (BA)/t$  V
c.  $\mathcal{E} = (BA)\, t$  V
d.  $\mathcal{E} = t/(BA)$  V
e.  None of these is correct.

2208    **22-1  Magnetic Flux and Faraday's Law,  Numerical,  e**

The plane of a circular, 200-turn coil of radius 5.25 cm is perpendicular to a uniform magnetic field produced by a large electromagnet.  This field is changed from 0.650 T to 0.150 T in 0.0100 s.  What is the magnitude of the emf induced in the coil?

a.  110 V
b.  170 V
c.  1.7 V
d.  26 V
e.  87 V

2209    **22-2  Motional emf,  Numerical,  c**

A 25-cm long conducting rod moves at a speed of 12 m/s in a plane perpendicular to a uniform magnetic field of magnitude 0.080 T.  What is the induced potential difference between the ends of the rod?

a.  24 V
b.  2.4 V
c.  0.24 V
d.  600 V
e.  6.0 V

2210    **22-2  Motional emf,  Conceptual,  b**

A conducting rod moving through a magnetic field creates a motional emf $\mathcal{E}$.  If the rod moves with twice the speed, what will be the motional emf?

a.  $\mathcal{E}$
b.  $2\mathcal{E}$
c.  $\mathcal{E}/2$
d.  $4\mathcal{E}$
e.  $\mathcal{E}/4$

**2211**    **22-2   Motional emf,   Numerical,   b**

In the diagram, $\mathbf{B} = 1.2$ T, $\mathbf{v} = 8.0$ m/s, $l = 30$ cm, and $R = 3.5\ \Omega$. What is the magnitude and direction of the current induced in the resistor $R$?

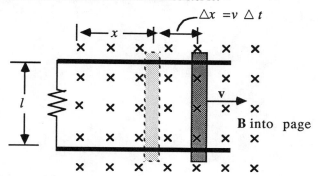

a.   0.82 A up
b.   0.82 A down
c.   1.2 A up
d.   1.2 A down
e.   2.9 A down

**2212**    **22-3   Eddy Currents,   Conceptual,   a**

Two identical bar magnets are dropped from equal heights.  Magnet $A$ is dropped from above bare earth, whereas magnet $B$ is dropped from above a metal plate.  Which magnet strikes first?

a.   Magnet $A$
b.   Magnet $B$
c.   Both strike at the same time.
d.   Whichever has the N pole toward the ground.
e.   Whichever has the S pole toward the ground.

**2213**    **22-4   Inductance,   Numerical,   e**

A coil with a self-inductance of 6.5 H carries a current that is changing at a rate of 50 A/s. What is the induced emf in the coil?

a.   0.13 V
b.   7.7 V
c.   32 V
d.   65 V
e.   320 V

**2214**    **22-4   Inductance,   Numerical,   e**

How many turns are needed in a solenoid of radius 10 cm and length 20 cm for a self-inductance of 6.0 H?

a.   30
b.   74
c.   500
d.   550
e.   5500

2215    **22-4  Inductance,  Factual,  c**

The self-inductance of a wire coil is a proportionality constant that relates

a.  electric field to current.
b.  electric flux to current.
c.  magnetic flux to current.
d.  magnetic field to current.
e.  voltage to current.

2216    **22-4  Inductance,  Conceptual,  d**

How would the self-inductance of a coil be changed if the same length of wire were wound onto a cylinder of twice the diameter and twice the length?

a.  It would be the same.
b.  It would be doubled.
c.  It would be quadrupled.
d.  It would be halved.
e.  It would be quartered.

2217    **22-4  Inductance,  Conceptual,  e**

How would the self-inductance of a coil be changed if half the length of wire were wound around the same cylinder?

a.  It would be the same.
b.  It would be doubled.
c.  It would be quadrupled.
d.  It would be halved.
e.  It would be quartered.

2218    **22-5  *LR*  Circuits and Magnetic Energy Density,  Conceptual,  c**

How would the energy stored in an inductor be changed if the current through the inductor were doubled?

a.  It would be the same.
b.  It would be doubled.
c.  It would be quadrupled.
d.  It would be halved.
e.  It would be quartered.

2219    **22-5  *LR*  Circuits and Magnetic Energy Density,  Numerical,  d**

What is the time constant of an *LR* circuit with a resistance $R = 25 \ \Omega$ and an inductance $L = 5.4$ mH?

a.  7.4 s
b.  4.6 s
c.  0.14 s
d.  $2.2 \times 10^{-4}$ s
e.  $1.5 \times 10^{-3}$ s

**2220**   **22-5** *LR* **Circuits and Magnetic Energy Density,  Numerical,  c**

How much energy is stored in the inductance in an *LR* circuit with a resistance $R = 25\ \Omega$ and an inductance $L = 5.4$ mH when a steady current has been achieved if the emf in the circuit is 9.0 V?

a.  Zero
b.  0.35 J
c.  $3.5 \times 10^{-4}$ J
d.  $7.0 \times 10^{-4}$ J
e.  $9.7 \times 10^{-4}$ J

**2221**   **22-6  Generators and Motors,  Conceptual,  d**

How would the maximum emf produced by a generator (a rotating coil) be changed if the period of rotation were doubled?

a.  It would be the same.
b.  It would be doubled.
c.  It would be quadrupled.
d.  It would be halved.
e.  It would be quartered.

**2222**   **22-6  Generators and Motors,  Conceptual,  e**

A motor sometimes burns out when its load is suddenly increased because the sudden decrease in its rotational frequency that results causes

a.  an increased back emf and an increased current flow.
b.  a decreased back emf and a decreased current flow.
c.  a decreased back emf and zero current flow.
d.  a increased back emf and a decreased current flow.
e.  a decreased back emf and an increased current flow.

**2223**   **22-6  Generators and Motors,  Numerical,  d**

A 200-turn coil rotates in a magnetic field of magnitude 0.25 T at a frequency of 60 Hz.  The area of the coil is 5.0 cm$^2$.  What is the maximum emf in the coil?

a.  1.5 V
b.  4.5 V
c.  9.0 V
d.  9.4 V
e.  24 V

CHAPTER 23    Alternating Current Circuits

2301    **23-1  Alternating Current in a Resistor,  Numerical,  b**

The rms value of house voltage in much of Europe is 220 V.  What is the maximum voltage?

a.  440 V
b.  310 V
c.  220 V
d.  160 V
e.  120 V

2302    **23-1  Alternating Current in a Resistor,  Numerical,  d**

A 1200-W heater and a 600-W toaster are plugged into the same 110-V electrical outlet.
What is the total rms current drawn by these two appliances?

a.  5.45 A
b.  10.9 A
c.  11.6 A
d.  16.4 A
e.  23.1 A

2303    **23-1  Alternating Current in a Resistor,  Numerical,  e**

An ac generator supplies 22 rms volts of electricity to a 30 $\Omega$ resistor at 50 Hz.  What is the
maximum current in the resistor?

a.  $3.3 \times 10^{-3}$ A
b.  $2.1 \times 10^{-2}$ A
c.  0.52 A
d.  0.73 A
e.  1.0 A

**2304   23-1  Alternating Current in a Resistor,  Conceptual,  b**

As the frequency in this simple ac circuit increases, the rms current through the resistor

a.  increases.
b.  does not change.
c.  may increase or decrease depending on the magnitude of the original frequency.
d.  may increase or decrease depending on the magnitude of the resistance.
e.  decreases.

**2305   23-1  Alternating Current in a Resistor,  Conceptual,  b**

As the frequency in this simple ac circuit increases, the rms power dissipated by the resistor

a.  increases.
b.  does not change.
c.  may increase or decrease depending on the magnitude of the original frequency.
d.  may increase or decrease depending on the magnitude of the resistance.
e.  decreases.

**2306   23-1  Alternating Current in a Resistor,  Conceptual,  a**

If the rms voltage in an ac circuit is doubled, the peak voltage is

a.  increased by a factor of 2.
b.  decreased by a factor of 2.
c.  increased by a factor of $\sqrt{2}$.
d.  decreased by a factor of $\sqrt{2}$.
e.  not changed.

**2307   23-2  Alternating Current in Inductors and Capacitors,  Numerical,  a**

At what frequency is the reactance of a 1.5-mH inductor equal to 5.0 $\Omega$?

a.  0.53 kHz
b.  0.13 kHz
c.  3.3 kHz
d.  21 Hz
e.  21 kHz

**2308   23-2  Alternating Current in Inductors and Capacitors,  Numerical,  b**

For an inductor,

a.  the voltage lags behind the current.
b.  the current lags behind the voltage.
c.  the current and the voltage are in phase.
d.  the current-voltage phase angle is greater than 90°.
e.  the current-voltage phase angle is less than 90°.

**2309    23-2   Alternating Current in Inductors and Capacitors,  Numerical,  b**

A 12-V rms ac power supply operating at 5.0 kHz is connected to a 20-$\mu$F capacitor.  What is the rms current in this circuit? (Neglect any resistance in this circuit.)

a.   1.2 A
b.   7.5 A
c.   19 A
d.   120 A
e.   11 A

**2310    23-2   Alternating Current in Inductors and Capacitors,  Numerical,  c**

At what frequency would the reactance of a 1.0-mH inductor be twice that of a 10-$\mu$F capacitor?

a.   10 kHz
b.   3.2 kHz
c.   2.2 kHz
d.   1.6 kHz
e.   1.1 kHz

**2311    23-2   Alternating Current in Inductors and Capacitors,  Conceptual,  b**

If the frequency in the diagramed circuit is doubled, the inductance of the inductor will

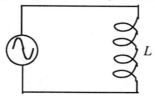

a.   increase by a factor of 2.
b.   not change.
c.   decrease by a factor of 2.
d.   increase by a factor of $2^2$.
e.   decrease by a factor of $2^2$.

**2312    23-2   Alternating Current in Inductors and Capacitors,  Conceptual,  a**

If the frequency in the diagramed circuit is doubled, the inductive reactance of the inductor will

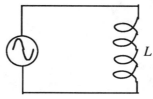

a.   increase by a factor of 2.
b.   not change.
c.   decrease by a factor of 2.
d.   increase by a factor of $2^2$.
e.   decrease by a factor of $2^2$.

2313    23-2  **Alternating Current in Inductors and Capacitors,  Conceptual,  c**

If the frequency in the diagramed circuit is doubled, the capacitative reactance of the circuit will

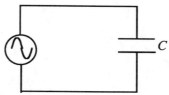

    a.   increase by a factor of 2.
    b.   not change.
    c.   decrease by a factor of 2.
    d.   increase by a factor of $2^2$.
    e.   decrease by a factor of $2^2$.

2314    23-3  **An *LRC* Circuit with a Generator,  Numerical,  c**

A series *LRC* circuit is driven by a 1.0-kHz oscillator.  The circuit parameters are $L = 5.0$ mH, $C = 4.0\ \mu F$, $R = 10\ \Omega$.  What is the impedance of this circuit?

    a.   8.4 $\Omega$
    b.   10 $\Omega$
    c.   13 $\Omega$
    d.   240 $\Omega$
    e.   81 $\Omega$

2315    23-3  **An *LRC* Circuit with a Generator,  Numerical,  a**

A series *LRC* circuit is driven by a 1.0-kHz oscillator.  The circuit parameters are $L = 5.0$ mH, $C = 4.0\ \mu F$, $R = 10\ \Omega$.  What is the resonance frequency of the circuit?

    a.   1.1 kHz
    b.   7.1 kHz
    c.   11 kHz
    d.   36 Hz
    e.   36 kHz

2316    23-3  **An *LRC* Circuit with a Generator,  Numerical,  d**

A series *LRC* circuit is driven by a 1.0-kHz oscillator.  The circuit parameters are $L = 5.0$ mH, $C = 4.0\ \mu F$, $R = 10\ \Omega$.  If the frequency of the oscillator is adjusted so that it is at the resonance frequency of the *LRC* circuit, and if it supplies 3.0 V rms, what is the rms current in the circuit?

    a.   0.23 A
    b.   0.36 A
    c.   0.21 A
    d.   0.30 A
    e.   0.42 A

**2317**    **23-3 An *LCR* Circuit with a Generator,  Conceptual,  a**

If the frequency in the diagramed circuit increases, the impedance

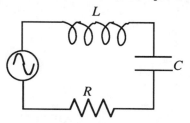

a.  may increase, decrease, or stay the same.
b.  will increase.
c.  will decrease.
d.  will not change.
e.  None of these is correct.

**2318**    **23-3 An *LCR* Circuit with a Generator,  Conceptual,  a**

The SI units of inductance times capacitance are

a.  seconds squared.
b.  hertz.
c.  volts.
d.  amperes.
e.  ohms.

**2319**    **23-4 The Transformer,  Conceptual,  c**

A transformer is used to change

a.  capacitance.
b.  frequency.
c.  voltage.
d.  power.
e.  None of these is correct.

**2320**    **23-4 The Transformer,  Numerical,  b**

A calculator typically uses 6.0 V for its operation.  If, instead of using batteries, you obtain this 6.0 V from a transformer plugged into 110-V house wiring, what must be the ratio of the primary to the secondary turns in the transformer?  (Ignore any changes in voltage due to rectification.)

a.  0.054
b.  18
c.  660
d.  0.066
e.  15

2321    **23-4  The Transformer,  Numerical,  b**

If the 8000-turn primary of a transformer is connected to a 50-kV transmission line and the secondary has 19 turns, what is the voltage output of this transformer?

a.  21 MV
b.  119 V
c.  110 V
d.  21 kV
e.  220 V

2322    **23-4  The Transformer,  Numerical,  d**

For the output current from the secondary coil of a transformer to be 10 times the input current to the primary coil, the ratio of the number of turns $N_2/N_1$ must be

a.  100
b.  10
c.  1
d.  0.1
e.  0.01

CHAPTER 24     # Light

**2401**    **24-1   Waves or Particles,   Factual,   d**

When a light ray strikes a boundary between two transparent media, part of it is transmitted. What is the bending of this transmitted ray called?

a.   Reflection
b.   Diffraction
c.   Interference
d.   Refraction
e.   Attenuation


**2402**    **24-1   Waves or Particles,   Conceptual,   c**

The diffraction of sound is more noticeable than the diffraction of light because

a.   ears are more sensitive to diffraction than eyes.
b.   sound frequencies are so much higher than light frequencies.
c.   sound wavelengths are so much longer than light wavelengths.
d.   sound bounces off objects better than light.
e.   sound is made of particles and light is a wave.


**2403**    **24-1   Waves or Particles,   Conceptual,   e**

Of electrons, light, and sound,  which has the longest wavelength and which has the shortest?

a.   Light has the longest; electrons have the shortest.
b.   Light has the longest; sound has the shortest.
c.   Electrons have the longest; light has the shortest.
d.   Electrons have the longest; sound has the shortest.
e.   Sound has the longest; electrons have the shortest.


**2404**    **24-2   Electromagnetic Waves,   Numerical,   b**

What is the frequency of 555-nm yellow light?

a.   16.7 kHz
b.   $5.4 \times 10^{14}$ Hz
c.   $5.4 \times 10^{15}$ Hz
d.   $1.7 \times 10^{7}$ Hz
e.   $5.4 \times 10^{17}$ Hz

2405    24-2   Electromagnetic  Waves,  Factual,  d

Which of the following statements about light in a vacuum is NOT correct?

a.  Light always travels with the same speed $c$, regardless of the motion of the source or
    observer.
b.  Light has wave-like properties.
c.  Light has particle-like properties.
d.  Light is an electromagnetic wave with its electric field vector pointing parallel to the
    direction of propagation.
e.  Light can be plane polarized.

2406    24-2   Electromagnetic  Waves,  Numerical,  b

Light that has a wavelength of 600 nm  has a frequency of

a.  $5.0 \times 10^{15}$ Hz
b.  $5.0 \times 10^{14}$ Hz
c.  $5.0 \times 10^{6}$ Hz
d.  $1.2 \times 10^{5}$ Hz
e.  None of these is correct.

2407    24-2   Electromagnetic  Waves,  Factual, c

Arrange the following types of electromagnetic radiation in order of increasing wavelength:
gamma rays, infrared light, ultraviolet light, visible light.

a.  Gamma rays are not electromagnetic radiation.
b.  Gamma rays, infrared, visible, ultraviolet
c.  Gamma rays, ultraviolet, visible, infrared
d.  Visible, ultraviolet, infrared, gamma rays
e.  Ultraviolet, visible, infrared, gamma rays

2408    24-2   Electromagnetic  Waves,  Factual,  c

A beam of light is propagating in the $x$ direction.  The electric field vector

a.  may oscillate in any arbitrary direction in space.
b.  must oscillate in the $z$ direction.
c.  must oscillate in the $yz$ plane.
d   must oscillate in the $x$ direction.
e.  must have a steady component in the $x$ direction.

2409    24-2   Electromagnetic  Waves,  Numerical,  c

What is the wavelength of a 150 MHz television signal?

a.  1.0 m
b.  1.5 m
c.  2.0 m
d.  2.0 cm
e.  50 cm

2410    24-2  Electromagnetic Waves,  Numerical,  d

The intensity of a laser beam is 450 $W/m^2$.  What is the rms value of the electric field of this laser beam?  (The permittivity of free space $\epsilon_0 = 8.85 \times 10^{-12}$ $C^2/N \cdot m^2$)

a.  $1.7 \times 10^5$ V/m
b.  $5.8 \times 10^2$ V/m
c.  $3.4 \times 10^5$ V/m
d.  $4.1 \times 10^2$ V/m
e.  $1.3 \times 10^3$ V/m


2411    24-2  Electromagnetic Waves,  Conceptual,  b

The detection of radio waves can be accomplished with either a dipole antenna or a loop antenna.  The dipole antenna detects the _____ of the wave,  and the loop antenna detects the _____ field of the wave.

a.  electric field; electric
b.  electric field; magnetic
c.  magnetic field; magnetic
d.  magnetic field; electric
e.  electric and magnetic fields; electric


2412    24-2  Electromagnetic Waves,  Factual,  c

Of x-rays, infrared radiation, and radio waves, which has the longest wavelength and which has the shortest?

a.  X-rays have the longest; radio waves have the shortest.
b.  X-rays have the longest; infrared radiation has the shortest.
c.  Radio waves have the longest; x-rays have the shortest.
d.  Radio waves have the longest; infrared radiation has the shortest.
e.  Infrared radiation has the longest; x-rays have the shortest.


2413    24-2  Electromagnetic Waves,  Numerical,  b

The nearest star to us, Alpha Centauri, is 4.30 light-years away.  What is this distance in kilometres?

a.  $4.1 \times 10^{10}$ km
b.  $4.1 \times 10^{13}$ km
c.  $4.1 \times 10^{16}$ km
d.  $6.8 \times 10^{11}$ km
e.  $6.8 \times 10^{14}$ km


2414    24-2  Electromagnetic Waves,  Conceptual,  d

Light wave $A$ has twice the frequency of light wave $B$.  The wavelength of light wave $A$ is _____ that of light wave $B$.

a.  equal to
b.  twice
c.  four times
d.  half
e.  one-fourth

**2415    24-3  The Speed of Light,  Conceptual,  a**

Mission Control sends a brief wake-up call to astronauts in a far away spaceship.  Five seconds after the call is sent, Mission Control can hear the groans of the astronauts.  How far away (at most)  from the earth is the spaceship?

    a.   $7.5 \times 10^8$ m
    b.   $15 \times 10^8$ m
    c.   $30 \times 10^8$ m
    d.   $45 \times 10^8$ m
    e.   The spaceship is on the moon.

**2416    24-3  The Speed of Light,  Numerical,  b**

Communications satellites are usually placed in synchronous orbits, a distance of $4.43 \times 10^7$ m from the center of the earth.  What is the time lag for a signal sent from one point on the earth's surface to another via such a satellite?  (The radius of the earth $R_E = 6.370 \times 10^6$ m.)

    a.   0.13 s
    b.   0.25 s
    c.   0.51 s
    d.   0.29 s
    e.   0.15 s

**2417    24-4  Reflection,  Conceptual,  e**

Light traveling in a medium with an index of refraction $n_1$ is incident on a boundary with a second medium with an index $n_2$.  Very little light is transmitted into the second medium. Which of the following statements must be true?

    a.   $n_1$ equals $n_2$
    b.   $n_1$ is somewhat greater than $n_2$
    c.   $n_2$ is somewhat greater than $n_1$
    d.   $n_2$ is much greater than $n_1$
    e.   Either index of refraction is much greater than the other.

**2418    24-5  Refraction,  Conceptual,  a**

As light passes from one medium into another, the angle of refraction is _____ in the medium with the _____ index of refraction and _____ speed of light.

    a.   smaller; larger; lower
    b.   smaller; larger; higher
    c.   larger; smaller; lower
    d.   larger: larger; lower
    e.   smaller; smaller; higher

**2419    24-5  Refraction,  Conceptual,  c**

Which of the following statements is true about the speeds of the various colors of light in glass?

    a.   All colors of light have the same speed in glass.
    b.   Violet has the highest speed, red the lowest.
    c.   Red has the highest speed, violet the lowest.
    d.   Green has the highest speed, red and violet the lowest.
    e.   Red and violet have the highest speed, green the lowest.

**2420    24-5   Refraction,  Factual,   e**

A wave traveling at speed $v_1$ in medium 1 passes into medium 2, where its speed is $v_2$. The frequency $f_1$ of the wave while it is in medium 1 is related to its frequency $f_2$ while it is in medium 2 by which of the following equations?   ($\theta_1$ and $\theta_2$ are the angles of incidence and refraction.)

a.   $f_1 \sin \theta_1 = f_2 \sin \theta_2$
b.   $f_1 v_2 = f_2 v_1$
c.   None of these is correct.
d.   $f_1 v_1 = f_2 v_2$
e.   $f_1 = f_2$


**2421    24-5   Refraction,   Factual,   a**

When light originally in a medium with an index of refraction $n_2$ is incident on the boundary surface of another medium with an index of refraction $n_1$ at a sufficient angle, which of the following conditions must be satisfied for total internal reflection to occur?

a.   $n_1 < n_2$
b.   $n_1 > n_2$
c.   $n_1 = n_2$
d.   Any of these may be correct.
e.   None of these is correct.


**2422    24-5   Refraction,   Factual,   c**

A ray of light passes from air into water, striking the surface of the water with an angle of incidence of 45°.  Which of the following four quantities change as the light enters the water:  (1) wavelength, (2) frequency, (3) speed of propagation, and (4) direction of propagation?

a.   1 and 2 only
b.   2, 3, and 4 only
c.   1, 3, and 4 only
d.   3 and 4 only
e.   1, 2, 3, and 4


**2423    24-5   Refraction,   Numerical,   a**

A ray of light strikes a slab of glass at an angle of incidence of 35°.  The angle of refraction in the glass is

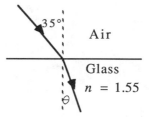

a.   22°
b.   63°
c.   27°
d   90°
e.   None of these is correct.

**2424   24-5   Refraction,   Numerical,   a**

A light ray traveling in glass strikes a glass-
water surface.  At angles greater than $\theta_c$
the light ray is totally internally reflected.
The value of $\theta_c$ is

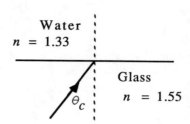

a.   59°
b.   31°
c.   45°
d.   Total internal reflection is impossible in this case.
e.   None of these is correct.

**2425   24-5   Refraction,   Numerical,   b**

The light ray in the diagram is incident on a
glass-air surface.  The index of refraction
of the glass is 1.744.  The critical angle for
total internal reflection is

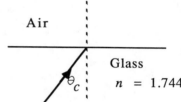

a.   48°
b.   35°
c.   30°
d.   The angle cannot be determined.
e.   None of these is correct.

**2426   24-5   Refraction,   Numerical,   a**

A ray of light traveling in air enters the end
of a rectangular block of a material that has
an index of refraction $n = 1.350$.  The

largest value of the angle $\theta$ for which total
internal reflection will occur at the upper
surface of the material is

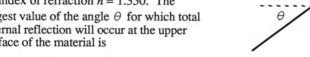

a.   65°
b.   48°
c.   56°
d.   78°
e.   None of these is correct.

**2427    24-5   Refraction,  Numerical,  e**

When a ray of light traveling in air is incident at $\theta =$ 50° on a plane-parallel slab of glass as illustrated, the light ray

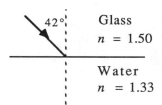

a.  is 100% reflected at the first surface.
b.  is 100% reflected at the second surface.
c.  emerges parallel to the incident ray and is not displaced to one side or the other of the incident ray.
d.  is absorbed if the wavelength is greater than 450 nm.
e.  None of these is correct.

**2428    24-5   Refraction,  Numerical,  d**

A light ray makes an angle of 42° with the normal to a glass-water surface on the glass side of the surface.  The angle $\theta$ in the water is

a.  The light is totally reflected.
b.  36°
c.  63°
d.  49°
e.  None of these is correct.

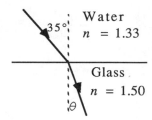

**2429    24-5   Refraction,  Numerical,  c**

A ray of light strikes a water-glass interface at an angle of incidence of 35°.  The angle of refraction is

a.  40.3°
b.  22.1°
c.  30.6°
d.  59.4°
e.  None of these is correct.

2430    24-6   Polarization,   Factual,   d

Light is an electromagnetic wave.  When visible light is plane polarized,

a.  the electric field vector is parallel to the magnetic field vector.
b.  the electric field vector is parallel to the direction of propagation.
c.  the electric field vector is in a fixed direction perpendicular to the direction of
    propagation but the magnetic field vector may be in any direction.
d.  the electric field vector is in a fixed direction perpendicular to the direction of
    propagation and the magnetic field vector is perpendicular to the electric field vector.
e.  None of these is correct.

2431    24-6   Polarization,   Conceptual,   b

Two polarizers have their transmission axes at an angle $\theta$.  Unpolarized light of intensity $I$
is incident upon the first polarizer.  What is the intensity of the light transmitted by the
second polarizer?

a.  $I (\cos^2 \theta)$
b.  $I (\cos^2 \theta)/2$
c.  $I (\cos^2 \theta)/4$
d.  $I (\cos \theta)$
e.  $I (\cos \theta)/4$

2432    24-6   Polarization,   Conceptual,   d

Which of the following is not a phenomenon whereby polarized light can be produced from
unpolarized light?

a.  Absorption
b.  Reflection
c.  Birefringence
d.  Diffraction
e.  Scattering

2433    24-6   Polarization,   Numerical,   d

Light known to be polarized in the horizontal direction is incident on a polarizing sheet.  It is
observed that only 15.0% of the intensity of the incident light is transmitted through the
sheet.  What angle does the transmission axis of the sheet make with the horizontal ?

a.  8.6°
b.  21°
c.  23°
d.  67°
e.  81°

2434    24-6   Polarization,   Numerical,   a

Light is reflected off the surface of a lake ($n = 1.33$).  What is the angle of incidence for
which the reflected light will be 100% polarized?

a.  53°
b.  49°
c.  45°
d.  41°
e.  37°

CHAPTER 25      Geometric Optics

**2501      25-1  Plane Mirrors,  Conceptual,  d**

What is the minimum length of plane mirror in which a standing woman can see her entire reflection?

a.  It must equal her height.
b.  It depends on how far from the mirror the woman stands.
c.  It depends on the focal length of the mirror.
d.  It must be one-half her height.
e.  It depends on the image distance.

**2502      25-1  Plane Mirrors,  Factual,  e**

A plane mirror forms

a.  a real image.
b.  an inverted image.
c.  an enlarged image.
d.  a focal image.
e.  a perverted image.

**2503      25-2  Spherical Mirrors,  Numerical,  a**

A concave spherical mirror has a radius of curvature of 50 cm.  An object is located 35 cm in front of the mirror.  The image is

a.  real, inverted, magnified 2.5 times, and 87.5 cm from the mirror.
b.  real, erect, magnified 2.5 times, and 87.5 cm from the mirror.
c.  virtual, erect, magnified 3.3 times, and 117 cm from the mirror.
d.  real, inverted, magnified 3.3 times, and 117 cm from the mirror.
e.  real, inverted, diminished 0.42 times, and 14.6 cm from the mirror.

**2504      25-2  Spherical Mirrors,  Numerical,  d**

In a convex mirror, an object 25 cm from the mirror is observed to produce an image 13.6 cm behind the mirror.  What is the focal length of the mirror?

a.  8.8 cm
b.  -8.8 cm
c.  30 cm
d.  -30 cm
e.  -60 cm

2505    25-2  Spherical Mirrors,  Numerical,  b

An object 0.50 cm high is 5.0 cm from a concave spherical mirror of focal length 20 cm. How high is the image and is it erect or inverted?

a.  0.40 cm, inverted
b.  0.67 cm, erect
c.  0.50 cm, inverted
d.  0.67 cm, inverted
e.  0.40 cm, erect


2506    25-2  Spherical Mirrors,  Conceptual,  a

If an object is closer to a convex mirror than the mirror's focal point, the

a.  magnification will be less than one.
b.  image distance will be greater than the object distance.
c.  magnification will be  equal to one.
d.  image will be real.
e.  image will be inverted.


2507    25-2  Spherical Mirrors,  Conceptual,  b

If an object is closer to a concave mirror than the mirror's focal point, the

a.  magnification will be less than one.
b.  image distance will be greater than the object distance.
c.  magnification will be  equal to one.
d.  image will be real.
e.  image will be inverted.


2508    25-2  Spherical Mirrors,  Conceptual,  a

If an object is further from a convex mirror than the mirror's focal point, the

a.  magnification will be less than one.
b.  image distance will be greater than the object distance.
c.  magnification will be  equal to one.
d.  image will be real.
e.  image will be inverted.


2509    25-2  Spherical Mirrors,  Conceptual,  e

If an object is further from a concave mirror than twice the mirror's focal length, the

a.  magnification will be less than one.
b.  image will be inverted.
c.  the image distance will be less than the object distance.
d.  image will be real.
e.  All of the above are correct.

**2510    25-3   Images Formed by Refraction,   Conceptual,   a**

When you stand in water up to your knees, your feet appear

  a.  closer than usual.
  b.  farther away than usual.
  c.  at the same location as usual.
  d.  To answer this you must know your height and the depth of the water.
  e.  To answer this you must know the index of refraction of water.

**2511    25-3   Images Formed by Refraction,   Conceptual,   e**

For the following diagram, which of the following statements is correct if $n_2$ is greater than $n_1$?

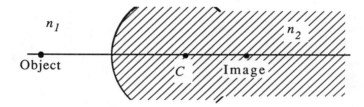

  a.  The object distance is greater than the image distance.
  b.  The image distance may be positive or negative.
  c.  The radius of curvature is negative.
  d.  The magnitude of the magnification is less than one.
  e.  The object distance is positive.

**2512    25-3   Images Formed by Refraction,   Numerical,   c**

A cat is looking at a goldfish inside a fishbowl.  The radius of the bowl is 15.0 cm.  The goldfish is 5.00 cm from the side of the bowl nearest the cat.  How far from the side of the bowl does the fish appear to be to the cat?  (For water, $n = 1.33$.)

  a.  7.5 cm
  b.  4.5 cm
  c.  4.1 cm
  d.  3.5 cm
  e.  2.5 cm

**2513    25-3   Images Formed by Refraction,   Numerical,   c**

The clear water of a lake is 1.5 m deep at the end of a dock.  A boy looks directly down from the end of the dock and sees a rock on the bottom of the lake.  How far below the surface does the rock appear to be?  (For water, $n = 1.33$.)

  a.  2.0 m
  b.  1.5 m
  c.  1.1 m
  d.  0.75 m
  e.  1.8 m

2514    **25-4   Thin Lenses,   Numerical,   d**

The lens of a slide projector has a focal length of +12.0 cm.  A slide 12.6 cm to the left of the lens forms the object for the lens.  The screen should be placed

    a.   25 cm to the left of the lens.
    b.   25 cm to the right of the lens.
    c.   250 cm to the left of the lens.
    d.   250 cm to the right of the lens.
    e.   390 cm to the right of the lens.

2515    **25-4   Thin Lenses,   Conceptual,   a**

If a real object is placed just inside the focal point of a diverging lens, the image is

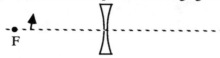

F

    a.   virtual, erect, and diminished.
    b.   real, inverted, and enlarged.
    c.   real, inverted, and diminished.
    d.   virtual, erect, and enlarged.
    e.   virtual, inverted, and diminished.

2516    **25-4   Thin Lenses,   Conceptual,   b**

A positive lens has a focal length $f$.  The only way to get a magnification of -1 is to

    a.   place a real object at the focal point.
    b.   place a real object at a distance $2f$ from the lens.
    c.   place a virtual object at a distance $2f$ from the lens.
    d.   Magnifications can never be negative.
    e.   None of these is correct.

2517    **25-4   Thin Lenses,   Conceptual,   d**

A positive lens has a focal length $f$.  The image is the same size as the object when

    a.   the object is at the focal point.
    b.   The image can never be the same size as the object.
    c.   the image is on the same side as the object and is the same distance from the lens as the object.
    d.   the image is on the opposite side from the object and is the same distance from the lens as the object.
    e.   None of these is correct.

2518    **25-4   Thin Lenses,   Numerical,   b**

A negative lens has a focal length of 25.6 cm.   A real object is 42.1 cm from the lens.  The object is 2.45 mm high.  The height and orientation of the image are

    a.   3.8 mm and inverted.
    b.   0.93 mm and erect.
    c.   6.4 mm and erect.
    d.   0.38 mm and erect.
    e.   None of these is correct.

**2519    25-4   Thin Lenses,   Numerical,   c**

A thin convex lens has a focal length of 10 cm.  An object 2 cm high is placed 20 cm from the lens.  Which one of the following statements is NOT true about the image formed?

a.   It is 2 cm high.
b.   It is 20 cm from the lens
c.   It is erect.
d.   It is real.
e.   All of these is correct.

**2520    25-4   Thin Lenses,   Numerical,   c**

A negative lens has a focal length $f$ = -20 cm.  A real object is 30 cm from the lens.  The image is

a.   virtual and 30 cm from the lens.
b.   real and 12 cm from the lens.
c.   virtual and 12 cm from the lens.
d.   real and 20 cm from the lens.
e.   None of these is correct.

**2521    25-4   Thin Lenses,   Numerical,   e**

A real object is 42 cm from a negative lens with $f$ = -21 cm.  The image is

a.   real and 14 cm from the lens.
b.   real and 42 cm from the lens.
c.   virtual and 42 cm from the lens.
d.   virtual and 21 cm from the lens.
e.   virtual and 14 cm from the lens.

**2522    25-4   Thin Lenses,   Numerical,   b**

A positive lens has a focal length of +30 cm.  A virtual object is 30 cm from this lens.  The image is

a.   at infinity.
b.   real and 15 cm from the lens.
c.   virtual and 15 cm from the lens.
d.   real and 60 cm from the lens.
e.   virtual and 60 cm from the lens.

**2523    25-4   Thin Lenses,   Numerical,   c**

A lens forms an erect image of a real object.  The image is twice the size of the object and appears to be 40 cm from the lens.  Determine the power of the lens in diopters.

a.   There is not sufficient information.
b.   -2.5 D
c.   +2.5 D
d.   +7.5 D
e.   None of these is correct

**2524    25-4  Thin Lenses,  Numerical,  d**

A negative lens with a focal length of -10.0 cm is on the same axis as a positive lens with a focal length of +20.0 cm as illustrated.  The distance between the lenses is 20.0 cm.  A real object that is 3.00 cm high is placed 20.0 cm to the left of the negative lens.  After the light has passed through both lenses, the image is

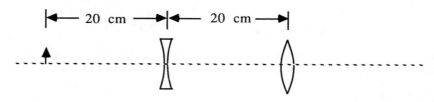

a.   3.0 cm high and virtual.
b.   1.0 cm high and virtual.
c.   1.0 cm high and real.
d.   3.0 cm high and real.
e.   None of these is correct.

**2525    25-4  Thin Lenses,  Numerical,  b**

Two lenses, one with a focal length $f_1$ = +20 cm and the other with a focal length $f_2$ = -20 cm are on the same axis and 60 cm apart as shown.

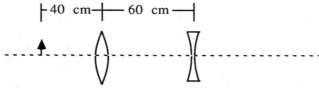

A real object is 40 cm to the left of the positive lens.  The image formed by the negative lens is

a.   real and 10 cm from the negative lens.
b.   virtual and 10 cm from the negative lens.
c.   at infinity.
d.   virtual and 20 cm from the negative lens.
e.   None of these is correct.

**2526    25-4  Thin Lenses,  Numerical,  a**

A negative lens with a focal length of -15 cm is  25 cm from a positive lens with a focal length of +20 cm on the same axis.

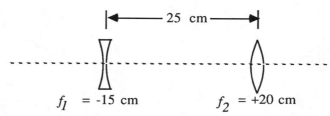

Parallel light from the left is incident on the negative lens.  The image formed by the positive lens is

a.   real and 40 cm from the positive lens.
b.   virtual and 20 cm from the positive lens.
c.   real and 20 cm from the positive lens.
d.   real and 13 cm from the positive lens.
e.   None of these is correct.

**2527    25-4  Thin Lenses,  Numerical,  e**

A thin converging lens made of Crown glass $n( =1.517)$ is flat on one side and has a radius of curvature of 50 cm on the other side.  An object is placed 45.0 cm to the left of this lens. Where is the image?

a.   120 cm to the right of the lens
b.   31 cm to the left of the lens
c.   31 cm to the right of the lens
d.   84 cm to the right of the lens
e.   84 cm to the left of the lens

**2528    25-4  Thin Lenses,  Conceptual,  d**

In order to project an image on a screen using a lens,

a.   the lens must be diverging and the object must be further from the lens than the second focal point.
b.   the lens must be converging and the object must be between the first focal point and the lens.
c.   the lens must be diverging and the image must be further from the lens than the second focal point.
d.   the lens must be converging and the object must be further from the lens than the first focal point.
e.   the lens must be diverging and the object must be between the first focal point and the lens.

**2529    25-4  Thin  Lenses,  Conceptual,  d**

In order to form a real image using a lens,

a.  the radius of curvature of the first surface must be positive and that of the second surface must be negative.
b.  the radius of curvature of the first surface must be negative and that of the second surface must be positive.
c.  the radius of curvature of the first surface must be positive and that of the second surface may be positive or negative.
d.  Either a or c is correct.
e.  Either b or c is correct.

**2530    25-4  Thin  Lenses,  Conceptual,  e**

In order to form a virtual image using a lens,

a.  the radius of curvature of the first surface must be positive and that of the second surface must be negative.
b.  the radius of curvature of the first surface must be negative and that of the second surface must be positive.
c.  the radius of curvature of the first surface must be positive and that of the second surface must be positive.
d.  Either b or c but not a is correct.
e.  Choices a, b, or c are all correct.

**2531    25-4  Thin  Lenses,  Conceptual,  d**

A real image is formed by a converging lens as shown in the diagram.  If a weak diverging lens is placed between the converging lens and the image, where will the new image be located?  Point *C* is at the location of the original image.

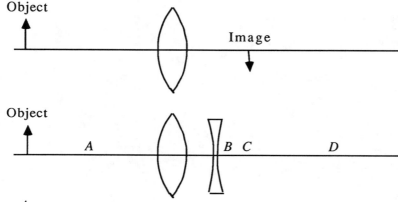

a.  *A*
b.  *B*
c.  *C*
d.  *D*
e.  It may be at either *A* or *B*.

**2532    25-5  Aberrations,  Conceptual,  c**

A spherical mirror exhibits

a.  both chromatic and spherical aberrations.
b.  neither chromatic nor spherical aberration.
c.  spherical but not chromatic aberration.
d.  chromatic but not spherical aberration.
e.  The type of aberration depends on the shape of the spherical surface.

CHAPTER 26     **Optical Instruments**

**2601**    **26-1  The Eye,  Numerical,  c**

A myopic eye cannot focus on objects that are more than 25 cm in front of it.  The power in diopters of the lens needed for distinct distant vision is

a.   +25 D
b.   +4.0 D
c.   -40 D
d.   -2.5 D
e.   None of these is correct.

**2602**    **26-1  The Eye,  Numerical,  c**

A myopic eye cannot focus on objects that are more than 16.5 cm away nor closer than 4.5 cm to it.  When glasses for normal distant vision are used, the new near point is

a.   3.5 cm
b.   16.5 cm
c.   6.2 cm
d.   10.5 cm
e.   None of these is correct.

**2603**    **26-1  The Eye,  Numerical,  b**

An eye can focus on objects a great distance away, but cannot focus on objects that are closer than 125 cm to the eye.  The power of the lens in diopters for normal near vision (25 cm) is

a.   +0.8 D
b.   +3.2 D
c.   +4.0 D
d.   -4.0 D
e.   None of these is correct.

**2604**    **26-1  The Eye,  Numerical,  c**

A hypermetropic eye cannot focus on objects that are more than 225 cm from the eye.  The power in diopters of the lens required for distinct distant vision is

a.   +2.25 D
b.   +4.4 x $10^{-3}$ D
c.   +0.44 D
d.   -0.44 D
e.   None of these is correct.

2605    **26-1  The Eye,  Conceptual,  c**

A typical farsighted person requires

a.  glasses with converging lenses to drive.
b.  glasses with diverging lenses to drive.
c.  glasses with converging lenses to read.
d.  glasses with diverging lenses to read.
e.  no glasses to read.

2606    **26-1  The Eye,  Conceptual,  b**

A farsighted person uses glasses to read.  The person will see _____ print that appears _____ than is actually the case.

a.  larger; closer
b.  larger; further away
c.  smaller; closer
d.  smaller; further away
e.  actual sized; further away

2607    **26-2  The Simple Magnifier,  Numerical,  e**

A person with near point $x_{np}$ uses a lens of focal length $x_{np}/5$ as a simple magnifier.  What magnification is obtained?

a.  10
b.  50
c.  0.1
d.  0.2
e.  5

2608    **26-2  The Simple Magnifier,  Numerical,  d**

A stamp collector with a normal near point (25 cm) needs a magnifying power of 10 to examine his stamps.  What power of magnifying glass should he buy?

a.  0.40 D
b.  2.5 D
c.  10 D
d.  40 D
e.  25 D

2609    **26-2  The Simple Magnifier,  Numerical,  b**

A stamp collector with a normal near point (25 cm) needs a magnifying power of 10 to examine his stamps.  If one of the stamps is 2.0 cm wide, what is the angle (in degrees) subtended by the stamp when it is viewed through the magnifier?

a.  23°
b.  46°
c.  0.80°
d.  4.6°
e.  1.6°

**2610    26-2  The Simple Magnifier,  Numerical,  a**

A simple magnifier gives a magnification of 8 times when it is used by a person with a normal near point (25 cm).  What is the magnifying power when it is used by a person whose near point is 15 cm?

a.  4.8
b.  13
c.  8.0
d.  15
e.  9.6

**2611    26-2  The Simple Magnifier,  Numerical,  c**

A jeweler's loupe (magnifying glass) has a focal length of 2 cm.  Assuming that the loupe is held so that it forms an image at the normal near point of 25 cm, what magnification does it provide?

a.  46
b.  54
c.  13.5
d.  50
e.  None of these is correct.

**2612    26-3  The Camera,  Numerical,  c**

The $f/2.8$ lens of a camera has focal length of 40 mm.  What is the usable diameter of the lens?

a.  2.8 mm
b.  5.6 mm
c.  14 mm
d.  20 mm
e.  28 mm

**2613    26-3  The Camera,  Numerical,  e**

You have just taken a picture at $f/8$ and 1/500 s when your light meter stops functioning. You wish to take another picture under the same light conditions at $f/22$ for greater depth of field.  What shutter speed setting should you use?

a.  1/1500 s
b.  1/1000 s
c.  1/500 s
d.  1/125 s
e.  1/60 s

**2614    26-3  The Camera,  Conceptual,  b**

You wish to take a winter photograph on a very bright day.  What should you do to minimize the exposure?

a.  Minimize the $f$/number and the shutter speed.
b.  Maximize the $f$/number and the shutter speed.
c.  Minimize the $f$/number and maximize the shutter speed.
d.  Maximize the $f$/number and minimize the shutter speed.
e.  Minimize the depth of field and the shutter  speed.

**2615    26-3  The Camera,  Conceptual,  d**

You are a photographer.  You wish to have as great a depth of field as possible without having too little exposure.  What will you do?

a.  Minimize the $f$/number and the shutter speed.
b.  Maximize the $f$/number and the shutter speed.
c.  Minimize the $f$/number and maximize the shutter speed.
d.  Maximize the $f$/number and minimize the shutter speed.
e.  None of these is correct.

**2616    26-4  The Compound Microscope,  Conceptual,  d**

Two people look at the same object through the same microscope.  Person $A$ has a near point of $x_{np}$ whereas person $B$ has a near point of $2x_{np}$.  If person $A$ sees the object magnified $m$ times, with what magnification does person $B$ see the object?

a.  $m$
b.  $m/2$
c.  $m/4$
d.  $2m$
e.  $4m$

**2617    26-4  The Compound Microscope,  Conceptual,  e**

A person uses two microscopes to view the same object.  Microscope $A$ is twice as long as microscope $B$ and contains lenses with focal lengths that are one-half those of $B$.  If microscope $A$ provides a magnification of $m$, then what magnification does $B$ provide?

a.  $m$
b.  $2m$
c.  $m/2$
d.  $8m$
e.  $m/8$

**2618    26-4  The Compound Microscope,  Numerical,  a**

A microscope is constructed with an objective of focal length 1.50 cm and an eyepiece of focal length 2.50 cm.  The two lenses are 20.0 cm apart.  What is the overall magnification of this microscope for a person with a normal near point (25 cm)?

a.  -110
b.  -130
c.  -160
d.  -120
e.  -85

**2619    26-4  The Compound Microscope,  Numerical,  c**

Two lenses are available for making a compound microscope: $f_o = 0.80$ cm and $f_e = 1.20$ cm.  How far apart must the lenses be to get a magnification of -300?  (Assume the normal near point of 25 cm.)

a.  11.5 cm
b.  12.7 cm
c.  13.5 cm
d.  13.9 cm
e.  15.0 cm

2620    **26-5   The Telescope,   Numerical,   b**

A simple refracting telescope has an objective of focal length 75 cm and an eyepiece of focal length 3.0 cm.  When viewed by the naked eye, the moon subtends an angle of about 0.009 radians.  What is the angle subtended by the moon when it is viewed through this telescope?

   a.   0.022 rad
   b.   0.22 rad
   c.   $3.6 \times 10^{-4}$ rad
   d.   0.078 rad
   e.   $3.0 \times 10^{-3}$ rad

2621    **26-5   The Telescope,   Conceptual,   a**

To provide large magnification, a telescope should have an objective with a _____ and an eyepiece with a _____ .

   a.   long focal length; short focal length
   b.   long focal length; long focal length
   c.   short focal length; short focal length
   d.   short focal length; long focal length
   e.   large diameter; short focal length

2622    **26-5   The Telescope,   Numerical,   c**

The 200-in reflecting telescope at Mt. Palomar has an objective mirror with a focal length of 16.8 m.  If an eyepiece with a focal length of 2.00 cm is used, what is the overall magnification of this telescope?

   a.   -250
   b.   -130
   c.   -840
   d.   -38
   e.   -300

**2623    26-5   The Telescope,   Conceptual,   c**

The lens system used in a Galilean telescope or opera glasses consists of a positive lens and a negative lens on the same axis. In the following ray diagrams the focal points of the positive lens are marked $F$ and $F'$ and those of the negative lens are marked $f$ and $f'$. The points $F$ and $f'$ coincide. A ray of light comes from a distant object, traverses the system, and enters an eye on the right side of the diagram. Which of the ray diagrams is correct?

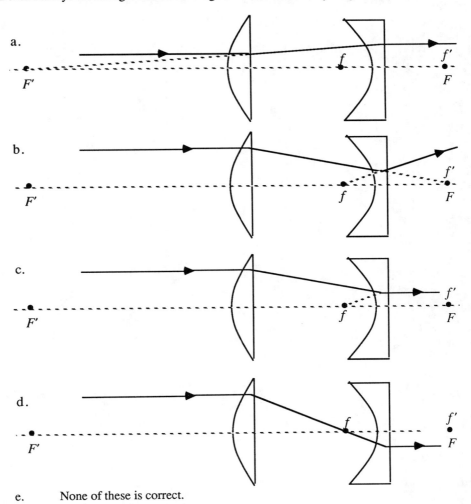

e.        None of these is correct.

CHAPTER 27   # Physical Optics: Interference and Diffraction

**2701   27-1   Phase Difference and Coherence,   Conceptual,   d**

A phase shift of 180° occurs when a light wave

a.   is transmitted through a boundary surface into a medium that is more dense than the medium from which the wave came.
b.   is transmitted through a boundary surface into a medium that is less dense than the medium from which the wave came.
c.   reflects from the boundary surface of a medium that is less dense than the medium in which the wave is traveling.
d.   reflects from the boundary surface of a medium that is more dense than the medium in which the wave is traveling.
e.   Both c and d  are correct.

**2702   27-1   Phase Difference and Coherence,   Conceptual,   b**

Which of the following is NOT necessary for the light waves from two sources to be coherent?

a.   They must have the same speed.
b.   They must have the same amplitude.
c.   They must have the same wavelength.
d.   They must have a constant phase difference.
e.   They must have the same frequency.

**2703   27-1   Phase Difference and Coherence,   Conceptual,   a**

Visible light from an ordinary source (such as a sodium lamp) can be used to produce interference effects that demonstrate the wave nature of light provided that

a.   the light beam from the single source is split into two (or more) beams that have a constant phase relationship to one another.
b.   the light is polarized.
c.   the light is not polarized.
d.   Interference effects cannot be demonstrated with ordinary light sources.
e.   None of these is correct.

**2704**   **27-2   Interference in Thin Films,   Conceptual,   e**

In order for us to see interference phenomena in a thin film,

   a.   the incoming light must be monochromatic.
   b.   the index of refraction of the thin film must be greater than the index of refraction of the material below it.
   c.   the index of refraction of the thin film must be less than the index of refraction of the material below it.
   d.   the incoming light must be multicolored.
   e.   None of these is correct.

**2705**   **27-2   Interference in Thin Films,   Conceptual,   d**

Why are fringes NOT observed if the angle of the wedge of air in the diagram is too large?

   a.   For a large angle, the small angle approximation (sin $\theta = \theta$) is not valid.
   b.   The light passing through the wedge of air loses its coherence.
   c.   The fringes overlap each other.
   d.   The fringes are too close together to be seen individually.
   e.   None of these is correct.

**2706**   **27-2   Interference in Thin Films,   Conceptual,   b**

For two identical rays of light to interfere destructively, their path lengths must

   a.   be equal.
   b.   differ by an odd number of half wavelengths.
   c.   differ by an even number of half wavelengths.
   d.   differ by an integral number of wavelengths.
   e.   None of these is correct.

**2707**   **27-2   Interference in Thin Films,   Numerical,   b**

A loop of wire is dipped in soapy water ($n = 1.33$) and is then held vertically, with a soap film in the loop. The film "sags" such that its thickness near the top of the loop is nearly zero. This is shown by the fact that the film appears black though illuminated by white light, which means that all of the reflected wavelengths interfere destructively. What is the thickness of the film where the first red band is observed by reflected white light? (Take the wavelength of red light to be 680 nm.)

   a.   130 nm
   b.   170 nm
   c.   220 nm
   d.   250 nm
   e.   340 nm

**2708**   **27-2   Interference in Thin Films,  Numerical,  d**

A wedge-shaped film of air is made by placing a small slip of paper of thickness 1.0 μm between the edges of two flat plates of glass 2.5 cm wide.  Monochromatic light of unknown wavelength is incident normally on the glass plates and is viewed by reflection. Dark fringes are seen at the edge where the two glass plates meet and at the other end where the paper is located. Three additional dark fringes are observed between those two.  What is the wavelength of the incident light?

a.   250 nm
b.   400 nm
c.   440 nm
d.   500 nm
e.   620 nm

**2709**   **27-2   Interference in Thin Films,  Numerical,  c**

A convex lens is placed on top of a flat plate of glass and is illuminated by monochromatic light of wavelength 600 nm.  A dark circle is observed at the center of the lens, surrounded by a series of concentric dark rings.  What is the thickness of the air space between the lens and the flat glass plate where the sixth dark ring is observed?

a.   3.90 μm
b.   3.60 μm
c.   1.80 μm
d.   1.95 μm
e.   2.10 μm

**2710**   **27-2   Interference in Thin Films,  Numerical,  b**

A material with $n = 1.25$ is applied to a lens ($n_g = 1.5$) to make a nonreflective coating due to destructive interference at a wavelength (in a vacuum) of 555 nm.  What minimum thickness of the coating is required?

a.   56 nm
b.   110 nm
c.   220 nm
d.   280 nm
e.   140 nm

**2711**   **27-3   The Michelson Interferometer,  Numerical,  b**

Suppose the speed of light along one arm of a Michelson interferometer were $1.5 \times 10^{-3}$ percent less than that along the other arm.  If the light's path in each arm is a total of 50 cm, by how many fringes is the interference pattern shifted, when light with a wavelength of 500 nm is used?

a.   5.0
b.   15
c.   25
d.   30
e.   150

2712    **27-3   The Michelson Interferometer,   Conceptual,   b**

If one mirror of a Michelson interferometer is moved back a distance equal to three wavelengths of the light being used, by how much will the fringe pattern shift?

a.  3 fringes
b.  6 fringes
c.  1.5 fringes
d.  12 fringes
e.  9 fringes


2713    **27-3   The Michelson Interferometer,   Conceptual,   d**

An evacuated container is placed in one arm of a Michelson interferometer and a fringe pattern is observed.  Nitrogen gas is then let into the container and the fringe pattern is observed to change.  This change is due to

a.  the increase in the wavelength of light in the container.
b.  the decrease of the index of refraction in the container.
c.  an increase in the length of the container.
d.  the decrease in the wavelength of light in the container.
e.  a change in spectral lines of the nitrogen.


2714    **27-4   The Two-Slit Inference Pattern,   Conceptual,   b**

Which of the following statements concerning Young's double-slit experiment is FALSE?

a.  The bands of light are caused by the interference of the light coming from the two slits.
b.  The results of the double-slit experiment supported the particle theory of light.
c.  Double-slit interference patterns can also be produced with sound waves and water waves.
d.  If the slits are moved closer together, the bands of light on the screen are spread farther apart.
e.  The pattern of light on the screen consists  of many bands, not just two bands.


2715    **27-4   The Two-Slit Interference Pattern,   Conceptual,   e**

The distance between the slits in a double-slit experiment is increased by a factor of 4. Assuming that the distance between the fringes is small compared to the distance from the slits to the screen, the distance between the adjacent fringes near the center of the interference pattern

a.  increases by a factor of 2.
b.  increases by a factor of 4.
c.  depends on the width of the slits.
d.  decreases by a factor of 2.
e.  decreases by a factor of 4.


2716    **27-4   The Two-Slit Interference Pattern,   Conceptual,   d**

In a double-slit experiment, the distance from the slits to the screen is decreased by a factor of 2.  Assuming that the distance between the fringes is small compared to the distance from the slits to the screen, the distance between adjacent fringes

a.  increases by a factor of 2.
b.  increases by a factor of 4.
c.  depends on the width of the slits.
d.  decreases by a factor of 2.
e.  decreases by a factor of 4.

**2717    27-4   The Two-Slit Interference Pattern,   Conceptual,   e**

The distance between the slits in a double-slit experiment is increased by a factor of 4. Assuming that the distance between the fringes is about the same as the distance from the slits to the screen, the distance between adjacent fringes

   a.   increases by a factor of 2.
   b.   increases by a factor of 4.
   c.   decreases by a factor of 2.
   d.   decreases by a factor of 4.
   e.   depends on which two fringes are being used for the measurement.


**2718    27-4   The Two-Slit Interference Pattern,   Numerical,   b**

Two slits separated by 1.0 mm are illuminated with light of a single unknown wavelength. The tenth bright line from the central point is observed at an angle of 0.34°. What is the wavelength of the light?

   a.   620 nm
   b.   590 nm
   c.   560 nm
   d.   450 nm
   e.   600 nm


**2719    27-4   The Two-Slit Interference Pattern,   Numerical,   c**

Two slits 0.50 mm apart are illuminated with light of wavelength 555 nm, and interference fringes are observed on a screen 6.0 m away.  What is the spacing between the fringes on the screen?

   a.   6.7 mm
   b.   3.3 mm
   c.   6.7 mm
   d.   10 mm
   e.   5.0 mm


**2720    27-4   The Two-Slit Interference Pattern,   Numerical,   b**

A narrow, horizontal slit is 0.50 mm above a horizontal plane mirror. The slit is illuminated by light of wavelength 400 nm. The interference pattern is viewed on a screen 10.0 m away from the slit. What is the distance from the mirror to the first bright line?

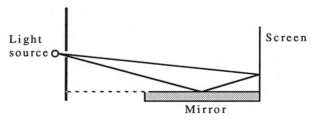

   a.   1.0 mm
   b.   2.0 mm
   c.   3.0 mm
   d.   4.0 mm
   e.   1.2 mm

2721   **27-5   Diffraction Pattern of a Single Slit,   Conceptual,   c**

When a parallel beam of light is diffracted at a single slit,

a.  the shadow is always sharp.
b.  the narrower the slit, the narrower the central diffraction maximum.
c.  the narrower the slit, the wider the central diffraction maximum.
d.  the width of the central diffraction maximum is independent of the width of the slit.
e.  None of these is correct.


2722   **27-5   Diffraction Pattern of a Single Slit,   Numerical,   d**

Light of wavelength 450 nm is incident on a narrow slit.  The diffraction pattern is observed on a screen 5.0 m away from the slit, and the central maximum is observed to have a width of 22 cm.  What is the width of the slit?

a.  4.5 μm
b.  5.0 μm
c.  10 μm
d.  20 μm
e.  0.20 μm


2723   **27-5   Diffraction Pattern of a Single Slit,   Numerical,   d**

Light of wavelength 650 nm is incident on a slit of width 25.0 μm.  At what angle is the second diffraction minimum observed?

a.  0.052°
b.  1.5°
c.  2.2°
d.  3.0°
e.  3.7°


2724   **27-5   Diffraction Pattern of a Single Slit,   Conceptual,   c**

In dealing with the diffraction pattern of a single slit, we are usually interested in the location of the first minimum in light intensity because

a.  it is the only one that can be determined accurately.
b.  it is the only one for which the small angle approximation holds.
c.  nearly all the light energy is contained in the central maximum.
d.  it is the only one for which the location is linearly proportional to the wavelength of the light.
e.  it is the only one that can be described by Fraunhofer diffraction.


2725   **27-5   Diffraction Pattern of a Single Slit,   Conceptual,   a**

As the width of the slit producing a single-slit diffraction pattern is slowly and steadily reduced (always remaining larger than the wavelength of the light), the diffraction pattern will

a.  slowly and steadily get wider.
b.  slowly and steadily get brighter.
c.  not change because the wavelength of the light does not change.
d.  slowly and steadily get narrower.
e.  None of these is correct.

**2726   27-6   Diffraction and Resolution,   Numerical,   a**

The headlights of a car are 1.2 m apart.  What is the maximum distance from the car at which you will be able to resolve the lights as two separate sources if the diameter of the pupil of your eye is 5.0 mm and the wavelength of the light is 555 nm?

   a.   8.9 km
   b.   11 km
   c.   4.4 km
   d.   5.4 km
   e.   13 km


**2727   27-6   Diffraction and Resolution,   Numerical,   b**

The 200-in reflecting telescope at Mt. Palomar has an objective mirror with a focal length of 16.8 m.  The effective aperture is the diameter of the big 200-in mirror (200 in = 5.08 m). For light in the blue region (450 nm), what is the smallest angle between two stars that this telescope can ideally resolve?  (In practice, the limit to resolution is really due to atmospheric turbulence.)

   a.   $8.9 \times 10^{-8}$ rad
   b.   $1.1 \times 10^{-7}$ rad
   c.   $7.3 \times 10^{-7}$ rad
   d.   $1.1 \times 10^{-4}$ rad
   e.   $8.9 \times 10^{-5}$ rad


**2728   27-6   Diffraction and Resolution,   Conceptual,   e**

Diffraction occurs when light passes

   a.   by a small particle.
   b.   through a small hole.
   c.   through a double slit.
   d.   by a sharp edge.
   e.   It occurs with all of the above.


**2729   27-6   Diffraction and Resolution,   Conceptual,   e**

The size of the smallest things that can be seen with an optical microscope is limited by diffraction.  Which of the following will help a microscopist see smaller things?

   a.   A more powerful microscope could be used.
   b.   The microscope could have a lens with a shorter focal length.
   c.   The microscope could have a lens with a longer focal length.
   d.   The diameter of the lens could be made smaller.
   e.   An illuminating light with a shorter wavelength could be used.


**2730   27-6   Diffraction and Resolution,   Conceptual,   a**

An antenna used for receiving television signals from a satellite has a diameter of 3 m.  The TV signals have a wavelength of 24 cm.  If the diameter of the antenna is reduced to 0.5 m, for what signal wavelengths would the antenna still have the same resolution?

   a.   4 cm
   b.   6 cm
   c.   8 cm.
   d.   144 cm
   e.   24 cm

**2731    27-7   Diffraction Gratings,   Numerical,   b**

The equation for a diffraction grating is $m\lambda = d\sin\theta$, where $m$ is the order of the spectrum produced, $\lambda$ is the wavelength, $d$ is the spacing of the slits in the grating, and $\theta$ is the angle of diffraction.  For a given grating, it is observed that a third-order line ($m = 3$) with $\lambda = 465.3$ nm overlaps a second-order line (has the same $\theta$ as a line with $m = 2$).  The wavelength of the second-order line is

    a.   304 nm
    b.   684 nm
    c.   913 nm
    d.   152 nm
    e.   372 nm

**2732    27-7   Diffraction Gratings,   Numerical,   b**

The grating equation is $m\lambda = d\sin\theta$, where $\theta$ is the angle of diffraction measured from the forward direction.  For a grating with $d = 3.5\lambda$, the maximum order $m$ of an interference maximum that can be observed for a specified $\lambda$ is

    a.   3.5
    b.   3
    c.   1
    d.   2
    e.   2.5

**2733    27-7   Diffraction Gratings,   Numerical,   e**

The grating equation is $m\lambda = d\sin\theta$, where $\theta$ is the angle of diffraction measured from the forward direction.  For a grating with $d = 4.5\lambda$, the maximum order $m$ of an interference maximum that can be observed for a specified $\lambda$ is

    a.   4.5
    b.   3
    c.   1
    d.   2
    e.   4

**2734    27-7   Diffraction and Resolution,   Conceptual,   a**

Two diffraction gratings have $N_1$ and $N_2$ slits per centimetre respectively.  If $N_1$ is greater than $N_2$, which grating has the greater resolving power?

    a.   The grating with $N_1$ slits per centimetre has the greater resolving power.
    b.   The grating with $N_2$ slits per centimetre has the greater resolving power.
    c.   Both have the same resolving power but the one with $N_1$ slits per centimetre has sharper spectral lines.
    d.   Both have the same resolving power but the one with $N_2$ slits per centimetre has sharper spectral lines.
    e.   The width of the individual slits must be known to answer the question.

CHAPTER 28    Relativity

**2801    28-1  Newtonian Relativity,  Factual,  b**

What is the principle of newtonian relativity?

a.   Absolute motion can be detected.
b.   Absolute motion cannot be detected.
c.   Relative motion can be detected.
d.   Relative motion cannot be detected.
e.   Both absolute and relative motion can be detected.

**2802    28-1  Newtonian Relativity,  Conceptual,  d**

You are in a room with no windows.  What simple experiment would obviously show whether you are on earth or in a space station that rotates to produce artificial gravity?

a.   Release a ball on the floor.
b.   Drop a ball from above the floor.
c.   Observe a body hanging on a spring, oscillating up and down.
d.   Spin a top.
e.   No such experiment could distinguish the two possibilities.

**2803    28-2  The Michelson-Morley Experiment,  Factual,  e**

What did Michelson conclude from the results of his famous experiment?

a.   The ether does not exist.
b.   The speed of light is measured to be the same in all reference frames.
c.   The speed of light is a constant relative to the ether.
d.   The earth moves relative to the ether.
e.   The earth does not move relative to the ether.

**2804    28-2  The Michelson-Morley Experiment,  Conceptual,  a**

If Michelson and Morley had performed a version of their experiment with sound waves, they would not have "heard a fringe shift" in which of the following cases?

a.   The experimental apparatus was on an open flat car that was not moving, and there was no wind.
b.   The experimental apparatus was on an open flat car that was not moving, and there was a wind.
c.   The experimental apparatus was on an open flat car that was moving, and there was no wind.
d.   The experimental apparatus was on an open flat car that was moving, and there was a headwind.
e.   All of the above are correct..

2805    28-2   The Michelson-Morley Experiment,   Numerical,   b

An airplane flies from point $A$ to point $B$, a distance of 100 km apart, and back again with an airspeed of 250 km/h.  What is the difference in the time for this round trip between a day when a wind of speed 50.0 km/h blows from $A$ toward $B$ and a day when a wind of speed 50.0 km/h blows in a direction perpendicular to $AB$?

a.   zero
b.   1.0 min
c.   5.5 min
d.   4.5 min
e.   10 min

2806    28-2   The Michelson-Morley Experiment,   Numerical,   a

Michelson obtained a value for the speed of light of $c = 299{,}796 \pm 4$ km/s  in the 1887 experiment on the ether with Morley.  If the total path length was 11.0 m, how big an error in the time it took for the light to travel through the apparatus corresponds to the error ($\pm 4$ km/s) in the speed of light?

a.   $4.9 \times 10^{-13}$ s
b.   $2.7 \times 10^{-3}$ s
c.   $3.7 \times 10^{-8}$ s
d.   $4.9 \times 10^{-10}$ s
e.   $9.2 \times 10^{-12}$ s

2807    28-3   Einstein's Postulates and Their Consequences,   Conceptual,   b

An observer sees a system consisting of a mass oscillating on the end of a spring moving past at a speed $u$ and notes that the period of the system is $T$.  Another observer, who is moving with the mass-spring system, also meausres its period.  The second observer will find a period that is

a.   equal to $T$.
b.   less than $T$.
c.   greater than $T$.
d.   either a or b depending on whether the system was approaching or receding from the
     first observer.
e.   There is not sufficient information to answer the question.

2808    28-3   Einstein's Postulates and Their Consequences,   Numerical,   d

A pion lives $2.5 \times 10^{-10}$ s in its rest frame. According to an observer in a laboratory in which the particle moves at a speed of $2.7 \times 10^{8}$ m/s, how long does the particle live?

a.   $1.1 \times 10^{-10}$ s
b.   $1.5 \times 10^{-10}$ s
c.   $4.3 \times 10^{-10}$ s
d.   $5.7 \times 10^{-10}$ s
e.   $7.9 \times 10^{-10}$ s

**2809    28-3    Einstein's Postulates and Their Consequences,   Numerical,   b**

A standard Canadian football field is 100 m long and 60 m wide.  A UFO streaks from one
end of the field to the other at a speed of 0.6c relative to the players on the field.  An
observer in the UFO measures the length of the field to be

    a.   60 m
    b.   80 m
    c.   100 m
    d.   125 m
    e.   167 m

**2810    28-3    Einstein's Postulates and Their Consequences,   Numerical,   a**

A standard Canadian football field is 100 m long and 60 m wide.  A UFO streaks from one
end of the field to the other at a speed of 0.6c relative to the players on the field.  An
observer in the UFO measures the width of the field to be

    a.   60 m
    b.   80 m
    c.   100 m
    d.   125 m
    e.   167 m

**2811    28-3    Einstein's Postulates and Their Consequences,   Numerical,   d**

A standard Canadian football field is 100 m long and 60 m wide.  A UFO streaks from one
end of the field to the other at a speed of 0.6c relative to the players on the field.  The aliens
in the UFO decide to watch the game on television as they head off toward Jupiter.  The
game begins at 1:30 PM and ends at 4:30 PM according to earthbound broadcasters.  The
elapsed time for the game according to the aliens is

    a.   1.8 hours
    b.   2.4 hours
    c.   3.0 hours
    d.   3.8 hours
    e.   5.0 hours

**2812    28-3    Einstein's Postulates and Their Consequences,   Numerical,   b**

As astronauts in a spaceship with a speed of 0.6c relative to the earth move outward from
the earth toward Jupiter, they observe a cosmic ray shower that contains protons moving
toward them at 0.2c relative to the earth.  They measure the speed of the protons to be

    a.   $0.80c$
    b.   $0.71c$
    c.   $0.95c$
    d.   $0.69c$
    e.   $0.45c$

**2813**   **28-3   Einstein's Postulates and Their Consequences,   Numerical,   c**

A pion lives $2.5 \times 10^{-10}$ s in its rest frame.  It travels 15 cm down a beam pipe in a particle accelerator before it decays to other particles.  How long is this distance in the rest frame of the pion?

   a.   34 cm
   b.   15 cm
   c.   6.5 cm
   d.   6.7 cm
   e.   2.9 cm

**2814**   **28-3   Einstein's Postulates and Their Consequences,   Numerical,   a**

A spaceship travels to the nearest star, Alpha Centauri, 4.3 light-years away at a speed of $0.95c$.  How long does the trip take from the point of view of the passengers on the ship?

   a.   1.4 y
   b.   1.0 y
   c.   4.5 y
   d.   14 y
   e.   0.44 y

**2815**   **28-3   Einstein's Postulates and Their Consequences,   Numerical,   c**

If a metrestick is measured by you to be 90 cm long as it moves past you in the direction of its length, what is its speed?

   a.   $5.7 \times 10^7$ m/s
   b.   $9.5 \times 10^7$ m/s
   c.   $1.3 \times 10^8$ m/s
   d.   $2.4 \times 10^8$ m/s
   e.   $2.7 \times 10^8$ m/s

**2816**   **28-3   Einstein's Postulates and Their Consequences,   Conceptual,   e**

Which of the following is NOT a consequence of Einstein's postulates?

   a.   Every observer in every reference frame measures the same value for the speed of light.
   b.   Moving clocks appear to run slow.
   c.   Moving objects appear to be contracted along the direction of motion.
   d.   Clocks synchronized in one reference frame are not synchronized in any frame moving relative to that reference frame.
   e.   Nothing can move at a speed greater than light.

**2817    28-3    Einstein's Postulates and Their Consequences,   Conceptual,   c**

You stand on a corner as a friend drives past in an automobile.  You both note the time interval required for the car to travel one block, and you both measure the distance traveled. The proper time interval is measured by _____ , and the proper distance is measured by _____ .

a.  you; you
b.  you; your friend
c.  your friend; you
d.  your friend; your friend
e.  your friend; both of you


**2818    28-3    Einstein's Postulates and Their Consequences,   Conceptual,   a**

A friend holding a metrestick and a clock drives past you.  The metrestick will appear too _____ to you, and the clock will appear _____ to you.

a.  short; slow
b.  long; slow
c.  short; fast
d.  long; fast
e.  short; normal


**2819    28-4    Clock Synchronization and Simultaneity,   Conceptual,   c**

You place two clocks that you consider to be synchronized 100 m apart along a road.  Your friend drives by at speed $V$ and observes the clocks to be out of synch by an amount $T$.  If you now place the clocks 200 m apart and your friend drives by at speed $2V$, what is the amount your friend will claim the clocks are out of synch?

a.  $T$
b.  $2T$
c.  $4T$
d.  $T/2$
e.  $T/4$


**2820    28-4    Clock Synchronization and Simultaneity,   Conceptual,   b**

Event $A$ is seen by an observer to occur before event $B$.  Which of the following statements is FALSE?

a.  Another reference frame must exist in which event $A$ precedes event $B$.
b.  A reference frame must exist in which event $B$ precedes $A$.
c.  A reference frame could exist in which the events are simultaneous.
d.  A reference frame could not exist in which event $B$ precedes event $A$.
e.  A reference frame could not exist in which event $B$ is never observed to occur.

**2821    28-4   Clock Synchronization and Simultaneity,   Numerical,   a**

In the twenty-second century, a hyperfast New York to Los Angeles train roars through St. Louis without stopping at a speed of 0.80$c$. The front of the train arrives at the St. Louis station at precisely 12:00 noon according to all the clocks on the train (which are all synchronized in the train's frame), and the passengers are called to lunch in the dining car. An observer on the station platform manages to catch a glimpse of a clock at the front of the train that reads exactly 12:00 noon. What is the time at this instant at the rear of the train, according to the observer on the platform, if the train is 500 m long in its rest frame?

a.   1.35 μs past noon
b.   1.35 μs before noon
c.   noon exactly
d.   1.35 ms past noon
e.   1.35 ms before noon

**2822    28-5   The Twin Paradox,   Conceptual,   e**

Castor and Pollux are identical twins. Both get into their individual spaceships and blast-off simultaneously. Castor's is the faster ship. Both return to earth simultaneously. Which of the following statements is TRUE?

a.   Castor is older only if he traveled in the same direction as Pollux.
b.   Castor is older only if he traveled in the opposite direction to Pollux.
c.   Pollux is older only if he traveled in the same direction as Castor.
d.   Pollux is older only if he traveled in the opposite direction to Castor.
e.   Pollux is older.

**2823    28-5   The Twin Paradox,   Conceptual,   d**

To thoroughly dispel the twin paradox, what kind of reference frame must be analyzed?

a.   a reference frame moving at high speed
b.   an inertial reference frame
c.   the ether
d.   a noninertial reference frame
e.   a reference frame in which the speed of light is variable

**2824    28-6   Relativistic Momentum,   Conceptual,   b**

As an object of mass $M$ approaches the speed of light, its momentum approaches

a.   zero
b.   infinity
c.   $Mc$
d.   $Mc^2$
e.   $c$

**2825    28-6    Relativistic  Momentum,  Numerical,  d**

A proton is accelerated in a cyclotron to one-third of the speed of light.  The proton travels
along arcs of a circle through the magnetic field of the cyclotron.  Near the beginning of its
path through the cyclotron, the speed of the proton is small and the radius of the arc is small.
Near the end of its path, the radius is large and the speed is $c/3$, so the motion of the particle
must be treated relativistically.  What must be the ratio of the average magnetic field at the
edge of the cyclotron to that at the center to compensate for the relativistic momentum of the
proton?  (HINT:  The cyclotron frequency $f = qB/2\pi m$ must remain constant for the proton
throughout its path.)

a.  0.94
b.  0.33
c.  1.3
d.  1.1
e.  1.7

**2826    28-7    Relativistic  Energy,  Numerical,  a**

A proton with a rest energy of 938 MeV has a speed of $0.99c$.  What is its momentum in
units of GeV/$c$?

a.  6.6 GeV/$c$
b.  0.93 GeV/$c$
c.  9.3 GeV/$c$
d.  3.3 GeV/$c$
e.  47 GeV/$c$

**2827    28-7    Relativistic  Energy,  Numerical,  c**

As astronauts in a spaceship with a speed of $0.6c$ relative to the earth move outward from
the earth toward Jupiter, they observe a cosmic ray shower that contains protons moving
toward them at $0.2c$ relative to the earth.  One of the protons has a rest energy of 3.0 GeV
and  momentum as measured by the astronauts of 4.0 GeV/$c$.  Its kinetic energy is

a.  7.0 GeV
b.  4.0 GeV
c.  5.0 GeV
d.  2.7 GeV
e.  2.0 GeV

**2828    28-7    Relativistic  Energy,  Numerical,  b**

An electron with a rest mass of 0.511 MeV travels at speed $v = 0.500c$.  What is its kinetic
energy?

a.  590 keV
b.  80 keV
c.  510 keV
d.  430 keV
e.  220 keV

**2829 28-7 Relativistic Energy, Numerical, b**

The energy released by the nuclear bomb that destroyed Hiroshima was equivalent to 12.4 kilotons of TNT. This is equivalent to $9.0 \times 10^{26}$ MeV. The mass that was converted into energy in this explosion was

a. 1.6 kg
b. $1.6 \times 10^{-3}$ kg
c. $1.4 \times 10^{14}$ kg
d. $1.1 \times 10^{10}$ kg
e. 120 kg

**2830 28-7 Relativistic Energy, Conceptual, b**

A proton and an electron are accelerated until their total energy is twice their rest masses. If the rest mass of the proton is $M_p c^2 = 931$ MeV and that of an electron is $M_e c^2 = 0.51$ MeV, the ratio of the velocity of the electron to that of the proton is

a. 0.5
a. 1.0
c. 1.5
d. 2.0
e. Not enough data are given.

**2831 28-7 Relativistic Energy, Numerical, a**

In a nuclear reaction, 0.0036 ($1.67 \times 10^{-31}$ kg) of mass is converted to the kinetic energy of a deuteron that is originally at rest. The kinetic energy of the deuteron is

a. 3.4 MeV
b. 3.6 eV
c. $3.9 \times 10^{-6}$ MeV
d. $3.2 \times 10^{18}$ eV
e. $4.2 \times 10^{8}$ eV

**2832 28-7 Relativistic Energy, Numerical, a**

The total yearly world consumption of energy is approximately $4.0 \times 10^{20}$ J. How much mass would have to be completely converted into energy to provide this amount of energy?

a. $4.4 \times 10^{3}$ kg
b. $1.3 \times 10^{12}$ kg
c. $1.3 \times 10^{4}$ kg
d. $4.4 \times 10^{5}$ kg
e. $2.2 \times 10^{4}$ kg

**2833 28-7 Relativistic Energy, Conceptual, a**

A particle of mass $M$ moving at speed $V \ll c$ has approximately what energy?

a. $Mc^2$
b. $MV^2/2$
c. $cMV$
d. $Mc^2/2$
e. $cMV/2$

**2834**  **28-8  General Relativity,  Conceptual,  c**

Imagine a kind of material that would exert an antigravitational force on you.  Which of the following statements about the material is FALSE?

a.  Light would be repelled by the material.
b.  An antigravitational red shift would be possible.
c.  A black hole could be made of this material.
d.  Clocks would run more quickly in regions where the magnitude of the antigravitational potential is large.
e.  An antigravitational blue shift would be possible.

**2835**  **28-8  General Relativity,  Conceptual,  c**

A set of twins work in an office building.  One works on the top floor and the other works in the basement.  Considering general relativity, which one will age more quickly?

a.  They will age at the same rate.
b.  The twin who works on the top floor will age more quickly.
c.  The twin who works in the basement will age more quickly.
d.  It depends on the speed of the office building.
e.  None of these is correct.

CHAPTER 29    The Origins of Quantum Theory

**2901    29-1   Blackbody Radiation,   Conceptual,   e**

Quantum of light $A$ has three times the energy of quantum of light $B$.  If the wavelength of $A$ is 400 nm, the wavelength of $B$ is

a.   133 nm
b.   200 nm
c.   230 nm
d.   693 nm
e.   1200 nm

**2902    29-1   Blackbody Radiation,   Conceptual,   d**

The amount of energy of a quantum of light of a given frequency is

a.   directly proportional to the speed of light.
b.   directly proportional to the wavelength of light.
c.   dependent on the intensity of light.
d.   always constant.
e.   None of these is correct.

**2903    29-1   Blackbody Radiation,   Numerical,   e**

The peak in the radiation spectrum emitted by a blackbody at $T = 1600$ K is at $\lambda = 1.90$ μm. What is the wavelength at the peak if $T = 3000$ K?

a.   3.6 μm
b.   2.6 μm
c.   1.9 μm
d.   1.4 μm
e.   1.0 μm

**2904    29-1 Blackbody Radiation,  Factual,  a**

The energy of a quantum of light is Planck's constant multiplied by the frequency of the radiation.  The SI units of energy of a quantum of light are

a.  J
b.  J·s
c.  J/s
d.  N/C
e.  None of these is correct.


**2905    29-1 Blackbody Radiation, Numerical, b**

An electron and a positron (an antielectron) each have an energy of 0.51 MeV.  They destroy one another to produce two identical photons.  The frequency of these photons is

a.  $4.1 \times 10^{11}$ Hz
b.  $1.2 \times 10^{20}$ Hz
c.  $3.7 \times 10^{20}$ Hz
d.  $1.6 \times 10^{9}$ Hz
e.  $2.2 \times 10^{20}$ Hz


**2906    29-1  Blackbody Radiation,  Numerical,  b**

What is the energy in electronvolts of a quantum of light of wavelength 555 nm?  (Planck's constant $h = 6.626 \times 10^{-34}$ J·s.)

a.  0.22 eV
b.  2.2 eV
c.  22. eV
d.  0.45 eV
e.  4.5 eV


**2907    29-2  The Photoelectric Effect,  Numerical,  e**

The maximum kinetic energy of electrons ejected from barium (whose work function is 2.50 eV) when it is illuminated by light of wavelength 350 nm is

a.  0.20 eV
b.  0.41 eV
c.  0.63 eV
d.  0.95 eV
e.  1.05 eV

**2908   29-2   The Photoelectric Effect,   Conceptual,   d**

In the photoelectric effect, the work function depends on the

a.  incident wavelength.
b.  applied voltage.
c.  light intensity.
d.  metal that the light strikes.
e.  current.

**2909   29-2   The Photoelectric Effect,   Conceptual,   c**

The maximum wavelength for the photoemission of electrons from a metal surface depends on the

a.  applied voltage.
b.  light intensity.
c.  metal that the light strikes.
d.  current.
e.  None of these is correct.

**2910   29-2   The Photoelectric Effect,   Conceptual,   e**

If the frequency of light causing photoemission of electrons is doubled, the kinetic energy of the ejected electrons will

a.  increase by a factor of $1/\sqrt{2}$.
b.  double.
c.  decrease by a factor of 2.
d.  increase by a factor less than two.
e.  increase by a factor more than two.

**2911   29-2   The Photoelectric Effect,   Numerical,   c**

Potassium has a work function of 2.3 eV for photoelectric emission.  Which of the following wavelengths is the longest wavelength for which photoemission will occur?

a.  400 nm
b.  450 nm
c.  500 nm
d.  550 nm
e.  600 nm

**2912   29-2   The Photoelectric Effect,   Factual,   e**

Albert Einstein was awarded the Nobel Prize for his

a.  theory of special relativity.
b.  theory of general relativity.
c.  explanation of Brownian motion.
d.  explanation of the Michelson-Morley experiment.
e.  explanation of the photoelectric effect.

**2913**    **29-2  The Photoelectric Effect,  Numerical,  d**

In a photoelectric experiment, the threshold frequency for a material is $3.2 \times 10^{14}$ Hz.  An electron ejected by a photon of frequency $9.4 \times 10^{14}$ Hz from this surface can be stopped by a stopping potential of

a.  0.0085 V
b.  1.6 V
c.  $2.6 \times 10^{-10}$ V
d.  2.6 V
e.  $3.6 \times 10^3$ V

**2914**    **29-2  The Photoelectric Effect,  Numerical,  a**

The work function for tungsten is 4.58 eV.  What is the kinetic energy of electrons emitted when light of wavelength 400 nm is incident on a tungsten surface?  (Planck's constant $h = 6.626 \times 10^{-34}$ J·s $= 4.136 \times 10^{-15}$ eV·s)

a.  No electrons will be emitted.
b.  1.5 eV
c.  7.7 eV
d.  2.9 eV
e.  0.74 eV

**2915**    **29-2  The Photoelectric Effect,  Numerical,  c**

Light of wavelength 400 nm is incident on a certain metal.  The stopping potential for the emitted electrons is measured to be 1.2 V.  What is the work function of this metal?  (Planck's constant $h = 6.626 \times 10^{-34}$ J·s $= 4.136 \times 10^{-15}$ eV·s)

a.  4.3 eV
b.  3.1 eV
c.  1.9 eV
d.  1.2 eV
e.  0.95 eV

**2916**    **29-2  The Photoelectric Effect,  Numerical,  c**

Photons that have an energy of 7.52 eV strike a material that has a work function of 4.22 eV.  The maximum kinetic energy of the electron emitted from this material is

a.  7.5 eV
b.  12 eV
c.  3.3 eV
d.  0.98 eV
e.  No electrons will be ejected by these photons.

**2917**    **29-3  X-Rays,  Numerical,  a**

An x-ray tube is operated at 40 kV.  What is the wavelength of the most energetic x-rays emitted from this tube?

a.  0.031 nm
b.  31 nm
c.  $1.7 \times 10^{-6}$ m
d.  $2.5 \times 10^{-5}$ m
e.  0.75 nm

**2918    29-3   X-Rays,   Conceptual,   d**

If the voltage across an x-ray tube is doubled, the wavelengths of the characteristic spectrum emitted by this tube will

a.  double.
b.  quadruple.
c.  be decreased to one-half of their original energy.
d.  remain constant.
e.  None of these is correct.


**2919    29-3   X-Rays,   Conceptual,   c**

If the voltage across an x-ray tube is doubled, the minimum wavelength of the bremsstrahlung radiation will

a.  double.
b.  quadruple.
c.  be decreased to one-half of its original wavelength.
d.  remain constant.
e.  None of these is correct.


**2920    29-3   X-Rays,   Numerical,   c**

The energy of an x-ray photon of wavelength $3.0 \times 10^{-10}$ m is

a.  $1.0 \times 10^{-16}$ J
b.  $9.9 \times 10^{-16}$ J
c.  $6.6 \times 10^{-16}$ J
d.  $2.2 \times 10^{-24}$ J
e.  $3.2 \times 10^{-29}$ J


**2921    29-4   Compton Scattering,   Conceptual,   b**

Quantum $A$ has twice the energy of Quantum $B$.  The ratio of the momentum of $A$ to that of $B$ is

a.  4
b.  2
c.  1
d.  1/2
e.  1/4


**2922    29-4   Compton Scattering,   Conceptual,   b**

A Compton-scattered x-ray photon has less energy than the incident photon.  The scattered photon therefore has

a.  the same wavelength as the incident photon.
b.  a longer wavelength than the incident photon.
c.  a shorter wavelength than the incident photon.
d.  It cannot be assigned a wavelength.
e.  None of these is correct.

**2923    29-4  Compton  Scattering,  Conceptual,  c**

An x-ray photon scattering off an electron imparts some of its energy to the electron (the Compton effect).  Which of the following statements is TRUE?

a.  The wavelength of the scattered photon is unchanged.
b.  The wavelength of the scattered photon is decreased.
c.  The wavelength of the scattered photon is increased.
d.  The scattered photon gains speed.
e.  The scattered photon is slowed down.

**2924    29-4  Compton  Scattering,  Conceptual,  e**

Which of the following formulas has the correct units for the linear momentum of a photon?

a.  $hc/\lambda$
b.  $c/\bar{n}$
c.  $1/\lambda$
d.  $\lambda/h$
e.  None of these is correct.

**2925    29-4  Compton  Scattering,  Numerical,  c**

When an x-ray  is Compton scattered at right angles to its initial direction, the shift in its wavelength is $\lambda_c = 2.4$ pm.  (1 picometre $= 10^{-12}$ m)  An x-ray with wavelength of 15.4 pm is Compton scattered at right angles to its initial direction.   The wavelength of the scattered x-ray is

a.  2.4 pm
b.  0.15 pm
c.  18 pm
d.  13 pm
e.  170 pm

**2926    29-4  Compton  Scattering,  Factual,  d**

In the Compton effect,

a.  an electron is stopped suddenly.
b.  an x-ray collides with an electron; the electron is ejected and the x-ray photon ceases to exist.
c.  a neutrino is produced in a nuclear decay.
d.  an energetic photon collides with an electron and both the electron and the photon are scattered.
e.  None of these is correct.

**2927    29-4  Compton  Scattering,  Numerical,  d**

What is the momentum (in SI units) of a photon of wavelength $\lambda = 560$ nm?  (Planck's constant $h = 6.626 \times 10^{-34}$ J·s.)

a.  $3.7 \times 10^{-42}$ kg·m/s
b.  $8.4 \times 10^{-25}$ kg·m/s
c.  $1.2 \times 10^{-30}$ kg·m/s
d.  $1.2 \times 10^{-27}$ kg·m/s
e.  $3.6 \times 10^{-27}$ kg·m/s

**2928    29-4   Compton Scattering,  Numerical,  e**

What is the shift in wavelength of a photon scattered at 160°?

a.  2.4 pm
b.  0.15 pm
c.  1.6 pm
d.  1.2 pm
e.  4.7 pm

**2929    29-5   Quantization of Atomic Energies: The Bohr Model,  Conceptual,  e**

The energy of the $n = 1$ level of hydrogen is -13.6 eV.  The energy of the $n = 4$ level is

a.  -6.8 eV
b.  -3.4 eV
c.  -54.4 eV
d.  -27.2 eV
e.  -0.85 eV

**2930    29-5   Quantization of Atomic Energies: The Bohr Model,  Numerical,  a**

The energy of the $n = 1$ level of hydrogen is -13.6 eV.  The wavelength of the emission line corresponding to the transition from $n = 4$ to $n = 3$ is

a.  $1.9 \times 10^{-6}$ m
b.  $8.2 \times 10^{-7}$ m
c.  $5.3 \times 10^{5}$ m
d.  $3.0 \times 10^{-25}$ m
e.  $1.6 \times 10^{14}$ m

**2931    29-5   Quantization of Atomic Energies: The Bohr Model,  Numerical,  c**

The energy of the $n = 1$ level of hydrogen is -13.6 eV.  The difference in energy between the $n = 3$ and $n = 4$ levels (magnitude only) is

a.  1.1 eV
b.  0.88 eV
c.  0.66 eV
d.  1.5 eV
e.  0.33 eV

**2932    29-5   Quantization of Atomic Energies: The Bohr Model,  Conceptual,  b**

The radius of the $n = 1$ orbit in the hydrogen atom is 0.053 nm.  What is the radius of the $n = 5$ orbit?

a.  5(0.053) nm
b.  25(0.053) nm
c.  0.053 nm
d.  (1/5)(0.053) nm
e.  (1/25)(0.053) nm

**2933    29-5   Quantization of Atomic Energies: The Bohr Model,  Conceptual,  a**

The radius of the $n = 1$ orbit in the hydrogen atom is 0.053 nm.  What is the radius of the $n = 3$ orbit of lithium, which has three protons in its nucleus?

a.  3(0.053) nm
b.  9(0.053) nm
c.  0.053 nm
d.  (1/3)(0.053) nm
e.  (1/9)(0.053) nm


**2934    29-5   Quantization of Atomic Energies: The Bohr Model,  Numerical,  c**

The energy levels of a hydrogen atom are inversely proportional to the square of the principal quantum number $n$.  The energy of the ground level of atomic hydrogen is -13.6 eV.  The energy of the second ($n = 2$) level of the hydrogen atom is

a.  +13.6 eV
b.  -13.6 eV
c.  -3.4 eV
d.  -54.8 eV
e.  +3.4 eV


**2935    29-5   Quantization of Atomic Energies: The Bohr Model,  Numerical,  b**

Light of wavelength 411 nm is observed from a hydrogen discharge.  What transition produces this emission?  The energy of the $n = 1$ level is -13.6 eV.

a.  $n = 1.13$ to $n = 1$
b.  $n = 6$ to $n = 2$
c.  $n = 3$ to $n = 3$
d.  $n = 2$ to $n = 6$
e.  $n = 5$ to $n = 1$


**2936    29-5   Quantization of Atomic Energies: The Bohr Model,  Conceptual,  c**

The radii of the Bohr orbits in atomic hydrogen are given by:

$$r = n^2 \frac{(h/2\pi)^2}{mkZe^2}$$

If the radius of the first Bohr orbit ($n = 1$) is 0.053 nm, the radius of the third Bohr orbit ($n = 3$) is

a.  0.16 nm
b.  0.018 nm
c.  0.48 nm
d.  0.35 nm
e.  1.3 nm

**2937    29-5   Quantization of Atomic Energies: The Bohr Model,   Conceptual,   a**

The equation derived by Bohr for the wavelengths $\lambda$ of the lines in hydrogen-like spectra is:

$$\frac{1}{\lambda} = Z^2 R\left(\frac{1}{n_2^{\,2}} - \frac{1}{n_1^{\,2}}\right)$$

The first member of the Balmer series of hydrogen has $\lambda$ =660 nm. Doubly-ionized $_3Li^6$ is hydrogen-like. The wavelength of the first member of the Balmer series for doubly-ionized $_3Li^6$ is

a.  73 nm
b.  5.9 x $10^3$ nm
c.  150 nm
d.  60 nm
e.  1.8 x $10^{-3}$ nm

**2938    29-5   Quantization of Atomic Energies: The Bohr Model,   Numerical,   a**

The energy of the $n$th level in a one-electron atom is $E_n = -13.6(Z^2/n^2)$ eV. Consider a beryllium ion with all but one of its electrons removed (a beryllium atom normally has four electrons). What is the energy of the electron when it is in the third lowest energy state?

a.  -24 eV
b.  -7.6 eV
c.  -1.5 eV
d.  24 eV
e.  7.6 eV

**2939    29-5   Quantization of Atomic Energies: The Bohr Model,   Numerical,   c**

The energy of the $n$th level in a one-electron atom is $E_n = -13.6(Z^2/n^2)$ eV. Consider a beryllium ion with all but one of its electrons removed (a beryllium atom normally has four electrons). What is the wavelength of a photon emitted when the electron makes the transition from the third lowest to the lowest energy state?

a.  1.03 x $10^{-7}$ m
b.  2.03 x $10^{-8}$ m
c.  6.43 x $10^{-9}$ m
d.  5.71 x $10^{-9}$ m
e.  1.03 x $10^{-27}$ m

CHAPTER 30     Electron Waves and Quantum Theory

**3001**    **30-1 The de Broglie Equations, Conceptual, c**

A proton has five times the momentum of an electron. If the electron has a de Broglie wavelength $\lambda$, then what is the de Broglie wavelength of the proton?

a. $\lambda$
b. $5\lambda$
c. $\lambda/5$
d. $25\lambda$
e. $\lambda/25$

**3002**    **30-1 The de Broglie Equations, Conceptual, b**

Electrons do not exhibit wave properties as readily as light because electrons typically have much _____ momenta than light and hence much _____ wavelengths.

a. greater; longer
b. greater; shorter
c. lesser; longer
d. lesser; shorter
e. greater; the same

**3003**    **30-1 The de Broglie Equations, Conceptual, d**

If a baseball, an electron, and a photon all have the same momentum, which would have the longest wavelength?

a. baseball
b. electron
c. photon
d. All would have the same wavelength.
e. It depends on the energy of the photon.

**3004**    **30-1 The de Broglie Equations, Numerical, a**

Which of the following particles has the longest wavelength?

a. a photon with a frequency of $3 \times 10^{19}$ Hz
b. a photon with an energy of $2 \times 10^{-13}$ J
c. an electron with a momentum of $6.6 \times 10^{-21}$ kg·m/s
d. a proton with a momentum of $6.6 \times 10^{-21}$ kg·m/s
e. All four have the same wavelength.

**3005    30-1   The de Broglie Equations,   Numerical,   d**

Suppose that the world could be changed so that the de Broglie wavelength of a 40-kg runner who goes 100 m in 10.0 s was 5.0 m.  What would the value of Planck's constant have to be?  (Assume that all other constants remain the same.)

a.  0.80 J·s
b.  1.25 J·s
c.  20 J·s
d.  2000 J·s
e.  2.0 x $10^5$ J·s


**3006    30-1   The de Broglie Equations,   Numerical,   c**

What is the speed of an electron whose de Broglie wavelength is 0.0010 m?

a.  7.3 x $10^{-7}$ m/s
b.  7.3 x $10^{-4}$ m/s
c.  0.73 m/s
d.  510 m/s
e.  5.1 x $10^5$ m/s


**3007    30-1   The de Broglie Equations,   Numerical,   d**

The wavelength of an electron is 1.33 nm.  What is its kinetic energy in electronvolts?

a.  1.18 eV
b.  1.08 eV
c.  0.922 eV
d.  0.850 eV
e.  3.40 eV


**3008    30-2   Electron Diffraction,   Factual,   c**

Davisson and Germer were responsible for

a.  the discovery of bremsstrahlung radiation.
b.  the first experimental evidence for Einstein's theory of relativity.
c.  confirmation of de Broglie's wave theory for matter.
d.  verification of Schrödinger's theory.
e.  the rise of vaudeville teams in the 1920s.


**3009    30-2   Electron Diffraction,   Conceptual,   c**

The electron microscope is a welcome addition to the field of microscopy because electrons have a _____ wavelength than light, thereby increasing the _____ of the microscope.

a.  longer; resolving power
b.  longer; breadth of field
c.  shorter; resolving power
d.  longer; breadth of field
e.  longer; intensity

**3010    30-3   Wave-Particle Duality,   Conceptual,   e**

The wave-particle duality theory is the first to give an adequate explanation of which of the following facts about the hydrogen atom?

a.  why the proton attracts the electron
b.  why the proton forms the nucleus of the atom
c.  why the electron orbits the proton
d.  why the mass of the atom is less than the sum of the individual proton and electron masses
e.  why a finite maximum energy is required to separate the proton and electron

**3011    30-3   Wave-Particle Duality,   Conceptual,   c**

The wave-particle duality theory is the first to give an adequate explanation of which of the following facts about the hydrogen atom?

a.  why more than one possible orbit exists for the electron
b.  why an infinite number of possible orbits  exists for the electron
c.  why only certain energies are possible for the orbiting electron
d.  why more than one momentum is possible for the orbiting electron
e.  None of these is correct.

**3012    30-4   The Uncertainty Principle,   Numerical,   c**

Suppose that a 40-kg runner in an imaginary world in which Planck's constant has the value 100 J·s must be located at the finish line to an accuracy of ±0.33 m (to be sure that he won the race!).  What would be the minimal uncertainty in his speed in that world?

a.  0.12 m/s
b.  0.13 m/s
c.  0.60 m/s
d.  1.2 m/s
e.  15.0 m/s

**3013    30-4   The Uncertainty Principle,   Numerical,   a**

An electron has a kinetic energy of 1.5 eV.  If its momentum is uncertain by ±2.5%, what is the minimum uncertainty in its position?

a.  0.50 nm
b.  5.0 nm
c.  1.0 nm
d.  2.0 nm
e.  1.6 nm

**3014    30-4   The Uncertainty Principle,   Numerical,   d**

A proton (rest energy = 938 MeV) is confined inside a space of length 3.0 fm = $3.0 \times 10^{-15}$ m, about the size of a light nucleus.  What is the minimum uncertainty in its momentum?

a.  $2.2 \times 10^{-17}$ kg·m/s
b.  $5.5 \times 10^{-18}$ kg·m/s
c.  $3.6 \times 10^{-18}$ kg·m/s
d.  $1.8 \times 10^{-20}$ kg·m/s
e.  $8.8 \times 10^{-19}$ kg·m/s

3015    **30-4  The Uncertainty Principle,  Conceptual,  b**

Can you ever be sure that a baseball in your room has absolutely zero kinetic energy?

a.  Of course!
b.  Of course not!
c.  Yes, but only if you have extremely sensitive instruments.
d.  Yes, but only if you can lower the temperature of your room to 0 K.
e.  Yes, but only if you wait for more than 6.02 x $10^{23}$ years.


3016    **30-5  The Electron Wave Function,  Conceptual,  c**

The single electron wave function tells us

a.  where the particle is.
b.  where the wave is.
c.  where the particle is likely to be.
d.  where the wave is likely to be.
e.  the electric field of the wave.


3017    **30-6  A Particle in a Box,  Conceptual,  a**

The electron wave function gives us a useful picture of a single electron as a _____ and a large group of identical electrons as a _____.

a.  cloud; wave
b.  wave; cloud
c.  cloud; cloud
d.  wave; wave.
e.  point particle; cloud


3018    **30-6  A Particle in a Box,  Conceptual,  b**

A "plasma" can be thought of as a collection of highly ionized atoms (that is, nuclei and electrons are essentially separated).  Which of the following is FALSE?

a.  Quantum theory is able to describe the physics of plasmas correctly .
b.  Only quantum theory can describe the physics of plasmas correctly.
c.  Classical theory is able to describe the physics of plasmas correctly.
d.  Both classical and quantum theory are able to describe the physics of plasmas correctly.
e.  Quantum theory and classical theory are nearly indistinguishable in their descriptions of the physics of plasmas.


3019    **30-6  A Particle in a Box,  Conceptual,  e**

A particle is confined in a one-dimensional box. The ground state energy is $E$. If a second particle of twice the mass is placed in a second box of twice the length, what will its ground state energy be?

a.  $E$
b.  $4E$
c.  $E/4$
d.  $8E$
e.  $E/8$

**3020    30-6   A Particle in a Box,   Numerical,   b**

A marble of mass 20 g is in a box of length 5.0 cm.  What is the difference in the energies of the two lowest energy states allowed for this marble?

a.   $3.5 \times 10^{-64}$ J
b.   $3.3 \times 10^{-63}$ J
c.   $1.4 \times 10^{-63}$ J
d.   $1.0 \times 10^{-65}$ J
e.   $3.5 \times 10^{-68}$ J

**3021    30-6   A Particle in a Box,   Numerical,   a**

What is the wavelength of the electromagnetic radiation emitted when an electron confined to a box of length 0.20 nm makes a transition from the $n = 3$ to the $n = 1$ level?

a.   16 nm
b.   46 nm
c.   100 nm
d.   210 nm
e.   520 nm

CHAPTER 31    Atoms, Molecules, and Solids

**3101    31-1   Quantum Theory of the Hydrogen Atom,   Numerical,   d**

In an atom with $\ell = 2$ and $m = 1$, what is the angle between the angular momentum vector and the $z$ axis?

a.  60°
b.  30°
c.  24°
d.  66°
e.  90°

**3102    31-1   Quantum Theory of the Hydrogen Atom,   Factual,   a**

For the principal quantum number $n = 4$, how many different values can the orbital quantum number $\ell$ have?

a.  4
b.  3
c.  7
d.  16
e.  6

**3103    31-1   Quantum Theory of the Hydrogen Atom,   Factual,   a**

The fine structure of the spectral lines of hydrogen is explained by differences in the

a.  principal quantum number.
b.  orbital quantum number.
c.  magnetic quantum number.
d.  spin quantum number.
e.  None of these is correct.

**3104    31-1   Quantum Theory of the Hydrogen Atom,   Factual,   c**

For the principal quantum number $n = 4$, how many different values can the magnetic quantum number $m$ have?

a.  4
b.  3
c.  7
d.  16
e.  6

**3105**    **31-1   Quantum Theory of the Hydrogen Atom,   Numerical,   d**

What is the total number of distinct electron states (including spin) when $n = 5$?

   a.   18
   b.   22
   c.   25
   d.   50
   e.   72

**3106**    **31-1   Quantum Theory of the Hydrogen Atom,   Factual,   a**

Bohr's quantum condition on electron orbits

   a.   required that the angular momentum of the electron about the hydrogen nucleus equal $nh/(2\pi)$.
   b.   required that no more than one electron occupy a given stationary state.
   c.   required the electrons to spiral into the nucleus while radiating electromagnetic waves.
   d.   required that the energies of an electron in a hydrogen atom be equal to $nE_0$, where $E_0$ is a constant energy and $n$ is an integer.
   e.   required none of the above.

**3107**    **31-1   Quantum Theory of the Hydrogen Atom,   Numerical,   e**

What is the energy of the $n = 5$ state of the hydrogen atom?

   a.   68 eV
   b.   0.54 eV
   c.   -68 eV
   d.   -2.72 eV
   e.   -0.54 eV

**3108**    **31-1   Quantum Theory of the Hydrogen Atom,   Numerical,   b**

A compact disk of a CD player has a moment of inertia $I = 2.50 \times 10^{-5}$ kg·m$^2$ and rotates at 500 rev/min. Taking $L = I\omega$ and using the quantization of angular momentum, what is the approximate value of $\ell$? ($\hbar = 1.055 \times 10^{-34}$ J·s.)

   a.   $1.2 \times 10^{32}$
   b.   $1.2 \times 10^{31}$
   c.   $7.4 \times 10^{32}$
   d.   130
   e.   $3.5 \times 10^{15}$

**3109**    **31-2   The Periodic Table,   Factual,   c**

How many of oxygen's eight electrons are found in the $p$ state?

   a.   0
   b.   2
   c.   4
   d.   6
   e.   8

**3110    31-2  The Periodic Table,  Factual,  b**

The $p$ state of an electronic configuration corresponds to

a.  $n = 2$
b.  $\ell = 2$
c.  $\ell = 1$
d.  $n = 0$
e.  $\ell = 0$

**3111    31-3  Atomic Spectra,  Numerical,  c**

The energy of a photon of visible light is on the order of

a.  $10^{-6}$ eV
b.  $10^{-3}$ eV
c.  $10^{0}$ eV
d.  $10^{3}$ eV
e.  $10^{6}$ eV

**3112    31-3  Atomic Spectra,  Factual,  a**

Which of the following characteristic x-ray lines results from the least energetic transition?

a.  $K_\alpha$
b.  $K_\beta$
c.  $K_\gamma$
d.  All of these characteristic x-ray lines are the same.
e.  None of these is correct.

**3113    31-3  Atomic Spectra,  Numerical,  d**

What is the wavelength of the $K_\alpha$ characteristic x-ray emitted by tungsten (Z=74)?

$$\lambda = \frac{hc}{(13.6 \text{ eV})(Z - 1)^2(1 - 1/n^2)}$$

where $h = 6.6 \times 10^{-34}$ J·s and the  mass of a proton = $1.67 \times 10^{-27}$ kg.

a.  0.0167 nm
b.  0.0174 nm
c.  0.0222 nm
d.  0.0228 nm
e.  0.310 nm

**3114    31-3  Atomic Spectra,  Numerical,  c**

A $K_\beta$ x-ray line of wavelength 0.1641 nm is emitted by a certain metal.  What is the value of $Z$ and which element is it?

a.  24, Cr
b.  25, Mn
c.  26, Fe
d.  27, Co
e.  28, Ni

**3115** **31-4 Molecular Bonding, Conceptual, d**

The dissociation energy of an ionic compound is the negative of the potential energy of the positive-negative ion system when the ions are

a. touching.
b. infinitely far apart.
c. still atoms and have not yet been formed into ions.
d. at the equilibrium separation.
e. completely dissolved in a solvent.

**3116** **31-5 Molecular Spectra, Conceptual, e**

If the rotational energy of a diatomic molecule is increased by 10%, the separation of the atoms

a. increases by a factor of 1.1
b. increases by a factor of 0.95
c. increases by a factor of 1.05
d. decreases by a factor of 1.1
e. decreases by a factor of 0.95

**3117** **31-5 Molecular Spectra, Numerical, b**

The two oxygen atoms in the $O_2$ molecule are separated by 0.12 nm. What are the values of the two lowest rotational energies of $O_2$?

a. $9.0 \times 10^{-5}$ eV and $1.8 \times 10^{-4}$ eV
b. $1.8 \times 10^{-4}$ eV and $3.6 \times 10^{-4}$ eV
c. $3.6 \times 10^{-4}$ eV and $7.2 \times 10^{-4}$ eV
d. $1.8 \times 10^{-4}$ eV and $11 \times 10^{-4}$ eV
e. $3.6 \times 10^{-4}$ eV and $22 \times 10^{-4}$ eV

**3118** **31-5 Molecular Spectra, Factual, b**

When examined with a grating spectrograph, the discharge from helium gas has bright radiation at relatively few discrete wavelengths; the discharge from nitrogen gas has radiation in bands with a very large number of discrete wavelengths. What is the reason for this difference in the spectra of these two gases?

a. The atoms of the helium gas have two electrons whereas the atoms of the nitrogen gas have many electrons; therefore, the nitrogen gas gives a more complicated spectrum.
b. The nitrogen gas has molecules that have rotational and vibrational energies that produce bands of closely spaced wavelengths in the spectrum.
c. The nitrogen gas discharge is hotter, which "smears out" the wavelengths of the radiation according to Planck's law for blackbody radiation.
d. The levels of the helium atoms can be obtained from the Bohr theory of atoms, which gives a few relatively discrete allowed energies, whereas nitrogen must be described by the band theory, which gives continuous bands of allowed energies.
e. None of these are the correct explanation.

**3119    31-5   Molecular Spectra,   Numerical,   c**

If the $H_2$ molecule has a rotational energy $E_{0r} = 4.00$ meV, what is the average distance between the two atoms?

   a.  $1.0 \times 10^{-13}$ m
   b.  $3.2 \times 10^{-11}$ m
   c.  $1.0 \times 10^{-10}$ m
   d.  $1.0 \times 10^{-20}$ m
   e.  $1.4 \times 10^{-10}$ m

**3120    31-7   Band Theory of Solids,   Factual,   d**

A metal is a good conductor because the valence energy band for electrons is

   a.  There are no valence electrons in a metal.
   b.  completely full.
   c.  full, but there is only a small gap to a higher empty band.
   d.  partly full.
   e.  None of these is correct.

**3121    31-7   Band Theory of Solids,   Factual,   b**

Insulators are poor conductors of electricity because

   a.  there is a small energy gap between the valence band and the next higher band where electrons can exist.
   b.  there is a large energy gap between the valence band and the next higher band where electrons can exist.
   c.  the valence band has a few vacancies for electrons.
   d.  the valence band is only partly full.
   e  None of these is correct.

**3122    31-8   Semiconductor Junctions and Devices,   Factual,   c**

When light strikes the *p*-type semiconductor in a *pn* junction solar cell,

   a.  only free electrons are created.
   b.  only positive holes are created.
   c.  both electrons and holes are created.
   d.  positive protons are created.
   e.  None of these is correct.

**3123    31-8   Semiconductor Junctions and Devices,   Factual,   b**

When a *pnp* junction transistor is used as an amplifier, a small signal in the _____ current results in a large signal in the _____ current.

   a.  collector; base
   b.  base; collector
   c.  emitter; base
   d.  emitter; collector
   e.  collector; base

**3124    31-8   Semiconductor Junctions and Devices,   Conceptual,   a**

An alternating-current generator is producing a voltage with a frequency of 60 Hz.  In the diagram, *D* is a solid state diode made from a *pn* germanium junction.  Which graph best describes the current *I* through the resistor *R* as a function of time?

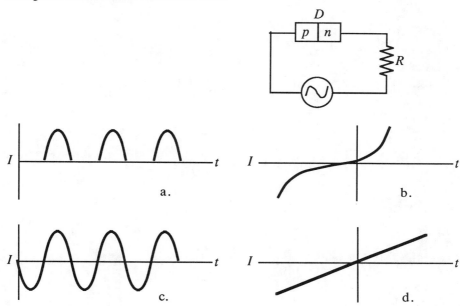

a.

b.

c.

d.

e.   None of these is correct.

**3125    31-8   Semiconductor Junctions and Devices,   Factual,   b**

A *pn* junction of germanium is connected through a resistor to a variable dc power supply as shown.  Which of the following graphs best describes the current *I* in the circuit as the voltage V of the power supply is varied in the range of approximately -10 V to +10 V?

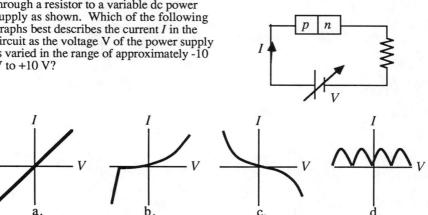

a.

b.

c.

d.

e.   None of these is correct.

CHAPTER 32    Nuclear Physics

3201    32-1   Properties of Nuclei,   Conceptual,   c

Why is there a greater ratio of neutrons to protons in the heavier elements?

a.  The greater the number of protons, the weaker the proton-neutron strong nuclear force.
b.  The greater the number of neutrons, the weaker the proton-neutron strong nuclear force.
c.  The greater the number of protons, the greater the electrostatic force of repulsion that must be overcome.
d.  The greater the number of neutrons, the greater the electrostatic force of repulsion that must be overcome.
e.  There is actually a lesser ratio of neutrons to protons in the heavier elements.

3202    32-1   Properties of Nuclei,   Conceptual,   e

The fact that nuclei all have the same density indicates that

a.  the strong nuclear force is different between protons than between neutrons.
b.  the hadronic force is different between neutrons than between a proton and a neutron.
c.  the hadronic force is the same between protons as it is between a neutron and an electron.
d.  the strong nuclear force does not exist between the proton and electron.
e.  the hadronic force is much the same between protons, between neutrons, and between a proton and a neutron.

3203    32-1   Properties of Nuclei,   Factual,   c

The superscript just before the symbol for an element represents the number of

a.  protons.
b.  neutrons.
c.  protons plus neutrons.
d.  protons minus neutrons.
e.  neutrons minus protons.

3204    32-1   Properties of Nuclei,   Factual,   c

Two isotopes of an element have

a.  the same number of nucleons in their nuclei.
b.  the same number of protons and the same number of neutrons.
c.  the same number of protons but different numbers of neutrons.
d.  a different number of protons and the same number of neutrons.
e.  a different number of protons and a different number of neutrons.

**3205    32-1   Properties of Nuclei,   Factual,   e**

Which of the following is a negatively charged particle found in the nucleus of an atom?

a.  proton
b.  electron
c.  neutron
d.  nucleon
e.  None of these is correct.


**3206    32-1   Properties of Nuclei,   Factual,   a**

The chemical characteristics of an atom (what element it is) are determined by

a.  its atomic number.
b.  its mass number.
c.  its neutron number.
d.  its nucleon number.
e.  All of these are correct.


**3207    32-1   Properties of Nuclei,   Factual,   a**

The subscript just before the symbol for an element represents the number of

a.  protons.
b.  neutrons.
c.  protons plus neutrons.
d.  protons minus neutrons.
e.  neutrons minus protons.


**3208    32-1   Properties of Nuclei,   Factual,   e**

The strong nuclear force acts

a.  between pairs of protons in the nucleus.
b.  between pairs of neutrons in the nucleus.
c.  between a proton and a neutron.
d.  between the nucleus and the electrons.
e.  Answers a, b, and c  are all correct.


**3209    32-1   Properties of Nuclei,   Numerical,   b**

What is the approximate radius of the $^{63}$Cu nucleus?

a.  0.38 fm
b.  6.0 fm
c.  12 fm
d.  24 fm
e.  100 fm

3210    32-1   **Properties of Nuclei,   Numerical,   d**

The following fusion reaction occurs in the sun:

$$^3_2\text{He} + ^4_2\text{He} \rightarrow\ ^7_4\text{Be}$$

The masses of nuclei are:

$^3\text{He} = 3.016\ 049$ u
$^4\text{He} = 4.002\ 604$ u
$^7\text{Be} = 7.016\ 930$ u

The energy released or absorbed by the reaction is

a.  920 MeV, absorbed
b.  1.6 MeV, absorbed
c.  920 MeV, released
d.  1.6 MeV, released
e.  270 MeV, released

3211    32-1   **Properties of Nuclei,   Numerical,   c**

Radon (Rn) is a gas.  Its nuclei decay with the emission of an alpha particle to form an isotope of polonium (Po):

$$^{222}_{86}\text{Rn} \rightarrow\ ^4_2\propto +\ ^{218}_{84}\text{Po}$$

The masses of the particles are:

$^{222}_{86}\text{Rn} =\quad 222.017\ 531$ u
$^4_2\propto\quad =\quad\ \ \ 4.002\ 603$ u
$^{218}_{84}\text{Po} = 218.008\ 318$ u

The rest energy of a unified mass unit is 931 MeV.  The kinetic energy of the ejected particle is

a.  6.26 MeV
b.  6.15 MeV
c.  6.04 MeV
d.  $6.61 \times 10^{-3}$ MeV
e.  5.73 MeV

**3212    32-1    Properties of Nuclei,    Numerical,    a**

When an alpha particle ($^4$He) with a kinetic energy of 6.54 MeV strikes a $^{27}$Al nucleus, a $^{30}$P nucleus is created and a neutron is ejected. Assume that the $^{30}$P nucleus has no final kinetic energy. Given the following masses for the different particles, what is the kinetic energy of the ejected neutron?

$$^4\text{He} = 4.002\ 603 \text{ u} \qquad\qquad ^1n = 1.008\ 665 \text{ u}$$
$$^{27}\text{Al} = 26.981\ 539 \text{ u} \qquad\qquad ^{30}\text{P} = 29.978\ 516 \text{ u}$$

a.  3.71 MeV
b.  2.83 MeV
c.  6.54 MeV
d.  9.37 MeV
e.  0.45 MeV

**3213    32-1    Properties of Nuclei,    Numerical,    a**

[For this question the students must be given Table 32-1 from the text or its equivalent.]

What is the total binding energy of $^{63}$Cu?

a.  551 MeV
b.  8.75 MeV
c.  555 MeV
d.  504 MeV
e.  62.9 MeV

**3214    32-1    Properties of Nuclei,    Factual,    b**

In this problem $Z$ is the atomic number, $N$ is the neutron number, and $A$ is the mass number. For stable isotopes with $A$ greater than 44, as $A$ increases, the ratio $Z/N$

a.  remains the same.
b.  decreases.
c.  equals $A - N$.
d.  increases.
e.  None of these is correct.

**3215    32-1    Properties of Nuclei,    Factual,    a**

In this problem $Z$ is the atomic number, $N$ is the neutron number, and $A$ is the mass number. For stable isotopes that have mass numbers between 2 and 20 and abundances of more than a fraction of a percent,

a.  $N = Z$ or $N = Z + 1$.
b.  $N = A$ and $Z = N - 1$.
c.  $Z = A = N$.
d.  $N = Z$ or $N = Z - 1$.
e.  None of these is correct.

3216    **32-2   Radioactivity,   Conceptual,   a**

The half-life of a radioactive substance is 5 minutes.  Which one of the following statements is TRUE of the decay of this substance?

a.   After 10 minutes, one-fourth of the original substance will remain.
b.   The amount of the substance remaining after a given time is proportional to the number of minutes.
c.   The amount of the substance remaining after a given time is inversely proportional to the number of minutes.
d.   After 10 minutes, none of the original substance will remain unchanged.
e.   None of these is correct.

3217    **32-2   Radioactivity,   Conceptual,   a**

In what type of radioactive decay are the mass numbers of the parent and daughter nuclei different ?

a.   alpha
b.   beta
c.   gamma
d.   both alpha and beta
e.   both beta and gamma

3218    **32-2   Radioactivity,   Conceptual,   b**

A radioactive nucleus with $Z = 92$ and $A = 235$ decays through a series of alpha, beta, and gamma emissions to a stable nucleus with $Z = 82$ and $A = 207$.  The number of alpha particles and the number of beta particles emitted during the entire process are

a.   8 alpha particles and 6 beta particles.
b.   7 alpha particles and 4 beta particles.
c.   7 alpha particles and 10 beta particles.
d.   14 alpha particles and 7 beta particles.
e.   None of these is correct.

3219    **32-2   Radioactivity,   Factual,   a**

Which of the following radiation products has the largest charge?

a.   alpha particles
b.   beta particles
c.   gamma rays
d.   neutrons
e.   All of these have the same charge.

3220    **32-2   Radioactivity,   Conceptual,   d**

A radioactive substance in the laboratory has a half-life of eight hours.  At noon today, a Geiger counter read 480 counts per minute above background.  At noon tomorrow, the counter should read about

a.   480 counts/minute.
b.   240 counts/minute.
c.   120 counts/minute.
d.   60 counts/minute.
e.   30 counts/minute.

3221    **32-2   Radioactivity,   Conceptual,   e**

A fission product, $^{96}_{30}$ Kr, is radioactive and decays in a series to the stable $^{90}_{40}$ Zr.  In this series, the particles ejected from the nucleus are

a.  one alpha particle and four beta particles.
b.  no alpha particles and two beta particles.
c.  one alpha particle and two beta particles.
d.  one alpha particle and three beta particles.
e.  no alpha particles and four beta particles.

3222    **32-2   Radioactivity,   Numerical,   b**

At a particular time, a radioactive source $A$ has a strength of 1.60 x $10^{11}$ becquerel and a half-life of 15.0 days, and a second source $B$ has a strength of 8.50 x $10^{11}$ becquerel. Sources $A$ and $B$ have the same strength 45.0 days later.  The half-life of $B$ is

a.  0.19 days.
b.  8.3 days.
c.  2.8 days.
d.  5.4 days.
e.  28 days.

3223    **32-2   Radioactivity,   Numerical,   d**

A nuclear explosion produces (among a lot of other things) 7.9 x $10^{23}$ Bq of iodine-131, which has a half-life of 8.05 days, and 5.7 x $10^{21}$ Bq of barium-140, which has a half-life of 12.8 days.  The total activity that remains after 145 days is

a.  3.5 x $10^{18}$ Bq
b.  1.16 x $10^{20}$ Bq
c.  2.2 x $10^{18}$ Bq
d.  5.2 x $10^{18}$ Bq
e.  7.3 x $10^{18}$ Bq

3224    **32-2   Radioactivity,   Numerical,   d**

Cesium-137 has a half-life of 31.0 years.  The time required for the cesium-137 now present to decrease to 1/30 its present value is

a.  930 years.
b.  30 years.
c.  465 years.
d.  152 years.
e.  1.6 years.

3225    **32-2   Radioactivity,   Factual,   b**

A β particle is

a.  an energetic photon emitted by a nucleus.
b.  an energetic electron or positron.
c.  an energetic proton emitted by a nucleus.
d.  an energetic neutron emitted by a nucleus.
e.  None of these is correct.

3226    **32-2  Radioactivity,  Numerical,  b**

A radiologist uses a radioactiove isotope of iodine, $^{123}$I, for thyroid scans. He receives a shipment of 15 millicuries (mCi) of this isotope at noon on Tuesday. The half-life of this isotope is 13.2 hours. How much activity remains at noon on Thursday of the same week?

a.  12 mCi
b.  1.2 mCi
c.  2.4 mCi
d.  4.2 mCi
e.  24 mCi

3227    **32-2  Radioactivity,  Conceptual,  b**

What are the number of protons $Z$ and the number of neutrons $N$ in the missing fragment of the following fission reaction?

$$^{1}_{0}n + ^{235}_{92}U \rightarrow ? + ^{140}_{55}Cs + 4\,^{1}_{0}n$$

a.  $Z = 55$ and $N = 37$
b.  $Z = 37$ and $N = 55$
c.  $Z = 92$ and $N = 37$
d.  $Z = 37$ and $N = 92$
e.  $Z = 37$ and $N = 58$

3228    **32-2  Radioactivity,  Conceptual,  c**

Of the several nuclear reactions listed below, which one is possible?

a.  $^{10}_{5}B + ^{4}_{2}He \rightarrow ^{13}_{7}N + ^{1}_{1}H$

b.  $^{23}_{11}Na + ^{1}_{1}H \rightarrow ^{20}_{10}Ne + ^{4}_{2}He$

c.  $^{10}_{5}B + ^{1}_{0}n \rightarrow ^{11}_{5}B + \beta^{-} + \nu$

d.  $^{14}_{7}N + ^{1}_{1}H \rightarrow ^{12}_{6}C + \beta^{-} + \nu$

e.  None of these is correct.

3229    **32-2  Radioactivity,  Conceptual,  b**

An alpha particle colliding with an electron that is initially at rest loses

a.  none of its energy.
b.  a little of its energy.
c.  half of its energy.
d.  most of its energy.
e.  all of its energy.

**3230    32-2  Radioactivity,  Factual,  d**

In which of the following are the particles listed in the order of increasing rest mass, that is, smallest first and largest last?

a.  electron, neutrino, alpha particle, neutron, proton
b.  neutrino, neutron, electron, alpha particle, proton
c.  neutron, electron, proton, neutrino, alpha particle
d.  neutrino, electron, proton, neutron, alpha particle
e.  electron, proton, neutron, neutrino, alpha particle

**3231    32-3  Nuclear  Reactions,  Numerical,  c**

[For this question the students must be given Table 32-1 from the text or its equivalent.]

Find the $Q$ value of the decay:    $^{218}_{84}\text{Po} \rightarrow {}^{208}_{82}\text{Pb} + {}^{4}_{2}\propto$

a.  8.75 MeV
b.  9.45 MeV
c.  9.67 MeV
d.  9.73 MeV
e.  9.89 MeV

**3232    32-3  Nuclear  Reactions,  Conceptual,  b**

Many elements show resonances in neutron capture.  What are these resonances?

a.  especially large $Q$ values for each neutron capture
b.  certain incident energies at which neutrons are most readily captured
c.  especially large $N$ values resulting from the capture of many neutrons
d.  especially large numbers of absorbed cross sections
e.  certain incident angles at which neutrons are most readily captured

**3233    32-4  Fission,  Fusion,  and  Nuclear  Reactors,  Conceptual,  a**

In the fusion process the total rest mass _____ , and in the fission process the total rest mass
_____ .

a.  decreases; decreases
b.  increases; decreases
c.  decreases; increases
d.  increases; increases
e.  stays the same; decreases

**3234    32-4  Fission,  Fusion,  and  Nuclear  Reactors,  Conceptual,  d**

The main purpose of a moderator in a nuclear reactor is to

a.  absorb the neutrons and thereby decrease the reaction rate.
b.  absorb the neutrons and thereby increase the reaction rate.
c.  slow down the neutrons and thereby decrease the reaction rate.
d.  slow down the neutrons and thereby increase the reaction rate.
e.  cool the reactor chamber.

3235    **32-4   Fission, Fusion, and Nuclear Reactors,   Conceptual,   b**

A light-water reactor uses _____ as fuel, and a heavy-water reactor uses _____ as fuel,

   a.  natural uranium; natural uranium
   b.  enriched uranium; natural uranium
   c.  enriched uranium; enriched uranium
   d.  natural uranium; enriched uranium
   e.  enriched uranium; plutonium

3236    **32-4   Fission, Fusion, and Nuclear Reactors,   Factual,   d**

Nuclear fusion takes place when

   a.  a large nucleus splits into two fragments with the release of a few neutrons.
   b.  an $\propto$ particle is ejected from the nucleus.
   c.  a positive $\beta$ particle is ejected from the nucleus.
   d.  small nuclei combine to form a larger one.
   e.  heavy hydrogen is accelerated.

3237    **32-4   Fission, Fusion, and Nuclear Reactors,   Numerical,   a**

Assuming that 200 MeV of energy is released per fission, the mass of $^{235}$U required to operate a $250 \times 10^6$ watt reactor for 1 year is approximately

   a.  100 kg
   b.  200 kg
   c.  400 kg
   d.  500 kg
   e.  1000 kg

3238    **32-4   Fission, Fusion, and Nuclear Reactors,   Factual,   c**

A reactor that produces more fuel than it uses is called a

   a.  fission reactor.
   b.  moderator reactor.
   c.  breeder reactor.
   d.  generating reactor.
   e.  fusion reactor.

3239    **32-4   Fission, Fusion, and Nuclear Reactors,   Numerical,   c**

[For this question the students must be given Table 32-1 from the text or its equivalent.]

How much energy is released by the following fusion reaction?

$$^1H + {}^1H \rightarrow {}^2H + \beta^+ + \nu$$

(The rest energy of $\beta^+$ is 0.511 MeV.)

   a.  2.0 MeV
   b.  1.4 MeV
   c.  0.93 MeV
   d.  1.9 MeV
   e.  1.0 MeV

**3240    32-4   Fission, Fusion, and Nuclear Reactors,   Numerical,   a**

If, on the average, each fission reaction of $^{235}$U releases 200 MeV of energy, how many nuclei of $^{235}$U fission per second in a 200-MW reactor?

a.  $6.3 \times 10^{18}$
b.  $6.0 \times 10^{23}$
c.  $1.0 \times 10^{19}$
d.  $1.6 \times 10^{19}$
e.  $2.7 \times 10^{18}$

**3241    32-4   Fission, Fusion, and Nuclear Reactors,   Numerical,   d**

If the reproduction factor in a reactor is $k = 1.01$, how many generations are needed for the power level to increase by a factor of 10?

a.  10
b.  70
c.  100
d.  230
e.  530

**3242    32-4   Fission, Fusion, and Nuclear Reactors,   Numerical,   b**

In an experimental inertial-confinement fusion reactor, inertial confinement has a useful duration of $\tau = 2.0 \times 10^{-10}$ s.  What must the density of the fusible material be in order to meet Lawson's criterion?

a.  $2.0 \times 10^{24}$ particles/cm$^3$
b.  $5.0 \times 10^{23}$ particles/cm$^3$
c.  $6.0 \times 10^{23}$ particles/cm$^3$
d.  $2.5 \times 10^{23}$ particles/cm$^3$
e.  $7.0 \times 10^{23}$ particles/cm$^3$

**3243    32-5   The Interaction of Particles with Matter,   Factual,   c**

A high-energy linear accelerator is used to produce x-rays with an energy of 18 MeV.  In this range of energies, the main contribution to the photon interaction cross section for the x-rays comes from

a.  the photoelectric effect.
b   the Compton effect.
c.  electron-position pair production.
d.  the Compton effect and the photoelectric effect together.
e.  None of these is correct.

**3244    32-5   The Interaction of Particles with Matter,   Conceptual,   e**

At very high energies, which process dominates in the absorption of a photon?

a.  photoelectric effect
b.  refraction
c.  diffraction
d.  Compton scattering
e.  pair production

3245    **32-5  The Interaction of Particles with Matter,  Conceptual,  c**

Beams of heavy charged particles are used in cancer therapy because they

   a.   are attracted to cancerous tissue.
   b.   can be "tuned" to destroy certain types of material.
   c.   can be "tuned" to destroy material at certain positions.
   d.   are an important diagnostic procedure.
   e.   pass through the body, causing no harm.


3246    **32-5  The Interaction of Particles with Matter,  Factual,  b**

At low energies near 1 MeV, the main contribution to the photon interaction cross section for the x-rays comes from

   a.   photoelectron production
   b.   Compton scattering
   c.   pair production
   d.   both  b and c
   e.   bremsstrahlung

CHAPTER 33   Elementary Particles

**3301**   **33-1  Spin and Antiparticles,  Factual,  d**

Positrons have only a short-term existence in our universe because

a.  they decay to other particles.
b.  their speeds are very high (near the speed of light).
c.  their speeds are very low (near zero).
d.  of the large number of electrons present in our universe.
e.  None of these is correct.

**3302**   **33-1  Spin and Antiparticles,  Factual,  b**

A particle and its antiparticle must have

a.  opposite spins.
b.  opposite charges.
c.  opposite masses.
d.  opposite forces.
e.  both opposite spins and opposite charges.

**3303**   **33-2  Hadrons and Leptons,  Factual,  c**

Particles that participate in the weak interaction are called

a.  quarks.
b.  hadrons.
c.  leptons.
d.  mesons.
e.  baryons.

**3304**   **33-2  Hadrons and Leptons,  Factual,  b**

Particles that participate in the strong interaction are called

a.  neutrinos.
b.  hadrons.
c.  leptons.
d.  electrons.
e.  photons.

3305   **33-2   Hadrons and Leptons,   Factual,   a**

Which of the following lists the four known types of forces in nature in order of decreasing strength?

a.   strong nuclear, electromagnetic, weak nuclear, gravitational
b.   electromagnetic, strong nuclear, weak nuclear, gravitational
c.   strong nuclear, gravitational, weak nuclear, electromagnetic
d.   strong nuclear, weak nuclear, electromagnetic, gravitational
e.   strong nuclear, electromagnetic, gravitational, weak nuclear

3306   **33-3   The Conservation Laws,   Factual,   e**

Which of the following is NOT conserved in a nuclear reaction or decay?

a.   mass-energy
b.   nucleon number
c.   baryon number
d.   charge
e.   All of these are conserved.

3307   **33-4   The Quark Model,   Factual,   a**

At the present time, the truly elementary particles are thought to be the

a.   quarks and leptons.
b.   hadrons and baryons.
c.   baryons and quarks.
d.   leptons and hadrons.
e.   quarks and photons.

3308   **33-5   Field Particles and Unified Theories,   Factual,   b**

In the present-day understanding of the behavior of elementary particles, the term *color* is used to denote

a.   the wavelengths of different $\gamma$ rays emitted by the particles.
b.   a property responsible for the strong forces between quarks.
c.   a property that distinguishes between protons and neutrons.
d.   a property that only leptons can possess.
e.   Color has nothing to do with elementary particles.

3309   **33-5   Field Particles and Unified Theories,   Factual,   d**

The field quanta associated with the hadronic force between quarks are called

a.   photons.
b.   gravitrons.
c.   GUT's
d.   gluons.
e.   vector bosons.

3310    **33-5   Field Particles and Unified Theories,   Factual,   e**

The field quanta that mediate the weak nuclear force are

a.   photons.
b.   gravitrons.
c.   GUT's
d.   gluons.
e.   vector bosons.